Inside Enigma

The Secrets of the Enigma and other Historic Cipher Machines

by Professor Tom Perera

Radio Society of Great Britain

Published by the Radio Society of Great Britain, 3 Abbey Court, Fraser Road, Priory Business Park, Bedford MK44 3WH, UK.

First published 2010

ISBN 9781-9050-8664-1

Publisher's note
The opinions expressed in this book are those of the author and not necessarily those of the RSGB. While the information pre-sented is believed to be correct, the author, publisher and their agents cannot accept responsibility for consequences arising from any inaccuracies or omissions.

Updates and revisions: New information about cipher machines is constantly coming to light as historic government archives are declassified and studied by historians. The following website contains cumulative updates, revisions and corrections for the information in this book: http://w1tp.com/enigma/enigma_book_updates.htm

Editing, typography and design: Mike Dennison, G3XDV, Emdee Publishing
Cover design: Kim Meyern
Production: Mark Allgar, M1MPA

Printed in Great Britain by Nuffield Press of Abingdon UK

Contents

DEDICATION

To my dear wife Gretchen who for over fifty years has encouraged my filling her life with countless thousands of "historic artifacts" and who tells me that if I die and leave her with all this "junk", she'll kill me! And for my wonderful children, Dan and Tom and grandchildren, Skyler, Austin, Wilder, and Jaro.

Tom Perera

Introduction

For thousands of years, man has had a desire to keep some of his messages secret. And of course as much effort has been put into decoding these secret messages as went into coding them in the first place.

During periods of conflict, the need for secrecy, and for breaking that secrecy, becomes most important and great resources are employed in this direction.

By the 20th century, electronic and mechanical advances permitted the use of sophisticated machines to take encryption to a new level.

Enigma was developed in the first quarter of the 20th century in Germany, but it was not until the preparations for World War 2 that it was produced in any quantity. It used such complex cipher techniques that it was to all intents and purposes unbreakable. As will be seen later in this book, the number of possible coding combinations is truly mind boggling.

That 'unbreakable' system should have been the greatest secret of the War. In fact a bigger secret was that not only had the Allies been able to read many of the Enigma messages throughout the conflict, but that this fact was concealed for thirty years after the War.

So how was it possible to decipher messages produced by an unbreakable system? Well, whilst it is true that the Enigma machine itself was virtually perfect, the Achilles heel was its human operators. A combination of espionage and sloppy interpretation of Enigma's operating instructions led to vulnerabilities which could be exploited by experts in Poland, the UK and the USA.

A SHORT HISTORY OF THE ENIGMA

The Enigma cipher machine was first patented by German Inventor Arthur Scherbius in 1918. (Note: the word cipher is also spelled cypher which is a primarily British variant.) It was initially designed to be used by commercial companies to keep their communications secret. When Germany began rebuilding its military in the 1930s, the government took over the Enigmas and began using them for all of their secret communications.

Poland was aware that Germany would probably invade them first and built a cipher bureau to try to read enciphered German messages. The Poles were the first to determine how the Enigma machine worked and how to go about decoding its messages. When Poland was invaded, the Polish mathematicians were already helping the Allied forces develop strategies and machines which allowed them to read many important German messages during the war.

A team of codebreakers working at Bletchley Park in England and initially using a replica Enigma machine supplied by the Poles was able to decode many of the Enigma-coded messages used by the German military even though the Germans changed the settings of the machine. The code name for the deciphering operation and the intelligence derived from it was "Ultra".

Each letter typed into the Enigma machine's keyboard was converted to some other letter of the alphabet and displayed in a lighted window. Since the entire mechanism rotated each time a letter was entered, pressing the same letter three times could produce three different encodings. The encodings were produced by hard-wired code wheels and patch panels. The three code wheels could be mounted in a variety of positions and each one could be set to any letter of the alphabet. In addition, a patch panel on the front of the machine could be set up in many ways, making a vast number of combinations of cipher keys possible.

WHAT IS COVERED IN THIS BOOK

There are very many books about Enigma and Ultra, covering the history of the WW2 efforts to break the code.

This book has chapters dealing with the mathematics behind the code, and the decryption efforts in Poland, the UK and the USA.

The main thrust of the book, however, is the machine itself, from its beginnings in the commercial world to its extensive use during the second half of the 20th century, well after it ceased to be as secure as its users believed.

In particular, Enigma machines used by the Germans, and the complex cipher machines developed by the Americans, Russians and Swiss are dealt with in great detail, with many of the component parts stripped down for closer examination.

ABOUT THE AUTHOR

As cipher machines and computers have taken on increasingly important roles in history, considerable interest has developed in collecting and studying these early technological innovations.

Although Tom Perera's primary interest lies in collecting and preserving antique telegraph equipment (the first form of widespread electrical digital communications), he also collects examples of these other instruments. He is particularly fascinated by the challenge of locating examples of WW2 Enigma cipher machines and travels to Europe frequently to try to find them. Since Enigmas are so scarce, Professor Perera often supplies Enigma machines for use as props in movies and documentaries and gives frequent lectures and demonstrations. More recently, he has found a fascinating Russian Cold War era Fialka cipher machine and documented it with detailed photographs, its instruction manual, and detailed rotor wiring data.

OTHER PUBLICATIONS BY PROF TOM PERERA

- **Perera's Telegraph Collectors Guide**:A complete telegraph collectors reference book with 300 photos and a price guide.
- **Telegraph Collectors Reference CD**:A collection of thousands of color photographs of telegraph instruments combined with several complete books on the history of telegraph, etc.
- **CD-ROM: The Story of the Enigma:** The material in this book and much more, including colour photographs, extra documents and videos

These publications are available from the following:
Radio Society of Great Britain: www.rsgb.org
American Radio Relay League: www.arrl.org
Artifax Books: www.artifaxbooks.com

(picture left): "I often feel as though I am is hunting for some rare species of animal in the German Alps" - *Prof Tom Perera*

ACKNOWLEDGEMENTS

The following are thanked for their permission to reproduce their words and photographs in this book:
- John Alexander
- F L Bauer
- Bletchley Park Trust
- British Public Records Office (now British National Archives)
- Dr David Hamer (various)
- Jim Bunch, Rich Hunting and Roger Hunting
- Dr A Ray Miller
- NSA / National Cryptological Museum
- Jim Oram
- Paul Reuvers
- Mark Simons
- US War Dept (M-209 Handbook)
- Frode Weirud

Chapter 1

Early Cipher Machines

Before looking at the machines, let us take a brief look at the techniques for transmitting the coded messages or CIPHERTEXT so that we can better understand the techniques used for intercepting and eventually deciphering it.

Until the mid nineteenth century, messages were carried by hand over long distances and could be intercepted and decoded only by capturing them through daring and dangerous attacks on the carriers. It took several *days* for a message to be carried the sixty miles from Washington to Baltimore and much longer to cover greater distances.

In 1844, this all changed when Samuel F B Morse demonstrated the use of the Electric Telegraph instruments to send a message *instantly* by an electrical signal in a wire from Washington to Baltimore.

The new Electric Telegraph used another code which quickly became the standard code for transmitting electrical messages. It was called the Morse code after its inventor. It gave each letter and number its own unique series of short and/or long electrical signals called dots and dashes. These electrical signals could be carried over the telegraph lines.

A slightly different version of the code (called the Continental or International Morse Code) was later sent without wires using early radio sets.

SECRET MESSAGES

Within a few years, America was criss-crossed with a network of telegraph wires. This telegraph network led to interconnected telephones, teletypes, fax, and now the internet.

Telegraph and the technology that evolved from it, such as telephone and radiotelegraph communications, made it easy and instantaneous to send and receive messages. However, it also made it easy and instantaneous for an enemy to intercept messages.

During World War 2, the Allies felt that it was important to educate people about how vulnerable the telephone lines were and used posters like the one shown on this page. Since they could not give every civilian a cipher machine, they relied on posters, such as the one show here, to educate the population not to talk about things that might be useful to the enemy.

MORSE AS A SECRET CODE

The International Morse Code was used by the German military to transmit Enigma-coded CIPHERTEXT during World War 2.

Part of the Continental/International version of the Morse Code is shown in the table below:

Educational Poster from WW2. [British Public Records Office]

Plaintext character	CONTINENTAL OR INTERNATIONAL CODE
a	•—
b	—•••
c	—•—•
d	—••
e	•
f	••—•
g	——•
h	••••
i	••
j	•———
k	—•—
l	•—••
m	——
n	—•
o	———
p	•——•
etc	etc

Part of the International Morse code used to transmit secret messages by both sides during WW2.

ENCODING BY MORSE
The transmitting station encodes the message as follows:

Inputting the plaintext message:
```
h e l p
```

Produces the MORSE message:

●●●● ● ●━●● ●━━●

This Morse message is sent to the receiving station by wire or radio

DECODING THE MORSE
The receiving station decodes the message as follows:

Inputting the MORSE message:

●●●● ● ●━●● ●━━●

Produces the plaintext message:
```
h e l p
```

Highly trained telegraph operators could read the MORSE messages by ear and write down the plaintext letters very rapidly. The speed record was about 75 five-letter words per minute (375 letters per minute).

At first, the Morse Code was used in its original form. But it soon became apparent that an enemy could easily read the Morse so CIPHERTEXT, and various methods were employed to encode the messages to keep them secret. These methods included code wheels and cipher machines.

A BIT OF HISTORY
Long before WW2 started, it had became important to develop unbreakable codes so that secret messages could be safely sent without fear of their being intercepted and deciphered.

Very early code wheel made in Denmark around 1915 by Alexis Kohl.
[NSA/National Cryptologic Museum]

Two thousand years ago, Julius Caesar used an early code to send a secret message. It is now called the Caesar Code and it has been modified in various ways over the years but its basic principles are still in use in the most modern computerized codes of today.

The Caesar Code is formed by simply shifting the alphabet by three letters as shown below:

Plaintext:
```
a b c d e f g h i j k l m n o p etc
```

CIPHERTEXT:
```
X Y Z A B C D E F G H I J K L M etc
```

ENCODING USING CAESAR CODE

With this Caesar Code, inputting the plaintext message:
```
help
```
Produces the CIPHERTEXT message:
```
EBIM
```
Please Note the convention of presenting the plaintext in small letters and the CIPHERTEXT in CAPITAL LETTERS.

DECODING CAESAR CODE
To decode the message, the CIPHERTEXT is converted into the original plaintext by simply reversing the procedure.

CIPHERTEXT:
```
X Y Z A B C D E F G H I J K L M  etc
```

Plaintext:
```
a b c d e f g h i j k l m n o p  etc
```

Inputting the CIPHERTEXT message:
```
EBIM
```

Produces the plaintext message:
```
help
```

HISTORIC CODE WHEELS AND DEVICES
The simplest machine for using the Caesar Code is a Code Wheel which has the plaintext on a fixed wheel and the CIPHERTEXT on a rotating concentric inner or outer wheel. A similar arrangement can be mounted on a drum, or might use strips of paper or cards.

Instructions for making your own code wheel can be found in a later chapter.

The following photographs of historic coding/decoding systems were taken in the NSA / National Cryptologic Museum during 2004.

MORSE KEYS
Over fifty years ago, I became interested and challenged by collecting, studying, and displaying the earliest telegraph instruments. This is my primary historical focus. My Telegraph Museum with over 3000+ telegraph instruments may be seen at: http://w1tp.com and I have published a telegraph collectors guidebook and a CD to document these historic beginnings of the information age (see details on page 4).

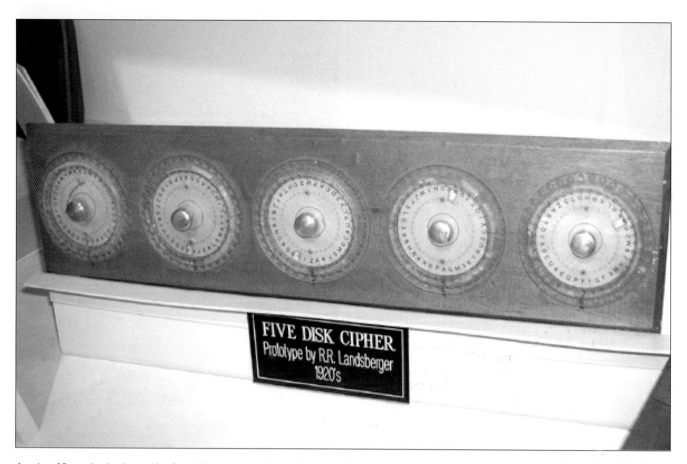

A series of five code wheels capable of producing a very complex cipher, produced in the 1920s. [NSA/National Cryptologic Museum]

Another early code wheel using concentric wheels. [NSA/National Cryptologic Museum]

Unusual shaped code wheel from the 1920s. [NSA/National Cryptologic Museum]

Another early code wheel. [NSA/National Cryptologic Museum]

A more recent cipher disk. [NSA/National Cryptologic Museum]

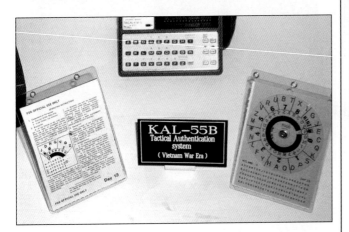

Code wheels used during the Vietnam War. [NSA/National Cryptologic Museum]

An alternative cipher system is to use a reel such as this one used by the Confederate Army in about 1863. This one, shown in its entirity in the top picture and in detail in the bottom one, was found in Mobile, Alabama. [NSA/National Cryptologic Museum]

Another early drum-based enciphering system. [NSA/National Cryptologic Museum]

Prototype of a revolving drum cipher by A G Damm, made in the 1920s. [NSA/National Cryptologic Museum]

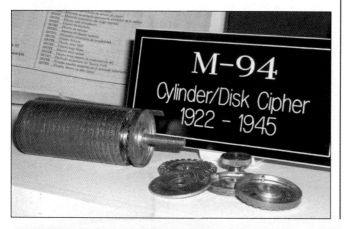

(above) The KL-99. A drum-based off-line encryption system used by the US Navy. [NSA/National Cryptologic Museum]

(left) M-94. A cylinder cipher with changeable wheels. [NSA/National Cryptologic Museum]

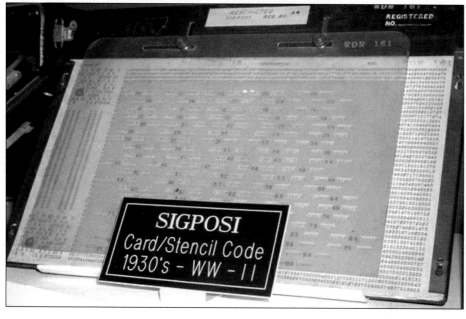

Another system uses strips of card as in this early WW2 cipher machine. [NSA/National Cryptologic Museum]

Another wartime strip cipher. [NSA/National Cryptologic Museum]

CODE AND CIPHER TOYS
It is easy to make your own cipher machine based on the Caesar Code, and full details on how to do this can be found in a later chapter.

Secret Codes have always fascinated people, especially children. In the 1930s, children could encode secret messages to each other *if* they had bought the right kind of breakfast cereal (the cereal box contained the code wheel) and agreed on a Starting Position or Key. They were using precisely the same basic technology that would soon be put to use by WW2 spies and Enigma machine operators.

The following photographs of historic code and cipher toys were taken at the NSA/National Cryptologic Museum 2006.

BETTER CODING TECHNIQUES
It would seem as though there would be a need for better coding principles than those used in the Caesar Code.

However, we will see that the Enigma cipher machine and even the most modern codes have their roots in this simple technique.

The Enigma code is very similar to the Caesar Code except that the Enigma machine shifts and rearranges the CIPHER-TEXT alphabet with *every* new plaintext letter that is typed in.

THE ENIGMA AS AN ELABORATE CODE WHEEL
The similarity between the operation of the Enigma and that of the code wheels mentioned earlier should be apparent by now. When the inner wheel of a code wheel is set to a 'Key' position, the code wheel allows plaintext on its outer wheel to be converted to CIPHERTEXT on its inner wheel.

Reversing the process on a code wheel that has been set to same the Key at the receiving end allows the CIPHERTEXT on the inner wheel to be converted to plaintext on the outer wheel.

SY KO/S.D.2 Strip cipher from the 1950s. [NSA/National Cryptologic Museum]

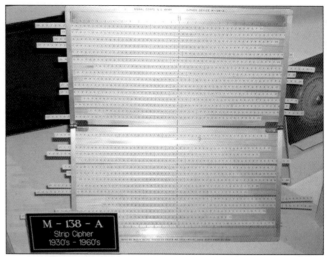

Another example of a strip cipher, used during and after WW2. [NSA/National Cryptologic Museum]

Code wheel in a "Federal Agent" toy from 1938. [NSA/National Cryptologic Museum]

PENELOPE
Call Sign Device
1950's

(right) 1950s strip cipher machine. [NSA/National Cryptologic Museum]

Captain Midnight code toys. [NSA/National Cryptologic Museum]

11

Code wheel toy of the 1930s. [NSA/National Cryptologic Museum]

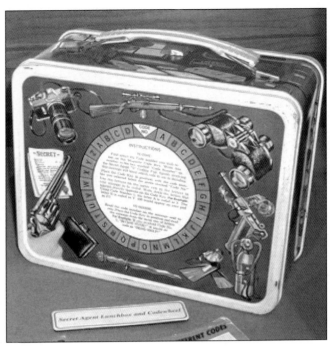

Secret Agent kit toy with a code wheel as part of the box. [NSA/National Cryptologic Museum]

The only difference between the operation of the code wheel and that of the Enigma, then, is the fact that the Enigma rotors which are the equivalent of the inner wheel in a code wheel, rotate once with every character typed into the keyboard. In the code wheel, the initial starting position or Key remains the same throughout the encoding/decoding processes and it is very easy to discover since there are only 26 possibilities. In the Enigma, the initial Starting Position or Key changes after the first character is typed. This fact and the additional complexity of the multiple rotors and the plugboard made the Enigma messages much harder to decipher than those of the code wheel.

UNBREAKABLE?
It was the need to develop a truly unbreakable encoding machine that led to the development of the Enigma.

The Enigma cipher machine was one of the devices which were invented to encipher plaintext messages to try to make them impossible for an enemy to read. This book traces the evolution, operation, and deciphering of the Enigma Cipher Machine.

The development of unbreakable codes and cipher machines was, of course, paralleled by the development of more and more sophisticated code breaking techniques. Many excellent books have been written about codes and codebreaking and some are listed in the bibliography and references section at the end of this book.

A Pre-1952 Timeline of Cryptologic Events originally produced by the (US) National Cryptologic Museum of NSA (web site http://www.nsagov/museum/index.cfm) can be found on page 18.

Chapter 2

Enigma Machines

WHAT THE ENIGMA MACHINE DOES

The Enigma cipher machine changes plaintext letters into CIPHERTEXT letters.

When a particular keyboard key is pressed, the voltage from a battery is sent through a series of switches and plugs that determine which of the 26 light bulbs will illuminate one of the 26 letters of the alphabet.

Pressing a keyboard key such as "h" causes a letter of the alphabet such as "A" to be illuminated. The keyboard key is called the "plaintext" and the illuminated letter is called the "CIPHERTEXT".

(Note: It is conventional to show the plaintext in lower-case and the CIPHERTEXT in capital letters.)

HOW THE ENIGMA MACHINE IS USED

If you type the word "hello" on the keyboard (the plaintext message), letters "AZRWK" (the CIPHERTEXT message) may be illuminated by the light bulbs.

The CIPHERTEXT message from the light bulbs, "AZRWK", is written down and then sent manually by telephone or radio or by a messenger to a receiving station that has another Enigma machine. Messages from one Enigma to another must be transferred and entered manually.

The receiving operator first sets his Enigma starting position or KEY so that it is the same as was used by the sending Enigma. He then types "AZRWK" into his Enigma machine which illuminates light bulbs "hello", the original plaintext message.

THE IMPORTANCE OF THE STARTING POSITION OR KEY

In order for all of this to work, the receiving Enigma machine **must** be set to the same Starting Position or Key as the sending Enigma machine was set to. Since there is an incredible number of possible starting positions (keys), even if an enemy has an Enigma machine, it is virtually impossible for them to decode the CIPHERTEXT since they would not know the proper starting position or key.

Itemised here is how the initial starting position or key is set before sending the first message of the day. (This description will make more sense after you have read about and seen the details of the construction of the Enigma Machine later in this chapter.)

Diagram showing how the Enigma machine encodes and decodes a message. The sending Enigma machine is on the left and the receiving Enigma machine is on the right. The original (plaintext) message is first typed into the left (sending) Enigma keyboard. The coded letters (CIPHERTEXT) that appear in the light bulb display are then manually written down on paper. The coded message (CIPHERTEXT) on the paper is then transferred by messenger, telephone, or radio to a receiving station.The coded message letters (CIPHER-TEXT) are then manually typed into the right (receiving) Enigma which decodes the message and displays the original message (plaintext) in the light bulb display above its keyboard. [www.w1tp.com/enigma Museum]

SETTING UP THE DAY'S STARTING POSITION

1 **Set the sequence of rotors (code wheels) on the shaft:** Set the position of the three numbered rotors or code wheels along the shaft from left to right. Any three of the five numbered rotors can be placed in any of the three positions on the shaft: left, middle and right. There are therefore 60 possible sequences of three rotors.

2 **Set the number or letter rings on each of the three rotors (code wheels):** Set the 'ring setting' of each rotor or code wheel. There are 26 possible settings on each of the three rotors. This gives $26^3 = (17,536)$ possible settings.

3 **Set the number or letter to be visible through the three windows at the start of coding:** Set 'starting positions' of the three rotors. There are 26 possible settings in each of the three windows. This gives $26^3 = (17,536)$ possible settings.

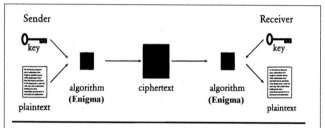

ENIGMA KEY:

1. Rotor Number and Location Along Axle.
2. Rotor internal Ring Setting.
3. Initial Starting Position of Each Rotor.
4. Jumper Cable Selections for Plug Board.

Diagram showing how the Enigma machine encodes and decodes a message. [Adapted from a diagram in Singh, 1999, *The Code Book*.]

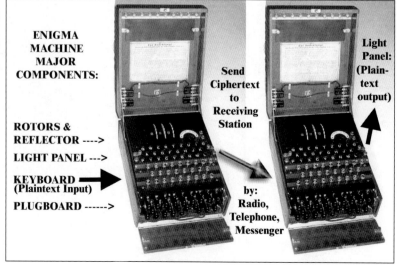

ENIGMA MACHINE MAJOR COMPONENTS:

ROTORS & REFLECTOR ---->

LIGHT PANEL --->

KEYBOARD (Plaintext Input)

PLUGBOARD ------>

Send Ciphertext to Receiving Station

by: Radio, Telephone, Messenger

Light Panel: (Plaintext output)

4 Insert double-plug patch / jumper cables into the plugboard (patch panel): Set jumper wire connections on plugboard. There are anywhere from 0 to 13 jumper wires which can be inserted into any of the 26 sockets. This gives: Sum from p = 0 to 13 of 26!/(26-2p)! x p! x 2 to the p power = 532,985,208,200,576 possible settings. Combining these possibilities give us a total of 26,672,901,348,424,004,787,290,112 or about 10^{26} possible starting settings or keys. Other ways of calculating this figure (discussed later) produce numbers as high as 10^{114} possible keys. As long as both the encoding Enigma and the decoding Enigma are set to this same starting position or key, the messages will be properly encoded and decoded.

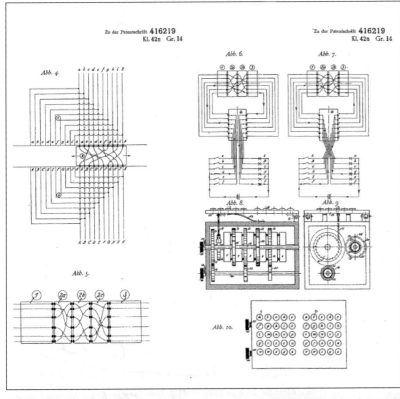

Scherbius' original 1918 patent covered rotor machines with up to 10 rotors.
[Courtesy of Paul Reuvers: www.cryptomuseum.com]

THE INVENTION OF THE ENIGMA CIPHER MACHINE

As with so many major inventions and innovations in history, the Enigma was almost simultaneously invented by four people.

The American Edward Hugh Hebern who had connected two electric typewriters together in 1915, made the first rotor drawings in 1917. However, he only filed an American patent in 1921. Thus he ended up being the last of the four inventors to patent the device. He lost his patent lawsuits and died in 1952.

The German inventor Arthur Scherbius was the first to patent the Enigma machine. He filed his German patent (number 416,219) on 23 February, 1918. His patent covered machines with up to ten rotors so it encompassed most of the subsequent designs. Scherbius died prematurely in an accident in 1929 and his company eventually became Heimsoeth & Rinke.

The Dutchman, Hugo Alexander Koch filed his patent on 7 October, 1919, about a year after Scherbius' patent. Scherbius ultimately decided to buy his patent and Koch died shortly thereafter.

The Hebern cipher machine. [NSA/National Cryptographic Museum]

Below: Arthur Scherbius was the first to patent the Enigma machine. [British Public Records Office]

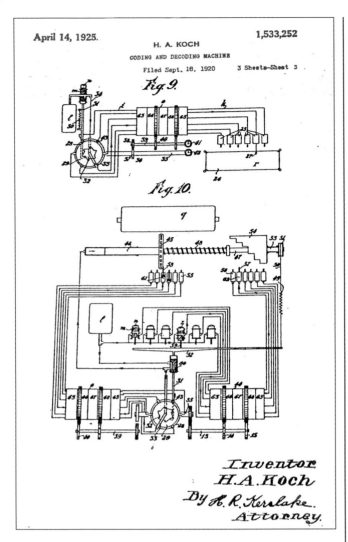

April 14, 1925.

H. A. KOCH

CODING AND DECODING MACHINE

Filed Sept. 18, 1920

1,533,252

3 Sheets-Sheet 3

Fig. 9.

Fig. 10.

Inventor
H.A.Koch
By H. R. Kerslake.
Attorney.

Koch's patent filed after Scherbius' patent. [On display in the NSA/National Cryptologic Museum

The Model A Enigma [F.L. Bauer, 1997]

The Model B Enigma. [F L Bauer, 1997]

Commercial Enigma Model D. [F L Bauer, 1997]

The Swede, Arvid Gerhard Damm, filed his patent on 10 October, 1919. His design included an unique 1/2-rotor system. It was eventually bought by Boris Hagelin who formed Aktiebolaget Ingenjorsfirmen Cryptoteknik. Hagelin technology led to the development of the C-36 Cipher Machine and eventually the M-209 set which was widely used by American and British troops in WW2 (see a later chapter in this book).

We will concentrate our attention on the work of Scherbius whose machines evolved into the German military Enigma. The following describes the models of Scherbius-inspired machines that were built by his company, Heimsoeth & Rinke. This material was compiled from the carefully researched books and articles by F L Bauer (1997).

THE VARIOUS EARLY COMMERCIAL MODELS OF ENIGMA

Scherbius set out to develop a machine that he could sell to commercial companies to help keep their business transactions secret.

The first Scherbius designs began with a modified typewriter that used coding wheels to convert plaintext into CIPHERTEXT and back again. These machines were heavy,

An advertising brochure for commercial Model D of the Enigma cipher machine.

The Model K Enigma machine and its companion power supply. This Enigma model includes a remote light bulb panel which allowed the decoded letters illuminated by the remote light panel to be read by an officer without allowing the Enigma operator to see the decoded letters. The machine appears to have four rotors but the leftmost wheel is actually a rotatable reflector. [Author's Enigma Museum: www.w1tp.com/enigma]

complex and expensive, and consequently they were not commercially successful.

The fourth practical Enigma machine was the model D, developed in 1927. With only a few minor changes, its basic design remained virtually unaltered in all subsequent models. Models A, B and D are illustrated on the previous page.

Enigmas were even offered to American companies as indicated by this American advertising brochure which drastically underestimates the number of possible 'key' or 'starting position' settings.

ENIGMA FAMILY TREE

Frode Weirud, Paul Reuvers, David Hamer, the author, and many others are working on trying to reconstruct the history of the development of the Enigma. Unfortunately, most of the records were destroyed during the bombings of WW2 and most of the remaining records were confiscated by the Allied forces. However, little pieces of history continue to surface as we hunt for them and interview the remaining German officers and personnel that were involved with the Enigma. For the latest discoveries please visit the websites of these historians who are listed in the acknowledgements section of this book.

The following historical summary is from the introduction in Paul Reuvers' book on the *Zahlwerk* Enigma G31.

"The history of the Enigma machine starts around 1918 when the first patents for its design were filed. In 1923, the first machines appeared under the Enigma brand. The early models (A and B) printed directly to paper and were therefore called *Schreibende* Enigma (Printing Enigma). These machines were bulky and above all very expensive.

"In 1924, a low-cost Enigma (model C) was introduced that produced its output on a panel with 26 (sometimes 28) lamps rather than on paper. This was called the *Gluhlampenmaschine* (Glow Lamp Machine). It was powered by a battery but needed the electrical energy only for lighting one lamp at a time. The wheels were moved by applying pressure on one of the keys on the keyboard. It is this design of the lamp machine that most of the later Enigma machines are based on.

"Following this text you will find a simplified Enigma family tree and a timeline for the development and use of the various Enigma models. From the top, the tree has two branches. The left branch shows the printing Enigma machines. Since the printing machines were quite impractical, this book will concentrate on the rightmost branch that shows the development of the glow lamp machine of which

ENIGMA CODING - MACHINES *about 800 000 possibilities!*

Type CI 4840

This American advertising brochure for the commercial Enigma cipher machine hugely underestimates its performance.

Enigma-C was the first. Enigma C was also the first Enigma machine to use a reflector (Umkehrwalze, UKW).

"Several models and variants were developed from Enigma-C such as *Funkschlussel-C* used by the *Kriegsmarine* and a special version for Sweden that contained some of the additional Swedish letters. Both of these variants had 28 letters rather than the more common 26. All Enigma-C machines had a fixed reflector that could, however, be mounted in a number of different positions.

"The Enigma-C eventually led to the development of the Enigma-D in 1926. Enigma-D had a rotatable reflector which means that it could be set of any of its 26 positions at the start of a message. The reflector did not move during encipherment.

Enigma-D was sold to a number of international customers such as banks, oil companies, governments and large enterprises.

"The German *Reichswehr*, (the predecessor of the *Wehrmacht*) adopted the Enigma in 1926 and the first machines, based on the Enigma-D were delivered in 1928. The *Reichswehr* improved the cryptographic strength of the machine by adding a so-called *Steckerbrett* (plugboard) to it. They also introduced the new name for this machine: Enigma-I so that it could be discriminated from the large printing Enigma-H which they called Enigma-II. The Enigma-I machines were also built by Chiffriermaschinen AG (later: Heimsoeth und Rinke). All machines used by the German *Wehrmacht* and *Luftwaffe* during WW2 are of the type Enigma-I. The variants that were later used by the *Kriegsmarine* (M1, M2, M3, and M4) were all derived from the Enigma-I. These are the only machines with a *Steckerbrett*. The majority of Enigma machines that have been found in recent years are of the type Enigma-I."

These developments and the various models that derived from these basic machines are shown on the Enigma Family Tree and the Enigma Timeline diagrams constructed by Paul Reuvers and Frode Weirud. Please remember that additions and corrections to these diagrams are possible at any time, so visit their websites for the most recent information. Following these diagrams you will find information on Enigma machine labels, manufacturers' codes, and manufacturers' names.

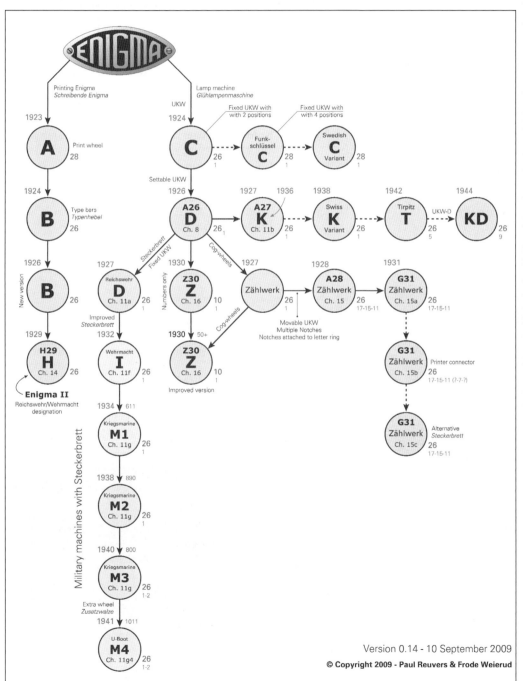

Version 0.14 - 10 September 2009
© Copyright 2009 - Paul Reuvers & Frode Weierud

Enigma Family Tree ©2009 by Paul Reuvers and Frode Weirud. Note: This is an evolving effort as new information is discovered. Please check: http://cryptomuseum.com for updates.

ENIGMA TIMELINE

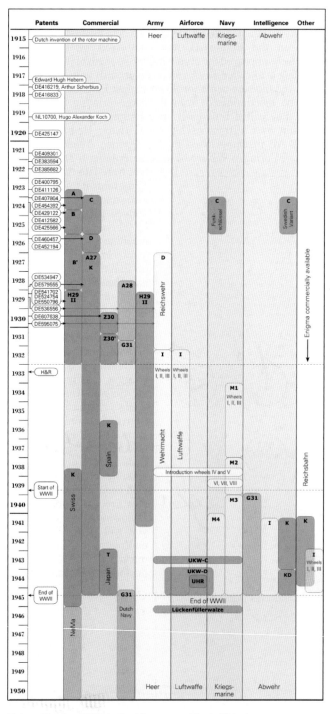

Enigma Timeline ©2009 by Paul Reuvers and Frode Weirud.
Note: This is an evolving effort as new information is discovered. Please check: http://cryptomuseum.com for updates.

ENIGMA FABRICATION CODES

Some of the Enigma machines have labels that are marked with a three letter fabrication code or *Fertigungskennzeichen* together with the serial number of the machine.

Enigma historian Frode Weirud has put together a table that shows the names of the manufacturers associated with each code. The Enigma's label might take the form as shown here for the 1944 model of the Naval Enigma M4:

```
Na 220 900
10233/gvx/44
```

or the form used on some Army/Luftwaffe machines:

```
A
00994/bac/43E
```

The fabrication codes for the known Enigma manufacturers are given below.

Code	Manufacturer
aye	Olympia Büromaschinenwerke A.-G., Erfurt, Mainzerhofplatz
bac	Ertel-Werk für Feinmechanik, Dipl. Ing. W. Preyss, München, Westendstr. 160
gvx	Konski & Krüger, Fabrik elektr. u. mechanischer Apparate, Berlin N 4, Chausseestr. 117
jla	Chiffriermaschinengesellschaft Heimsoeth u. Rinke, Berlin-Wilmersdorf, Uhlandstr. 136
jmz	Atlas-Werke A.-G., Maschinenfabrik, Bremen 11, Steinhöft 11

Enigma Manufacturing Codes. All of the above material is from Frode Weirud: http://cryptocellar.web.cern.ch/cryptocellar/Enigma/efabcode.html.

BASIC COMPONENTS OF THE ENIGMA MACHINE

Before we discuss how the Enigma machine works, I think it is important to become familiar with its basic components.

The Case

The Enigma case has a latch on the front which allows the cover to be raised. The lower half of the front also hinges down to allow access to the plugboard. The back of the case has a leather carrying handle.

Front of the Enigma case.
[w1tp.com/enigma]

Back of an Enigma case.
[w1tp.com/enigma]

Zur Beachtung!
Beachte die Gebrauchsanleitung für die Chiffriermaschine (H. Dv. g. 13)

1. Zur Säuberung der Walzenkontakte alle Walzen mehrmals gegenseitig vor- und rückwärtsdrehen.
2. Zur Säuberung der Tastenkontakte sämtliche Tasten vor Einschaltung des Stromes mehrmals kräftig herunterdrücken und hochschnellen lassen, wobei eine Taste dauernd gedrückt bleibt.
3. Bei Einstellung der in den Fenstern sichtbaren Zeichen beachten, daß die Walzen richtig gerastet sind.
4. Die unverwechselbaren doppelpoligen Stecker sind bis zum Anschlag in ihre Buchsenpaare einzuführen. Die vordere Holzklappe ist danach zu schließen, da sonst 3 Lampen zugleich aufleuchten können.
5. Leuchtet bei Tastendruck keine Lampe auf, so sind die Batterie, ihre Kontaktfedern, ihre Anschlüsse am Umschalter und der Umschalter zu prüfen.
6. Leuchten bei Tastendruck eine oder mehrere Lampen nicht auf, so sind die entsprechenden Lampen, die Kontakte unter ihnen, die Kabel der doppelpoligen Stecker, die Steckerbuchsen einschließlich ihrer Kurzschlußbleche, die Walzenkontakte, die Arbeitskontakte unter den jeweils gedrückten Tasten und die Ruhekontakte unter den mit ihnen korrespondierenden Tasten zu prüfen und bei etwa vorhandenen Verschmutzungen und Oxydationen zu säubern. (Siehe auch Ziffer 2).
   Von Maschine Nr. A 4388 ab dient zur Lampenprüfung die Öffnung auf der rechten Lampenfeldseite.
   Von Maschine Nr. A 4388 ab dienen zur Kabelprüfung die äußerste linke und rechte Buchse, der mittleren Reihe am Steckerbrett und die Kabelprüflampe auf der linken Lampenfeldseite.
7. Walzenachse und Walzenbuchsen sind sauber zu halten und wie alle übrigen Lagerstellen hin und wieder mit harz- und säurefreiem Öl leicht einzufetten. Die festen Kontakte der Walzen sind alle 6—8 Wochen mit Polierpapier überzuschleifen und mit einem wenig getränkten Öllappen abzureiben. Die Tastenkontakte, die Lampenkontakte und die Kurzschlußbleche sind vor Öl zu schützen.
8. Schlüsselangaben erfolgen entweder durch Zahlen oder Buchstaben.
   Zum Umsetzen der Zahlen in Buchstaben oder umgekehrt dient nachstehende Tafel:

A	B	C	D	E	F	G	H	I	J	K	L	M	N	O	P	Q	R	S	T	U	V	W	X	Y	Z
01	02	03	04	05	06	07	08	09	10	11	12	13	14	15	16	17	18	19	20	21	22	23	24	25	26

Instructions inside top cover. These explain how to clean and maintain the machine and include a table to convert Enigma rotors with 26 letters (A-Z) to those with 26 numbers (1-26). [w1tp.com/enigma Museum]

Case Cover

The inside of the cover contains (top to bottom):

- A clip to hold messages for the operator to type into the keyboard (shown here but very seldom found)
- Ten spare light bulbs
- A green filter to enhance readability or reduce nighttime glare of the illuminated letters
- A brief set of Maintenance Instructions (metal or white paper)
- Two extra plugboard cables

Top Panel

When closed, the top panel shows the keyboard, light panel, rotor setting wheels and power switch.

Opened up, the rotors and internal 4v battery box are revealed.

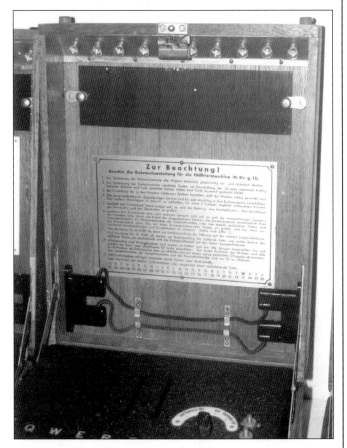

German Army Enigma case cover showing message clip, spare light bulbs, green filter, Maintenance Instructions, and extra plugboard cables. [w1tp.com/enigma Museum]

The closed top panel of the Enigma. [w1tp.com/enigma Museum]

A view of the light panel with the green filter in place.

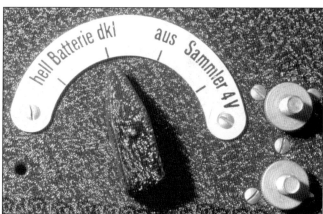

A close-up view of the power switch: (left-to-right): HEIL = Battery high, reduce power to bulbs to prolong their life; DKL = Battery low, Increase power to bulbs to make them readable; AUS = Power off; SAMMLER 4V = External 4 volts connected to external terminals. [w1tp.com/enigma Museum]

Top panel open. (w1tp.com/enigma Museum)

Top panel in open position with rotors being removed.

Manufacturer's label inside Enigma.

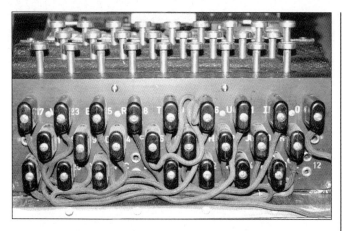

Plugboard with 12 of the possible 13 jumper cables in place.
[http://w1tp.com/enigma Museum]

Close-up of a plug showing the different size pins. Note the number 20 indicating that 'T' is the 20th letter of the alphabet.

The plugboard hinged out from the body of the machine.
[http://w1tp.com/enigma Museum]

Detail of the self-shorting bars that short out the two pins when no plug is inserted. [http://w1tp.com/enigma Museum]

Plugboard (German: *Steckerbrett*)

A possible 13 jumper cables can be used, each with a two-pin plug at each end. The plugs have one large pin at the top and one small pin at the bottom to ensure that they are not inserted the wrong way round. The sockets incorporate a self-shorting bar that operates when no plug is inserted.

Rotors and Reflectors

There are many variations of the basic Enigma rotors. A number of representative typical rotor and reflector photographs are shown here. Many more pictures are available on the CD *The Story of the ENIGMA* (see the info on page 4). The CD also includes the internal rotor wiring data for all of the standard rotors which Dr David Hamer has given me permission to include.

I will start by showing the most common rotors. I will then introduce the boxes that carried the additional rotors and next show the common reflector.

Reflector (left) and three typical German Army Enigma rotors (right) and input disc (far right) in place in Enigma. Note the locking lever on the left is in its locked operating position - pushed toward back of the machine.
[http://w1tp.com/enigma Museum]

A similar view to the one above but with the locking lever on the left in the open position - pulled towards the front of the machine. This allows the reflector to slide to the left as shown to allow removal of the rotors.
(http://w1tp.com/enigma Museum)

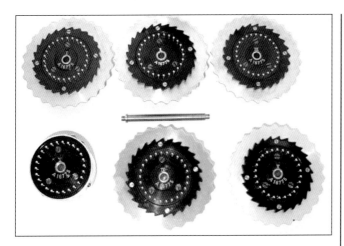

A complete set of five typical German Army Enigma rotors numbered: I, II, III, IV, and V along with the reflector and shaft. [http://w1tp.com/enigma Museum]

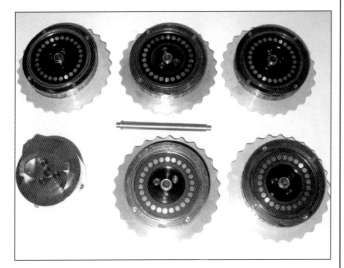

The other side of a complete set of five typical German Army Enigma rotors along with the reflector and shaft. [http://w1tp.com/enigma Museum]

Assembled (left) and disassembled view of a typical Enigma rotor. Note the complex interconnecting wires between the input side (right) and the output side (left). [NSA/National Cryptologic Museum]

One of the styles of wooden boxes used to store and transport the additional two interchangeable rotors which could be used in the three-rotor German Army Enigma. [http://w1tp.com/enigma Museum]

The widely used type B reflector. [http://w1tp.com/enigma Museum]

HOW THE ENIGMA MACHINE WORKS

The Enigma machine is like a fancy flashlight. Pushing a keyboard switch turns on a light bulb. This simple analogy will be helpful in understanding the workings of the machine.

Put very simply, Enigma works as follows: When you press a keyboard key to type in a plaintext letter, a switch is closed and an electrical voltage (4v) passes through a set of wheels and a plugboard, and finally lights a light bulb which illuminates a CIPHERTEXT letter of the alphabet.

The basic components are listed below. They are the same in both an Enigma machine and a flashlight.

- Battery
- Switch (keyboard)
- Electrical circuit (rotors and plugboard)
- Light bulb

Detailed Path of the Voltage from Battery to Bulb

1 *Battery -4v.* An internal 4 volt battery or an external DC source.
2 *Keyboard key contacts.* The normally open contacts are closed when a key is pressed. This passes the voltage along the appropriate letter's wire to the input disk or input connector.
3. *Input disk or input connector.* The input disk carries the voltage into the right end of the set of three rotors and the reflector.
4 *Rotors.* 3 (rightmost), 2 (middle) and 1 (leftmost). The voltage enters the rightmost rotor (3) from the input disk or input connector and travels left through its wiring to the middle rotor (2), then left through its wiring to the leftmost rotor (1) where it travels left through this rotor's wiring to the reflector.
5 *Reflector.* The reflector receives the voltage from the leftmost rotor (1) and its internal wiring sends the voltage back out along a different wire.
6 *Rotors again.* 1 (leftmost), 2 (middle), and 3 (rightmost), The voltage enters the leftmost rotor (1) from the reflector and travels right though its wiring to the middle rotor (2), then right through its wiring to the rightmost rotor (3) where it travels right through this rotor's wiring to the input disk or input connector.
7 *Input disk or input connector.* The input disk or input connector receives the voltage from the rightmost rotor (3) and carries it to the plugboard.
8 *Plugboard.* If no plug is inserted in the socket in the plugboard, an internal shorting bar simply passes the voltage out to the keyboard's normally-closed contacts. If a plug *is* inserted into the socket in the plugboard, the plug carries the voltage over to some other socket and from there to a different keyboard key's normally-closed contacts.
9 *Keyboard switches again.* The normally-closed contacts on the keyboard pass the voltage directly along to the appropriate light bulb.
10 *Light bulbs.* When a specific light bulb is illuminated, it lights up a single letter on the light panel.

Note that the rightmost rotor (3) is made to rotate one step by every keypress. At some point in its 26-step rotation, it makes the middle rotor (2) rotate one step. Similarly, the middle rotor (2) eventually causes the leftmost rotor to rotate one step. This causes a different light bulb to be illuminated even if the same keyboard key is pressed repeatedly. The exact point where a right rotor causes the rotor to its left to rotate one step is determined by the internal ring setting of the rotor.

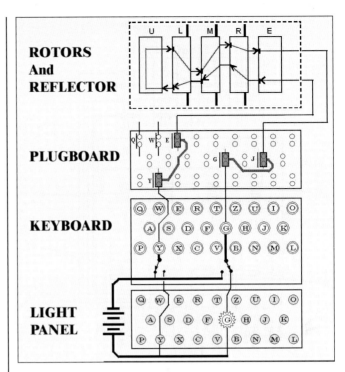

Graphical representation of current flow through an Enigma machine. [Diagram from Calbocovocoressi (2001)]

The diagram above was adapted from Calvocoressi (2001) *Top Secret Ultra* by Enigma historian Jim Jaeger. It presents the flow of electricity as it passes through the various parts of the machine. It starts from the battery shown to the left of the light panel. Press keyboard key "Y" and you can trace the voltage as it passes up through the switch under the key. Follow it as it continues up to the plugboard. A jumper in the plugboard transfers the electricity from the letter "Y" to the letter "E".

The electricity then flows up into the input disk (E), through the three rotors (R, M, L) to the reflector (U), back through the three rotors (L, M, R) to the input disk (E), and out to the plugboard again at letter "J". A plugwire connects letter "J" to letter "G". The electricity then continues down through the normally closed keyboard key switch "G" to light the light bulb that illuminates the letter "G" on the light panel. Note that many diagrams that you may encounter omit the passage of the voltage back through the normally-closed keyboard contacts. This diagram is correct and complete, as is the German diagram shown later.

ENIGMA MACHINE ELECTRICAL WIRING DIAGRAM

You can visually trace the battery voltage through the Enigma in the original German wiring diagram shown next.

Follow the arrows through the normally open keyboard key "Q" contacts down to the plugboard. The plugboard (with no jumper cable in place) passes the voltage directly on to the input disk or input connector. It passes through the rotors from right to left, the reflector, and then back through the rotors left to right to the input disk or input connector.

The voltage enters the plugboard as letter "E" and travels through the jumper cable to letter "W". It then passes through

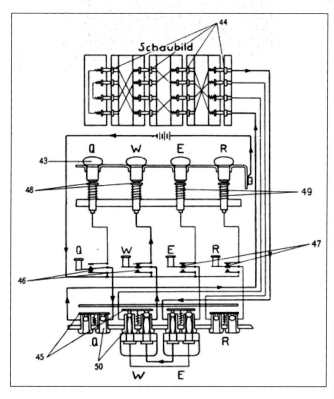

Wiring diagram of the German Army Enigma cipher machine (clockwise from top:): (44) Rotor contacts; (49) Lamp contact springs; (47) Normally closed key contacts; (50) Jacks in patch panel; (45) Bypass contacts for unused jack panel sockets; (46) Normally open key contacts; (48) Lamp contacts; (43) Light bulbs.

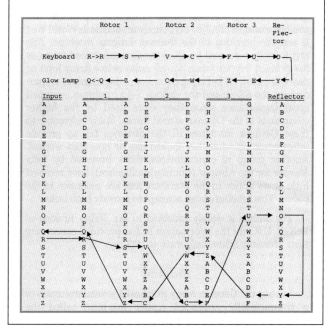

Another representation of how one letter (in this case a letter "R") is enciphered as another (a "Q"). [(From Mowry, 2003)

the normally closed contacts of the keyboard key "W" and lights up the bulb which illuminates the letter "W" in the light panel. This is how the plaintext letter "Q" is enciphered as the CIPHERTEXT letter "W".

Next, another diagram shows how the letter "R" electrical voltage passes through the rotors and comes out as the letter "Q".

It is a bit confusing because it shows the input disk on the left and the reflector on the right. In an Enigma machine, the input disk is actually on the right and the reflector is on the left. Keep this minor difference in mind as we trace the voltage through the rotors.

The voltage from the letter "R" coming into the input disk (on the left in this diagram) is converted into the letter "Q" as it passes through the rotors (1, 2 and 3), the reflector, the rotors (3, 2 and 1) again, and out of the input disk.

HOW THE ENIGMA MACHINE WAS USED - REVISITED
Having seen in detail how the Enigma is constructed, we can use that new knowledge to appreciate how the machine was used. To recap what we said at the beginning of the chapter:

Encoding
The Enigma cipher machine changes plaintext letters into CIPHERTEXT letters. It consists of a battery and a keyboard and a series of switches and plugs that determine which of the 26 light bulbs will illuminate one of the 26 letters of the alphabet when a particular keyboard key is pressed.

Pressing a keyboard key such as "h" causes a letter of the alphabet such as "A" to be illuminated. The keyboard key is called the "plaintext" and the illuminated letter is called the "CIPHERTEXT".

If you type the word "hello" on the keyboard (the plaintext message), letters "AZRWK" (the CIPHERTEXT message) may be illuminated by the light bulbs.

Transmission
The CIPHERTEXT message "AZRWK" is written down and then sent manually by telephone or radio to a receiving station.

Decoding
The receiving operator types "AZRWK" into another Enigma machine which illuminates light bulbs "hello" (the original plaintext message).

In order for this to work, the receiving Enigma machine **must** be set to the same starting position (key) that the sending Enigma machine used. Since there are an incredible number of possible starting positions, even if an enemy has an Enigma machine, it is virtually impossible for them to decode the ciphertext since they would not know the proper starting position (key). This is illustrated in diagrams at the start of this chapter.

The Enigma machine operator was trained to follow a set of steps before putting the machine into operation on a given day. These steps established the critically important Daily Key or initial settings of the machine.

The reason that the daily key was so important was that **it had to match** the initial setting or daily key set up on the receiving machine in order for the Enigma encoded CIPHERTEXT messages to be properly decoded into plaintext.

The daily key had four components that had to be set correctly. The key and its components were contained in the secret 'codebook' provided to every Enigma installation. It was the

Diagram showing how the input side of a rotor is connected to the output side through a maze of interconnecting wires. [From Mowry, 2003]

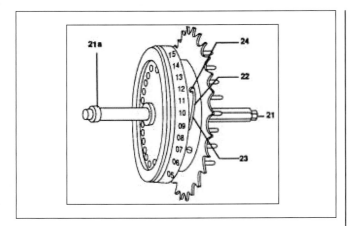

Example of a wiring maze

A B C D E F G H I J K L M N O P Q R S T U V W X Y Z

Z Y X W V U T S R Q P O N M L K J I H G F E D C B A

Setting the rotor position along the shaft. First, the rotors and shaft must be removed from the Enigma as shown here. [www.w1tp.com/enigma Museum]

Some of the important parts of the rotors (coding cylinders). Note especially the retainer spring (24) used to allow adjustment of the ring settings; lifting it allows rotation of the number/letter ring relative to the rotor. (21a) Axle shaft collar; (24) Retaining spring stud for adjusting ring settings; (22) Retainer spring for adjusting ring settings; (21) Axle shaft; (23) Retainer spring button for adjusting ring settings

capture of several of these on-site codebooks that provided many of the critical clues that allowed Enigma messages to be decoded, rather than any flaw in the design of the machine itself.

SETUP OF THE DAILY KEY OR INITIAL SETTING
The daily key or initial setting consists of the following four components:

(a) Rotor Position Along its Shaft
Each Army Enigma machine had three rotors that were slid onto an easily removable shaft or axle. Each rotor carried a number: I, II or III. Since the rotors could be placed on the shaft in any order, there were 3! (three factorial) = 6 possible orders.

Later Army Enigma machines were supplied with two more spare rotors IV and V giving 60 possible orders. The later German Navy Enigmas used four rotors internally and they were supplied with eight rotors numbered I to VIII. This gave many more possible settings.

To set the rotor position along the shaft, the rotors and shaft must first be removed from the Enigma, then the rotors are slid off the shaft and replaced in the desired order as shown in the pictures.

(b) Internal Rotor Ring Settings
Each rotor could have its internal ring wheel set at any one of 26 possible positions. The effect of these settings was to vary the point at which a complete revolution of the right rotor

Setting the rotor position along the shaft: The rotors are slid off the shaft and replaced in the desired order. [/w1tp.com/enigma Museum]

kicked in a single step of the next rotor to the left. Since there were three rotors, the number of possible settings was 26^3 (17,576). Actually, only two of the three wheels could increment a wheel to its left so the number of effective settings was 26^2 (676).

The photographs overleaf show how the ring settings can be adjusted.

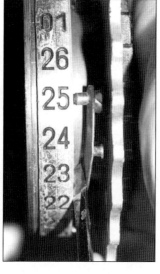

Setting the internal ring setting for a rotor. The locating pin, shown against number 25 in the left hand picture, must be pulled out to allow the ring with the numbers/letters to be rotated. Once the index pin has been pulled out, the ring with the numbers/letters may be rotated to any of the 26 possible positions. [www.w1tp.com/enigma Museum]

Setting the initial rotor starting window position or ground setting. The thumbwheel of each of the three rotors is moved until the appropriate letter/number appears in the window next to that thumbwheel. [From: Mowry, 2003]

(c) Initial Rotor Starting Window Position

One of the 26 numbers on each rotor could be set to appear in each window on the top of the Enigma machine as shown above. The number showing in each window was part of the Daily Key or initial setting, and there were $26^3 = (17,576)$ possible settings.

The plugboard with no jumper cables plugged in. [www.w1tp.com/enigma Museum]

(d) Plugboard Setting

Anywhere between 0 and 13 plug cables could be inserted into the 26 sockets in the plugboard. The calculation of the number of possible plugboard settings is complex and the formula is:

$$\sum_{p=0}^{p=13} \left(\frac{26!}{(26-2p)! \times p! \times 2p} \right) = 5 \times 10^{15}$$

This is 532,985,208,200,576 possible settings.

THE GRAND TOTAL OF POSSIBLE SETTINGS

Combining all of these possibilities give us a total of 26,672,901,348,424,004,787,290,112 or about 10^{26} possible starting settings.

Note that you may encounter other calculations for this figure. They differ with respect to the number of known and unknown factors. The calculation above is correct *if* you know the wiring of each rotor, the reflector, and the input disk. If you do not know these wiring diagrams, there are a great many more possibilities ranging up to 10^{114}. This was the case when Rejewski started trying to decipher Enigma messages as described later.

The NSA / National Cryptologic Museum book by Dr A. Ray Miller called *The Cryptographic Mathematics of Enigma* is available free on their website (http://www.nsa.gov/about/_files/cryptologic_heritage/publications/wwii/engima_cryptographic_mathematics.pdf) and in printed form directly from the museum. It is the first published mathematical analysis which explains very clearly how the number of possible keys is calculated.

There is more on the mathematics of Enigma in a later chapter.

Chapter 3
German Military Enigma Machines

The following is an illustrated chronological outline of the evolution of the German military Enigma cipher machines, based on the research of F L Bauer, 1997.

The differences between models often reflect differences between specific components of the Enigma (see the previous chapter).

1926 saw an early German Navy Model Enigma with three rotors. It was nicknamed the Glow Lamp machine.

Also manufactured in 1926 was the Funkschlussel C machine. It had 28 contacts, three rotors and four reflector positions. It was first intercepted by the Poles in 1928. Minor modifications appeared in 1933.

The 1928 Model G Enigma machine (shown below) appears to have four-rotors but the leftmost thumbwheel is actually used to turn a rotatable reflector. F L Bauer reports that this machine had no plugboard. This Enigma was specially constructed for supply to some governments that were friendly to Germany. Two hundred Model G machines were supplied to the German High Command (OKW) for an unknown "special purpose".

The T Model Enigma machine (below) has a rotatable reflector to the left of the three rotors and no plugboard. Five hundred of these specially wired machines are known to have been given to the Japanese Navy for joint communications.

The Enigma I (1930) became the standard German Army (*Heer*) model. It was now supplied with a plugboard (*Steckerbrett*) installed. A picture showing the principal parts of this machine is shown overleaf.

German Military Enigma Models at the NSA/National Cryptologic Museum. The G Model is on the left and the T Model on the right.

Enigma II was a large, eight-rotor printing model with 26 contacts, one position reflector and a German keyboard. The Polish Cipher Bureau detected that it was being used in 1933 for high-level military communications. It was, however, soon withdrawn from use after it was found to be unreliable and to jam frequently.

In 1934, the *Wehrmacht* version was agreed upon by the Navy (*Reichsmarine*) and the Army (*Heer*) so as to maintain inter-service compatibility. It was also introduced by the Air Force (*Luftnachrichtentruppe*) in 1935.

Army (*Heer*) Enigmas were released with only three rotors until December 12, 1938 when sets of five rotors developed in 1934 were released. Three rotors resided in the machine and two were carried separately in a special wooden box. Reflector "A" was replaced by Reflector "B" on November 1, 1937.

The Navy Enigma used three rotors out of a set of seven by 1938, and by 1939 three rotors were used out of a set of eight.

Reflector "C" was introduced in 1941. The Pluggable Reflector "D", introduced on 2 January, 1944, was first seen in Norway traffic nets.

The *Uhr* box was a 1944 addition enabling easy changing of the plugboard.

The four-rotor *Kriegsmarine* Enigma cipher machine was used on the Triton net in 1942. More on this machine later.

ENIGMA MACHINE MAJOR COMPONENTS:

ROTORS & REFLECTOR ---->

LIGHT PANEL --->

KEYBOARD ------->

PLUGBOARD ------>

The standard German Army three-rotor Enigma cipher machine. [www.w1tp.com/enigma Museum]

The standard German Air Force (*Luftwaffe*) Enigma cipher machine. [NSA/National Cryptologic Museum]

The Navy (*Kriegsmarine*) four-rotor Enigma cipher machine. Note that this example has a leftmost rotor with a black bakelite thumb wheel. They were usually all metallic. [NSA/National Cryptographic Museum]

German *Geheimschreiber* Model T-52 made by Siemens and codenamed STURGEON (ca. 1935). [NSA/National Cryptologic Museum]

German cipher machine codenamed TUNNY. [NSA / National Cryptologic Museum]

The Funkschlussel M4. (1942) with 'beta' rotor *Griechenwalze* which could be turned but was not moved by the mechanism. It was first used only by U-Boats in the Atlantic.

Another rotor 'gamma' was introduced on July 4, 1943. To ensure compatibility with the old three-rotor enigmas, old reflector "b" or "c" was split into a fixed thin reflecting disk: "b dunn" or "c dunn" and a turnable additional rotor 'beta' or 'gamma' was added.

Pictured on this page are two more historically important German cipher machines: the Tunny and the *Geheimschreiber* Model T-52.

GERMAN MILITARY ENIGMA MACHINE ACCESSORIES

In addition to additional rotors and boxes to store them in, there are several Enigma accessories which added to the versatility and usefulness of the machine.

The Enigma Uhr Box

This box contains 26 cables which plug into the 26 sockets on the plugboard on the Enigma. A switch allows the Enigma operator to select which sockets are connected to each other. This eliminates the tedious and time-consuming process of plugging individual patch cables into the sockets to change the plugboard settings.

It is thought that the name of the box, "Uhr" which is German for "clock" or "hour" may indicate that the dial was supposed to be changed on a regular time schedule.

Uhr box for automatic plugboard switching. [NSA/National Cryptologic Museum]

Remote light panel for Enigma. [NSA/National Cryptologic Museum]

The Enigma External Light Panel

This light panel had a connector which made electrical contact with all of the contacts that normally illuminated light bulbs on the internal Enigma light panel. All of the internal light bulbs were removed before the external light panel connector was installed.

The external panel display was placed out of sight of the Enigma keyboard operator so that he could not see the decoded message as it came in. This was done so that only an appropriate officer could see the decoded message illuminated by the external light panel.

The Enigma Printer

This printer plugged into all of the contacts that normally illuminated light bulbs on the internal Enigma light panel. The internal light bulbs were removed before the printer was installed.

When an electrical signal that would have activated an internal light bulb was received, it activated the printer which printed the letter on a paper tape.

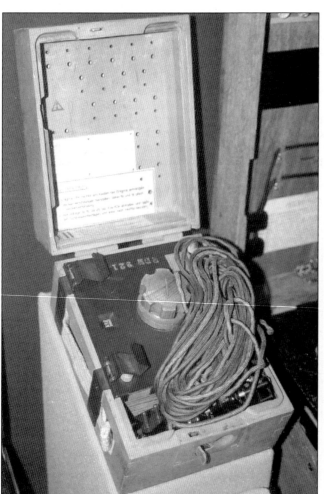

The Uhr box shown in its packed state and in use.

Enigma printer. [NSA/National Cryptologic Museum]

The Enigma Instruction Manuals

These manuals (pictured below) contained instructions for setting up the Initial Starting Position or Key for the Enigma as well as instructions about maintenance which explained how to clean the contacts and replace the bulbs.

Several Enigma Manuals in various languages are included on the CD: *The Story of the ENIGMA* (see the details on page 4 of this book).

SOME WW2 GERMAN ENIGMAS IN DETAIL

German Navy Four-rotor Enigma Cipher Machine

This four-wheel Enigma cipher machine was manufactured in 1944. By this point in the War, the German Navy suspected that the Enigma coded messages were being intercepted and they added a fourth rotor to the three-rotor Enigmas used by the Army and Air Force.

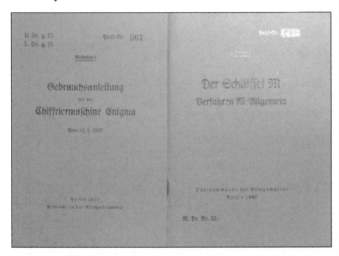

(pictured left) Enigma Instruction Manuals for the Army (*Heer*) (left) and Navy (*Kriegsmarine* 4-rotor) (right). [w1tp.com/enigma Museum]

The instruction label inside the cover with the two spare plug cables and the serial number plate.

Since the Enigma code had to be readable by all of the armed services, they designed the Navy four-rotor Enigma so that fixing the leftmost rotor in the 'A' position made the machine work exactly as though it was a three-rotor machine. In addition, the leftmost rotor was never rotated by the mechanism. This simplified the work of the Allies as they learned to decode the messages from the new four-rotor machine.

Illustrated on the left is one of the few surviving examples of the four-rotor Marine Enigma machine. It is in reasonably good condition considering its age. The inside of the cover is complete with spare light bulbs, special filter plate, instructions and two spare plug cables.

The following photographs show many views of the machine and its inner workings.

A rare German Navy four-rotor Enigma cipher machine.

Top view of the entire German Navy four-rotor Enigma.

The Military identification label of the German Navy four-rotor Enigma.

(right) German Navy four-rotor Enigma: A closer view of the plugboard.

German Navy four-rotor Enigma with the cover over the light bulbs removed.

The plugboard of the German Navy four-rotor Enigma.

German Navy four-rotor Enigma with the entire panel open.

Closeup of the four rotors of the German Navy Enigma.

Three rotors and their shaft have been removed. The reflector and leftmost rotor are on the left and the input wheel is on the right.

The reflector on the left and the input wheel on the right. Note that there is no rotational drive mechanism for the leftmost rotor.

The back cover plate has been removed to show the place where the rotors are mounted and the mechanism that advances the rotors with each keypress.

The reflector on the left, the special Beta rotor, and the three rightmost rotors on their shaft.

The three rightmost rotors and their shaft.

German Navy four-rotor Enigma with the top cover removed to show the light bulbs and the place where the rotors were mounted.

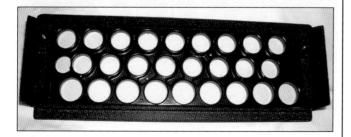

The plastic bezel that shields the light bulbs and mounts the transparent sheet carrying the letters.

The wooden box top and bottom with the Enigma removed.

The back of the box of the German Navy four-rotor Enigma, showing the carrying handle and the serial number tag

Another German Navy four-rotor Enigma cipher machine. This machine was found without its rotors, reflector, and without some of the label tags. The detail below shows the light filter in place over the light bulbs.

Pre WW2 German Enigma Cipher Machine

This is an early pre-WW2 version manufactured in 1937 and later used by the German Army.

The previous chapter of this book shows the front page of the English version of the advertising brochure for this machine. Also the front page of the German language handbook showing an early version that does not have a patch panel.

Two views of the 1937 German Army Enigma: (left) with all covers in place, and (right) with covers moved to show the light bulbs and battery case.

(below): A closeup of the patch panel, or *steckerboard,* of the pre-War Enigma machine.

A view of the K Enigma (right) next to a WW2 German Army Enigma for size comparison.

Model 'K' Enigma Cipher Machine

The Enigma-K (pictured above and below) was developed in 1926 and produced and sold to the Swiss Army in the 1930s. It has four adjustable wheels and no plugboard. The right three code wheels (German '*walze*') are similar to the standard Enigma machine wheels, and the left wheel is actually a completely adjustable reflector (German '*umkehrwalze*') which can be set to any one of the 26 possible letters.

The machine was also supplied with an external and internal display as well as a multiple-voltage power converter transformer in a separate box which converted voltages ranging from 110 - 250 volts AC to the required 3.5 volts to operate the lamps. The remote display made it possible for the officer-in-charge to read the decoded text without the cipher machine operator being able to see it. This was useful for top-secret messages.

Some of these German made machines, were bought by the Swiss before the War. The code was broken by several countries, including Britain and the US. The latter codenamed it "Indigo".

A closer view of the K Enigma with 'H' key pressed on keyboard and 'X' key illuminated in the light panel.

A closer view of the three rotors of the K Enigma on the right and reflector on the left.

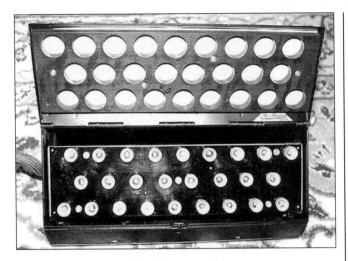

A closer view of the remote display light panel of the model 'K' Enigma.

A view of the K Enigma and power converter with wooden covers closed.

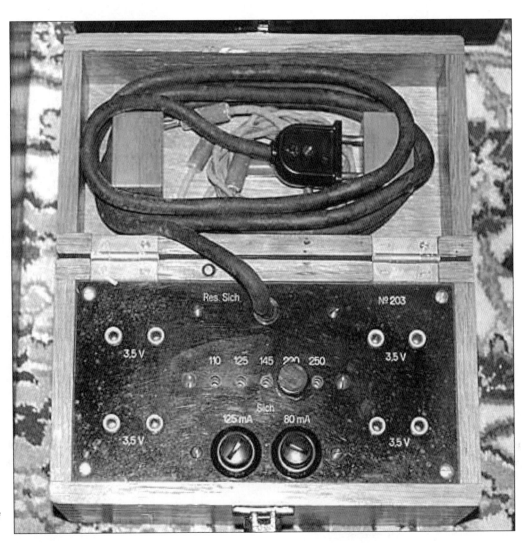

Model 'K' Enigma: A closer view of the power transformer box.

German Army WW2 Enigma Cipher Machine

This German Army model Enigma machine is in excellent condition as you can see from these pictures. It is shown with a complete set of rotors I, II, and III as well as the two additional rotors, IV and V which were interchanged with the three standard rotors to add complexity to the code settings.

The front of the WW2 German Army Enigma showing the plugboard, keyboard, light panel and rotor thumbwheels.

A view of the code wheels with the cover raised.

Set of five code wheels for the German Army machine.

Front of the Enigma with the cover closed, showing the latch.

Top of the German Army Enigma machine with the cover closed.

German Army WW2 Enigma: The mechanism which rotates the wheels.

(above) A view of the electrical contacts on the input wheel that brought voltages to and from the rotors from the plugboard.

Bottom of the German Army Enigma machine with the cover closed.

A view of the side of the Enigma machine with the cover closed.

Another German Army WW2 Enigma cipher machine. It also has the plastic cover for the rotors which are not present.

ENIGMA CIPHER MACHINE CODE WHEELS

There were several types of code wheel used in German Enigmas. Examples are shown in detail on the next few pages.

Set of Navy Code Wheels

Illustrated here is a boxed partial set of the original code wheels (German 'walze') for a Marine Enigma machine in the original carrying box.

The box is marked as the property of the German Marine High Command in Norway.

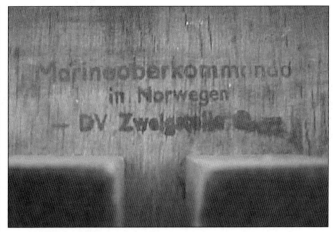

The Marine High Command label.

The complete box with some of the rotors.

The sides of all five code wheels.

A closer view of the five code wheels in the box.

View of the pin contacts on wheel number four.

The flat contacts of a code wheel.

(above) The front of the box in the closed position showing the latch, and (below) the back of the box showing the handle and serial number.

Boxed Sets of WW2 German Army Enigma Cipher Machine Code Wheels (Rotors)

The German Army Enigma machines had places for three rotors: I, II and III. The machines were also supplied with two additional rotors, numbers IV and V, which were stored in a special box to allow them to be carried around with the machine without damaging them.

Shown here is the box that was classically supplied to protect and transport the additional wheels.

Typical German Army Codewheels (Rotors)

(right) The three rotor wheels of a typical German Army Enigma on their shaft.

(above) Detail of the drive cogs that rotate the typical German Army code wheel.

Typical German Army rotors, with one slid off the shaft.

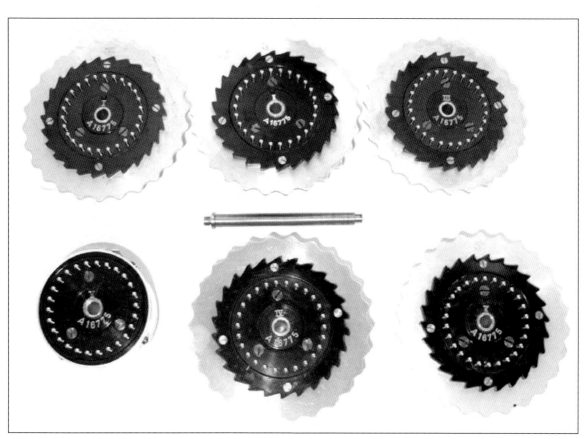

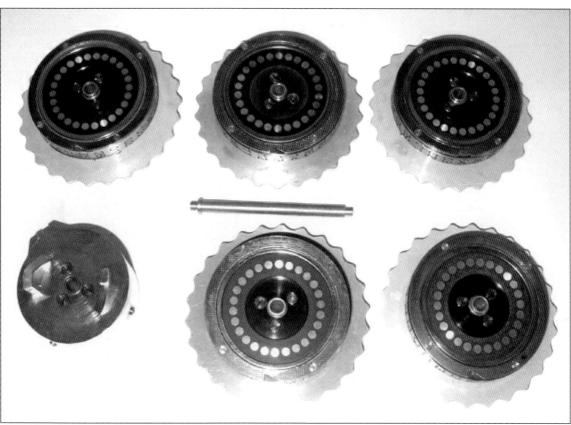

All five rotors, the reflector and shaft viewed from both sides.

The Widely Used 'B' reflector (German *Umkehrwalze-B*) for WW2 German Army Enigma Cipher Machines

The common 'B' reflector. Other pictures of this reflector and its position in the machine can be seen in the previous chapter.

The 'B' reflector in place in the Enigma machine.

Reverse side of the German Army WW2 'B' reflector.

Close-up view of the 'B' reflector.

Exceptionally Rare Programmable 'D' Reflector Wheel (German '*Umkehrwalze-D*') for WW2 German Army Enigma Cipher Machines

Called the D-reflector, this reflector wheel was used in the German Army (*Heer*) Enigma machine and it was first observed on 2 January, 1944 in Norwegian traffic. The D-reflector has 25 wires and tiny plugs, and each wire can be plugged into each of the 25 positions.

The D-reflector with the cover removed.

A close-up view of the plugs and wires on the D-reflector.

A Very Rare Vertically Boxed Set of Wheels

Vertically boxed sets of original WW2 Army Enigma code wheels (rotors).

Set of Enigma Rotors With Black Thumbwheels

These rotors have a black bakelite thumbwheel instead of the metal thumbwheel found on most rotors. Near the end of the war, Germany was very short on metal and was forced to make the rotors out of bakelite.

Both sides of the rotor with its bakelite thumbwheel.

The numbers and the ring setting adjustment on the black thumbwheel rotor.

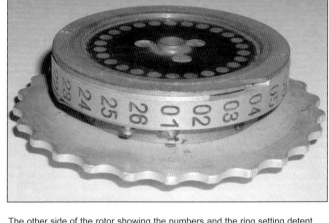

The other side of the rotor showing the numbers and the ring setting detent.

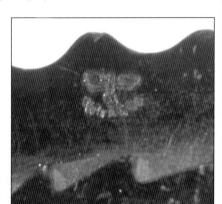

A closeup view of the German eagle emblem stamped into the bakelite thumb wheel.

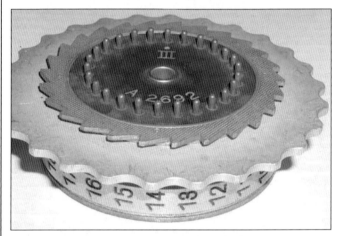

A different view showing the metal cog wheel.

A Set of Early Metal Enigma Rotors

This unusual set of Enigma rotors came from Italy. The rotors have metal cog wheels, an unusual looking dot over the roman numbers indicating the rotor number, and an unusual German eagle inspection stamp.

The unusual eagle inspection stamp.

Special Purpose Rotors from Hitler's Headquarters

These rotors, on display in the NSA / National Cryptological Museum, were specially wired and carried red-colored letters. They were primarily used by Hitler's Headquarters (NSA/National Cryptological Museum).

Rotor Shaft

This shaft is in 'as-found' condition typical of storage in a wet basement [w1tp.com/enigma Museum].

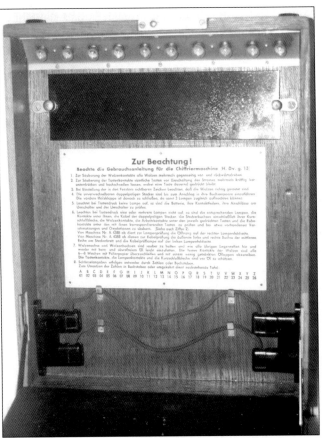

GERMAN THREE-ROTOR ENIGMA COVERS

The following two photographs from the w1tp.com/enigma Museum show variants of the German three-rotor Army Enigma cover.

The top one has a paper instruction sheet and the usual placement of green glare shield / filter.

The bottom one shows a paper instruction sheet and an alternate placement of green filter. This cover also shows unusual metal sockets for the spare plugboard cables.

Other Enigma covers are shown earlier in this chapter, and in the previous one.

HARD TO FIND LIGHT BULBS FOR GERMAN ENIGMA MACHINES.

Here are pictures of two boxes of the original light bulbs for the German enigma machines. These bulbs are flattened so that they do not come into contact with the plastic numerals in the display. Using round light bulbs usually results in cracking the plastic numerals in the display.

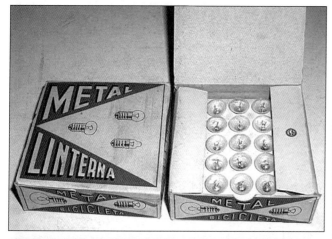

A view of the label on the side of the boxes.

A close-up view of one light bulb showing its flattened top.

DISASSEMBLY OF THE GERMAN ENIGMA MACHINE

These pictures show disassembly in the following order:

- Box
- Plugboard
- Metal Case
- Light panel
- Keyboard
- Frame
- Rotors

Disassembly of the Box

The Enigma machine is held in the wooden case by four screws. You can see one being removed in the picture. [http://w1tp.com/enigma Museum]

The Enigma machine base after removal from box. [http://w1tp.com/enigma Museum]

Another view of the very heavy cast iron base of the Enigma machine.
[w1tp.com/enigma Museum]

The right side of the Enigma showing the sheet metal cover plates.
[w1tp.com/enigma Museum]

Disassembly of the Plugboard

Plugboard with twelve of the possible thirteen jumper cables in place.
[http://w1tp.com/enigma Museum]

The wires are removed from the plugboard and it is unscrewed from the front of the Enigma machine with the screws shown in this photograph.
[w1tp.com/enigma Museum]

The plugboard is unscrewed from the front of the machine and swung out away from the machine. This reveals the self-shorting bars that short out the two sockets when no plug is inserted. [http://w1tp.com/enigma Museum]

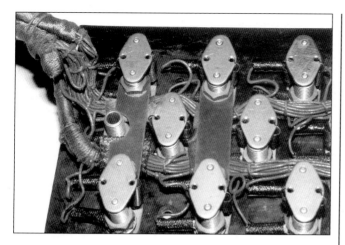

The plugboard is connected to the Enigma by these neatly cabled wires. Also note the self-shorting bars that short out the two sockets when no plug is inserted. [w1tp.com/enigma Museum]

Internal wiring of plug. [http://w1tp.com/enigma Museum]

Back of plugboard showing details of the self-shorting bars that short out the two sockets when no plug is inserted. Ignore the special test socket in the middle and note that the two sockets on the left are shorted together because no plug is inserted. On the right, you can see how the inserted plug pushes the shorting bar away from the two sockets allowing them to make electrical contact with the pins on the plug. [http://w1tp.com/enigma Museum)]

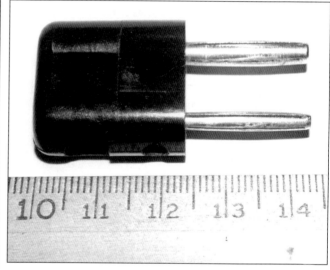

Detailed view of plug showing different size pins. [http://w1tp.com/enigma Museum]

Disassembly of the metal case

The Enigma machine with the metal case removed. [http://w1tp.com/enigma Museum]

Plugboard socket for letter 'T' (letter number 20) showing plug with large and small pins about to be inserted. [http://w1tp.com/enigma Museum]

Disassembly of the Light Panel

Unscrewing the side and back sheet metal panels allows them to be removed from the rest of the machine along with the top cover. They are shown on the right in this photo. [http://w1tp.com/enigma Museum]

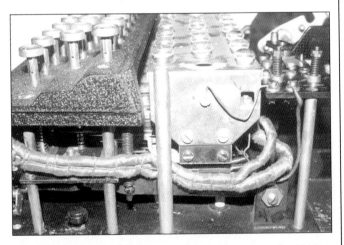

The entire metal light bulb panel serves as one contact for the screw-in contacts of the bulbs. It is connected to the power switch by the bare wire in the foreground. It is insulated from the rest of the machine by the brownish phenolic strip. (http://w1tp.com/enigma Museum)

Removing the two screws from the brownish phenolic strip at each end allows the light bulb panel to be removed. Note the cabled wires connecting the light panel to the rest of the machine. [http://w1tp.com/enigma Museum]

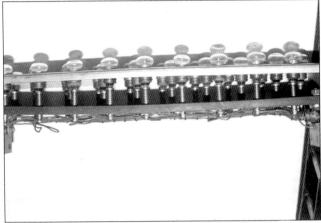

The entire light bulb panel showing the individually spring-loaded contacts for each light bulb. Note the cabled wires connecting the light panel to the rest of the machine. [http://w1tp.com/enigma Museum]

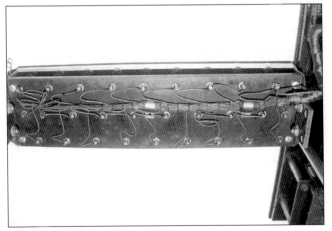

The back of the light bulb panel showing the individually wired contacts for each light bulb. Note the cabled wires connecting the light panel to the rest of the machine. [http://w1tp.com/enigma Museum]

A closer view of the light bulbs and their connections. [http://w1tp.com/enigma Museum]

Label warning users to use only light bulbs that are less than 12mm high. Using higher bulbs allows them to come into contact with the transparent plastic letter sheet and might damage this sheet. [http://w1tp.com/enigma Museum]

The underside of the light panel bezel showing the compartments for each bulb. If the bulbs are too high, they may press against the underside of the plastic sheet that carries the letters and they might distort or damage it. [http://w1tp.com/enigma Museum]

The light bulbs showing the special low-profile bulbs designed to be short enough not to damage the plastic letter panel. [http://w1tp.com/enigma Museum]

The spare light bulbs are stored in the cover of the wooden box. They are shown here along with the rare message clip. The message clip is used to hold the message while the Enigma operator types its letters into the keyboard. [http://w1tp.com/enigma Museum]

Disassembly of the Keyboard

The front of the keyboard showing how depressing a key both makes an electrical contact and presses down on the large bar that advances the rotors with each keypress. [http://w1tp.com/enigma Museum]

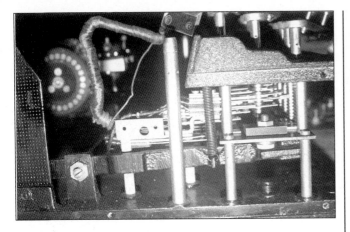

Side view of the metal bar that causes the rotors to turn with each keypress. [http://w1tp.com/enigma Museum]

This picture shows how pressing a key opens one set of electrical contacts and closes another. Each key shaft has a pin sticking out of it. When the key is pressed, the pin moves the common contact from the normally-closed contact on the top to the normally-open contact on the bottom. [http://w1tp.com/enigma Museum]

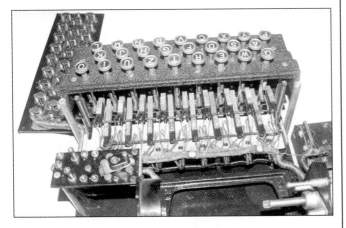

Back view of the keyboard showing the electrical contact matrix. [http://w1tp.com/enigma Museum]

Closer view of the electrical contacts on the keyboard. Note the screw-pins sticking out of each key's shaft which move the contacts. [http://w1tp.com/enigma Museum]

Disassembly of the frame

The fully disassembled Enigma showing the heavy cast iron base and frame surrounded by the modular light bulb panel (left), keyboard (bottom middle), and plugboard (right). [http://w1tp.com/enigma Museum]

The Enigma frame showing where the rotors and reflector fit and the push bars that cause the rotors to rotate with each keypress. The input disk can be seen on the right. [http://w1tp.com/enigma Museum]

The Enigma frame showing the input disk or input connector and the push bars that cause the rotors to rotate with each keypress. [http://w1tp.com/enigma Museum]

The input disk or input connector which brings the electrical voltages to, and accepts them from, the Rotors. [w1tp.com/enigma Museum]

Disassembly of the Rotors

A rotor disassembled and mounted at the NSA/National Cryptographic Museum. A complete rotor is on the left and the parts are distributed to the right. Note the complex connections made by the green wires between the input and output sides of the rotor.

Another perspective of the disassembled rotor. [NSA/National Cryptographic Museum]

A close view of the wiring maze that connects the 26 input contacts to the 26 output contacts inside the rotor. [NSA/National Cryptographic Museum]

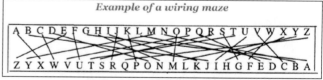

The maze of interconnecting wires that connect the input side of a rotor to the output side of a rotor. This maze is composed of the green wires in the preceding photograph. [From: Mowry, 2003]

GERMAN MILITARY ENIGMAS IN ACTION

Photographs showing German military Enigma machines in action are very rare since the German military did not want people to know what they were using for encipherment. The pictures on this page are among the very few that show Enigmas in the field.

The first set of three photographs appears to be an early Enigma field communications station

They were discovered by Rick Murdock who participates in WW2 re-enactments with the Grossdeutchland group of re-enactors

This is an unidentified field encampment showing a communications truck and a tent in which you can see several Enigma machines in operation. [Photo provided by German Grossdeutchland re-enactor Rick Murdock]

This is a closer view in the tent at an unidentified field encampment showing several Enigma machines in operation. [Photo provided by German Grossdeutchland re-enactor Rick Murdock]

Below is another view of the Enigmas in action in a tent at an unidentified field encampment. Although the photograph is very poor, it is included because it may provide some useful information for military historians. [Photo provided by German Grossdeutchland re-enactor Rick Murdock]

(right) An Enigma being used in the field.. [The NSA/National Cryptologic Museum]

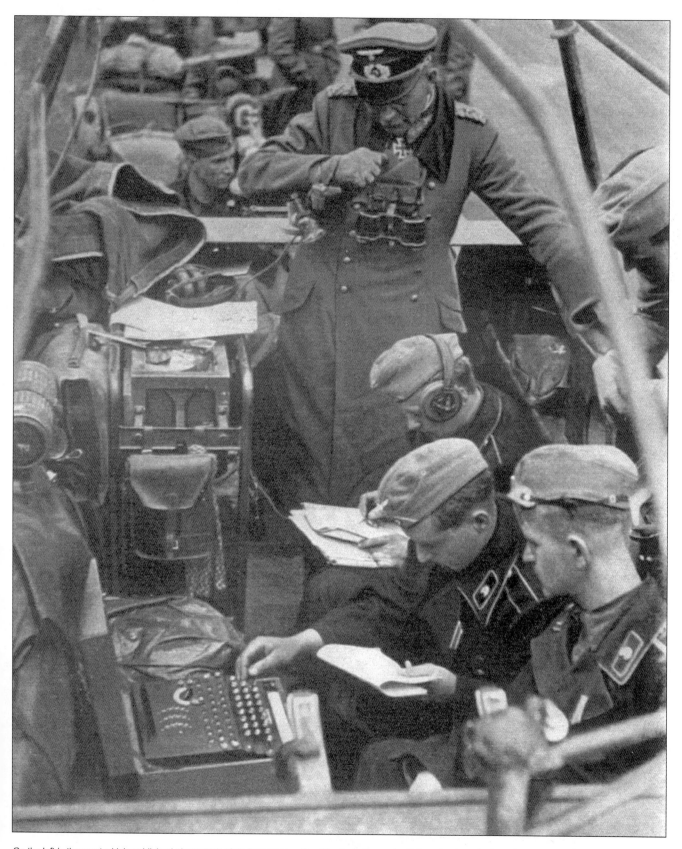

On the left is the most widely publicized photograph of an Enigma in action. The Army three-rotor Enigma is shown in the vehicle of Field Marshal Guderian. Note the number of operators needed to operate the Enigma. Two are operating the Enigma and one is handling communications while Guderian watches intently. [The NSA/National Cryptologic Museum]

ENIGMAS AT WW2 RE-ENACTMENTS

WW2 re-enactments are held in many countries and perhaps the largest is the one held on the first weekend in June at the Mid-Atlantic Air Museum in Reading, Pennsylvania.

Over 1500 re-enactors dressed in authentic uniforms, carrying authentic weapons and riding in authentic vehicles or aircraft, turn the Reading airport into a battlefield for three days. A crowd of 30,000 attends and watches demonstrations of radio equipment, armament, machine guns, flame throwers, search lights and artillery.

A replica of a French village is 'invaded' every few hours with frighteningly realistic compressed-air operated machine guns and explosions. Famous and not-so famous veterans take the stage and recount hair-raising experiences that they lived through during the war. In the evening 1940s bands play wartime music for dancing and reminiscing.

Visit: http://www.maam.org/maamwwii.html for more information.

Sometimes Enigma machines are shown and demonstrated in the German field encampments. The photos on this page were taken at the 2008 re-enactment.

Craig O'Brien, G3UZM, is shown in his German field tent dressed in an authentic German uniform at the 2008 Reading, Pennsylvania WW2 re-enactment. He is demonstrating one of the author's Enigmas. Behind the Enigma you can see his fully functional and authentic German radio transmitter and receiver. [author's photo]

An 80-year-old former German fighter pilot in his full-dress uniform inspects one of the author's Enigma machines. His comment was: "So *this* is why we lost the war . . . I have never seen one before". [author's photo.]

The author's Enigma display at the re-enactment included German Army, Air Force, and Navy Enigmas, an American M-209, and some accessories. [author's photo]

Chapter 4

The Mathematics of the Enigma

The most interesting mathematical aspect of the Enigma is the calculation of the total number of possible settings of the 'Day's Key' or 'Initial Setting' I have mentioned these calculations several times earlier in this book, and the calculations are clarified and explained in an excellent book published by the NSA / National Cryptologic Museum: *The Cryptographic Mathematics of Enigma* by Dr A Ray Miller. It is the first published mathematical analysis which explains very clearly how the number of possible Keys is calculated.

The book is available free of charge as an Adobe PDF file on the web site of the NSA / National Cryptologic Museum (http://www.nsa.gov/about/cryptologic_heritage/museum/) and in printed form directly from the Museum. A good friend of mine was interested in the mathematics of the Enigma. He saw the *The Cryptographic Mathematics of Enigma* for sale on *ebay.com*. He bid on it as it went up to $127.00. He enjoyed the interesting but rather short book until he paid a visit to the NSA museum in Maryland to see their Enigma machines. As he went in the front door, he saw a large stack of *The Cryptographic Mathematics of Enigma* books being distributed free at the front door!

For the convenience of the reader, I have reproduced in this chapter the full text of *The Cryptographic Mathematics of Enigma* (minus the illustrations which are similar to those reproduced elsewhere in this book).

Unfortunately, other books use different calculations and assumptions so you may find other values in print. This can be very confusing.

WHY CALCULATIONS DIFFER

The calculation of the number of possible locations of the three rotors on the shaft is fairly straightforward but some authors use only three rotors (six possible locations) and some use all of the five rotors that were available later in the evolution of the Army Enigma (sixty possible locations).

The calculation of the possible ring settings depends on whether you consider all three rings on all three rotors or only the rightmost two rings. These rings determine when the next rotor to the left will step or increment. The ring on the leftmost rotor, therefore, does not actually do anything, so some authors leave it out of the calculation.

The Ground Setting or Initial Setting of the rotors is straightforward.

The calculation of the possible arrangements of 0 - 13 jumper cables on the 26 socket plugboard is complex but it is also straightforward. However, some authors take into account the fact that many Enigma machines were only supplied with six, eight or ten jumper cables and restrict their calculations to take this factor into account.

Some authors consider every possible wiring arrangement for every rotor (and reflector) and the input disk, and some consider just the one wiring arrangement that was actually used in each rotor/reflector. Since Marian Rejewski and the Polish mathematicians knew absolutely nothing about the wiring of the rotors or reflector at the start of their work (see

the chapter on solving the Enigma), they were faced with this most complex situation.

HOW MANY POSSIBLE KEYS?

These differences result in calculations of the possible number of Keys that range from a high of 10 to the 114th power (10^{114}) and even 10 to the 145th power (10^{145}) for the four-rotor Navy Enigma) down to considerably lower figures. The early Polish codebreakers were faced with this high figure and after they had worked out the actual wiring of the rotors, reflector, and input disk, the number of possible Keys decreased dramatically, making their work and the work of subsequent codebreakers at Bletchley Park much easier. Their feat seems incredible since there are only about 10^{80} atoms in the entire observable universe and they were dealing with 10^{114} or 10^{145} possible Keys.

David Kahn in his book *Seizing the Enigma* (1991) emphasizes this point by saying that if a thousand cryptologists each had an Enigma to test at the rate of four Keys every minute every day all day, it would take 1.8 billion years for them to try all the possible Keys.

WAS IT UNBREAKABLE?

The total number of possible Keys is the number of Initial Settngs that a codebreaker would have to try before finding the one that deciphered the code. The number is so large that it would take a thousand codebreakers a thousand man-years to decode a single message. For this reason, the Germans believed that the Enigma machine code was unbreakable.

It is now clear that they were correct! The Enigma machine produced a CIPHERTEXT that *could not be deciphered* even using the fastest and most powerful computers of today. As we will see, it was human error, operational errors, and military tactics that made deciphering possible.

Although the Enigma machine had one technical mathematical flaw - a typed-in plaintext letter could *never* produce the same CIPHERTEXT letter - it was not enough to allow the CIPHERTEXT to be decoded mathematically. We will see how the messages were eventually deciphered in a later chapter.

Here is a summary of the operations necessary for setting the 'Day's Key' or 'Initial Setting'. Please keep them in mind as we see how the Keys were discovered in the next chapter of this book.

a. Rotor position on rotor shaft
b. Internal rotor ring settings
c. Initial rotor starting window position
d. Plugboard setting

Now follows the full text of *The Cryptographic Mathematics of Enigma* by Dr A Ray Miller, published by the NSA / National Cryptologic Museum > > > > > > > > > > > > >

The Cryptographic Mathematics of Enigma

written by Dr A Ray Miller

The Enigma cipher machine had the confidence of German forces who depended upon its security. This misplaced confidence was due in part to the large key space the machine provided. This paper derives for the first time the exact number of theoretical cryptographic key settings and machine configurations for the Enigma cipher machine. It also calculates the number of practical key settings Allied cryptanalysts were faced with daily throughout World War 2. Finally, it shows the relative contribution each component of the Enigma added to the overall strength of the machine.

ULTRA was the greatest secret of World War 2 after the atom bomb. With the exception of knowledge about that weapon and the probable exception of the time and place of major operations, such as the Normandy invasion, no information was held more tightly . . . . The security implies ULTRA's significance. ULTRA furnished intelligence better than any in the whole long history of humankind. It was more precise, more trustworthy, more voluminous, more continuous, longer lasting, and available faster, at a higher level, and from more commands than any other form of intelligence - spies or scouts or aerial reconnaissance or prisoner interrogations . . . . It may be concluded that ULTRA saved the world two years of war, billions of dollars, and millions of lives.

David Kahn, *Seizing the Enigma*

The Enigma cipher machine is one of the best known cipher machines in the world. Initially broken by Polish cryptanalysts, Enigma decrypts from British and later American efforts were given the cover name ULTRA to reflect the value of the information. Today the Enigma stands as a silent sentinel to the folly of those who placed their absolute confidence in its security. But it also stands in renowned tribute to the cryptanalysts who pitted their minds against a problem of seemingly invincible odds and who scaled its lofty heights.

Just how difficult was the Enigma cipher machine? Much has been written in recent years about the attacks against Enigma or the intelligence value of the ULTRA decrypts. However, little has been said about the defenses of the machine itself and why it was so trusted by its German designers. This paper sheds some light on that topic by calculating the incredible number of possible key settings and machine configurations, a number which led German forces to place undeserved confidence in Enigma's security. (Note 1)

This is the first time the exact numerical value in all significant digits has been published. Both the theoretical and the practical strength of the machine is calculated. The paper also provides an in-depth discussion of Enigma's construction.

An Enigma cipher machine consisted of five variable components: (Note 2)

1. a plugboard which could contain from zero to thirteen dual-wired cables
2. three ordered (left to right) rotors which wired twenty-six input contact points to twenty-six output contact points positioned on alternate faces of a disc

The illustrated booklet *The Cryptographic Mathematics of Enigma* by Dr A Ray Miller is published by the NSA / National Cryptologic Museum.

About the Author
Dr. A Ray Miller received a BS in computer science from the University of Central Florida in 1979. He received an MS and a PhD in computer science from the University of Illinois in 1984 and 1987, respectively. While in school, he worked at the Naval Experimental Computer Simulation Laboratory, the Department of Computer Science at the University of Illinois, and the Center for Supercomputing Research and Development. Dr. Miller has been employed at the National Security Agency since 1987 and has taken a tour at the Supercomputing Research Center. He has received several awards and commendations, including the 1991 Computer and Information Sciences Institute Award for Excellence, NSA's highest award in computer science. Dr. Miller is the author of several papers.

Produced by: The Center for Cryptologic History.
For more information contact: Public Affairs Office, National Security Agency, 9800 Savage Rd, Ft. Meade, MD 20755-6248

3. twenty-six serrations around the periphery of the rotors which allowed the operator to specify an initial rotational position for the rotors
4. a moveable ring on each of the rotors which controlled the rotational behavior of the rotor immediately to the left by means of a notch (Note 3)
5. a reflector half-rotor (which did not in fact rotate) to fold inputs and outputs back onto the same face of contact points

p	Combinations	p	Combinations
0	1	7	1,305,093,289,500
1	325	8	10,767,019,638,375
2	44,850	9	53,835,098,191,875
3	3,453,450	10	150,738,274,937,250
4	164,038,875	11	205,552,193,096,250
5	5,019,589,575	12	102,776,096,548,125
6	100,391,791,500	13	7,905,853,580,625

Nothing else on the machine which could be used to set the initial state of the cryptologic was variable. Additional necessary equipment included a mechanical system (stepping levers and ratchets) for forcing rotor rotation, a twenty-six-letter keyboard, twenty-six light bulbs for the output letters, and a battery for powering the light bulbs. What we wish to determine is the number of different ways of configuring the variable components in the system which contributed to the cryptographic strength of the machine. Although in practice the Germans did not use Enigma to its fullest potential, Allied cryptanalysts could not *a priori* rule out any valid theoretical configuration.

The first variable component was the plugboard. Twenty-six (for A-Z) dual-holed sockets were on the front panel of Enigma. A dual-wired plugboard cable could be inserted making a connection between any pair of letters. Enigma cryptographers had a choice of how many different cables could be inserted (from zero to thirteen) and which letters were connected. The plugboard functioned like an easily modifiable stationary rotor positioned to the right of the three rotating rotors. (Note 4)

There were three elements which must be considered when calculating the number of possible plugboard connections: the number of cables used, which group of sockets was selected to receive those cables, and the interconnections within that group of sockets (ie, the specific letter-pairs created by each cable). We will consider socket selection first. There were twenty-six sockets on the plugboard. Each individual cable consumed two sockets (one for each end of the cable). Given the choice of p ($0 \geq p \geq 13$) plugboard cables inserted into the plugboard, there were therefore

$(26/2p)$ different combinations of sockets which could have been selected.

Having calculated the number of different groups of sockets, we will now determine how many ways in which those p cables could have been inserted into the $2p$ selected sockets. After inserting the first end of cable #1 into a socket, the second end of the first cable had $2p - 1$ free sockets from which to choose (within that group). After inserting the first end of cable #2 into a socket, the second end of the second cable had $2p - 3$ free sockets from which to choose. This pattern continues down to cable #p; when its second end needed to be inserted into the plugboard, only one free socket was left open. It should be clear at this point that the total number of ways in which p cables (Note 5) could have been inserted into $2p$ open sockets (with each cable consuming two sockets) is given by the equation $(2p - 1) \times (2p - 3) \times (2p - 5) \times ... \times 1$.

Therefore, given p cables inserted into the plugboard, the number of different connections which could have been made by an Enigma operator is given by the combination of the above two elements or

$(26/2p)$ x $(2p-1)$ x $(2p-3)$ x $(2p-5)$ x ... x 1
= $26!/((26-p)!$ x $p!$ x $2^p)$

The third and final element which must be factored in is the number of cables used, or p. Using the equation just calculated, the number of plugboard combinations for all possible values of p is given in the table. One interesting characteristic of the machine is that the maximum number of combinations did not occur at 13 as might be expected, but rather when the operators used eleven plugboard cables. (Note 6)

Since the combinations possible for each value of p were mutually exclusive, the total number of possible plugboard combinations is given by the sum of the above numbers, or

$$\sum_{p=0}^{13} \frac{26!}{(26-2p)! \times p! \times 2^p} = 532,985,208,200,576$$

The second variable component was the three ordered (left to right) rotors which wired twenty-six input contact points to twenty-six output contact points positioned on alternate faces of a disc. This equation is straightforward. There are of course 26! unique discs which could have been constructed. (Note 7) Of those 26! any one of them could have been selected by the cryptographers to occupy the leftmost position. The middle position could have been occupied by one of the 26! - 1 discs which were left. And the rightmost disc could have been selected from any one of the 26! - 2 discs still remaining. The total number of ways of ordering all possible disc combinations in the machine is therefore:

26! × (26! - 1) × (26! - 2)
or (Note 8)
65,592,937,459,144,468,297,405,473,480,371,753, 615,896,841,298,988,710,328,553,805,190,043,271,168,000, 000.

The third variable component of Enigma was the initial rotational position of the three rotors containing the wired discs. This was specified by the cryptographers and set by the machine operators by means of twenty-six serrations around the rotor periphery. Since each of the three rotors could be initially set into one of twenty-six different positions, the total number of combinations of rotor key settings was 26^3 or 17,576.

The fourth variable component of the machine was a moveable ring on each of the rotors; each ring contained a notch in a specific location. (Note 9) The purpose of the notch was to force a rotation of the rotor immediately to the left when the notch was in a particular position. The rightmost rotor rotated every time a key was pressed. The rightmost rotor's notch forced a rotation of the middle rotor once every 26 keystrokes. The middle rotor's notch forced a rotation of the leftmost rotor once every 26 × 26 keystrokes. Since there were no more rotors, the leftmost rotor's notch had absolutely no effect whatsoever. (The reflector, positioned to the left of all rotors, did not move.)

Therefore, only two notches contributed to the cryptographic strength of the machine. Since each of them could have been positioned in any one of twenty-six possible locations, 26^2 or 676 combinations were possible.

The fifth and final variable component of Enigma was the reflector. The reflector had twenty-six contact points like a rotor, but only on one face. Thirteen wires internally connected the twenty-six contact points together in a series of pairs so that a connection coming in to the reflector from the rotors was sent back through the rotors a second time by a different route. The internal wiring could be constructed in the following fashion. Connecting one end of the first wire to contact point #1, the other side of the wire had twenty-five different contact points to which it could be connected. Thus the first wire consumed two contact points and had twenty-five different possibilities. The second wire also consumed two contact points, and had only twenty-three different connection possibilities remaining from the unconsumed contact points. The third wire consumed two more contact points and had twenty-one possibilities for connection. The pattern should be apparent by now; the number of distinct reflectors which could have been placed into Enigma was (Note 10):

$$25 \times 23 \times 21 \times \ldots \times 1 = 26/(13! \times 2^{13})$$
$$= 7,905,853,580,625$$

(It is interesting to notice that the number of different reflector combinations is also the same as the number of possible plugboard combinations when $p = 13$ cables were used. This should not be surprising; in both cases the value represents the number of possible pair-wise combinations which can be made given twenty-six choices and thirteen connecting wires.)

We now have everything we need in order to calculate the theoretical number of possible Enigma configurations. It is simply the product of all five values calculated above. That astounding number is:

3,283,883,513,796,974,198,700,882,069,882,752,878,379, 955,261,095,623,685,444,055,315,226,006,433,615,627,409, 666,933,182,371,154,802,769,920,000,000,000

which is approximately 3×10^{114}. To see just how large that number is, consider that it is estimated that there are only about 10^{80} atoms in the entire observable universe. No wonder the German cryptographers had confidence in their machine!

The three-rotor, single-notched Enigma was by far the most common model in use by German forces. Later in the war, however, the German Navy adopted a variant version of the Enigma cipher machine which used four rotors, and rings which contained either a single or a dual notch. Let's recalculate the theoretical number of key settings and machine configurations for a naval Enigma to see how those modifications increased the strength of the machine.

Step 1 is the number of plugboard combinations. Obviously the fourth rotor and the extra notches had absolutely no effect on this value; it is unchanged at 532,985,208,200,576.

Step 2 is the selection and the ordering, left to right, of the wired rotor discs. The previous value calculated was 26! × (26! - 1) × (26! - 2). It is tempting to simply add in the factor (26! - 3). However, the new fourth rotor was not interchangeable with the other rotors; it could be placed in only one location. (Note 11) This meant that selection of the fourth rotor was independent, and since there were 26! ways that the rotor's disc wiring could have been constructed, (Note 12) the new equation is given by:

$$26! \times (26! -1) \times (26! -2) \times 26! \text{ or}$$

26,453,071,587,484,435,966,565,383,350,966,637, 647,029,992,367,895,564,609,744,699,959,788,953,452,189, 042,702,687,102,042,112,000,000,000,000.

Step 3 is the initial rotational positions of the wired discs. As all four could have been in any one of twenty-six possible positions, the number of combinations is 26^4 or 456,976.

Step 4 is the initial positions of the moveable notched rings. The German Navy added a second notch to some rings in order to increase the irregularity of the rotational behavior of the rotors. We will therefore calculate all possible combinations of single or dual notched rings in each of the rotor positions. For a ring containing a single notch, we've already seen that the notch could have been placed in one of twenty-six possible orientations. A ring containing two notches, on the other hand, had 26 × 25 possible orientations. Since these two cases were mutually exclusive of each other, the total number of combinations is expressed as the sum of the two values or $26 + (26 \times 25) = 26^2$. Now on the three rotor Enigmas, as previously stated, the notch locations mattered only for the rotors placed into the rightmost and middle positions. As it turns out, that is also true for the four rotor naval Enigmas as well. Since the fourth rotor had no ratchets and the Enigma had no fourth stepping lever, the fourth rotor did not move; once the Enigma operator had set the initial rotational position by hand, it remained constant for the duration of the message. (Note 13) So then the total number of possible single or dual notched ring positions on the rightmost and middle two rotors is given by 26^4 or 456,976.

Step 5 is the reflector wiring. Because of cramped conditions on board ship, the Germans did not want to add the extra space required for the fourth rotor, thereby making the Enigma wider than it was before. Instead, they made a special half-width reflector so that the machine could continue to fit into the same sized space. However, the total number of possible wiring configurations does not change from what we calculated above, or 7,905,853,580,625. (Note 14)

We are now ready to determine the theoretical number of possible naval Enigma configurations assuming four rotors and single or dual notches in the rings. It is the product of all five values calculated above or:

23,276,989,683,567,292,244,023,724,793,447,227,628, 130,289,261,173,376,992,586,381,072,041,865,764,882,821, 864,156,921,211,571,619,366,980,734,115,647,633,344,328, 661,729,280,000,000,000,000,000,

which is approximately 2×10^{145}.

The numbers derived thus far are only theoretical values which reflect how many initial cryptographic machine states were possible. In practice, once the war started, Allied crypt-analysts had a much easier job. As a final exercise, we'll calculate the number of possible cryptovariables cryptanalysts were likely to encounter when trying to determine the daily keys. Some information was known by the Allies to be effectively constant.

In step 1, the plugboard, the most common value of p used was 10. Since the number of cables was known, all that needed to be determined on a daily basis was which twenty letters had a cable patch inserted and the ten pairs created by those twenty letters. This is already given in the table under $p = 10$ as the value 150,738,274,937,250.

In step 2, the selection and ordering of the rotor discs, things changed over time. Initially only three rotor discs were created for general-purpose use. (Special-purpose machines, as previously stated, had their own set of wirings.) Later, two additional rotor discs were introduced, making a total of five. The German Navy added an additional three rotor discs, bringing their total to eight. And finally, one and then two extra fourth rotor discs (without rotation ratchets) were added by the Navy, giving them ten possible discs.

We will assume the general-purpose case of five discs and further assume the wiring of each of the discs is known. We will also assume this is an Enigma machine with three rotors. What Allied cryptanalysts had to determine was which three of the five possible discs were chosen, and in which order they were placed into the machine. This is simply 5 x 4 x 3 = 60 possible combinations which needed to be checked.

In step 3, the initial rotational position of the rotors was an unknown key setting for which there were 26^3 or 17,576 possible values.

In step 4, the position of the notched rings, we will assume single notches on all of the rings. (Dual notched rings were not introduced until the Navy added their extra three rotor discs.) This is 26^2 or 676. (Note 15)

In step 5 we will assume the operators are using a single reflector in which the wiring is already known so the number of combinations here is simply 1.

Thus the possible cryptovariable space Allied cryptanalysts were typically faced with during the Second World War when attempting to read Enigma traffic is the product of the above five values, or 107,458,687,327,250,619,360,000, which is approximately 1×10^{23} or, stated another way, about one hundred thousand billion billion. (Note 16) Although that value is much smaller than the total number of atoms in the entire observable universe, it is still quite an impressive number! This is all the more true considering Allied cryptanalysts were faced with continually changing message keys at least daily - for every different radio network the Germans constructed.

With such daunting odds facing any cryptanalyst, it is not surprising that the German cryptographers felt secure using the Enigma. The strength of the large numbers, numbers so vast they are really beyond true comprehension, led the Germans to have absolute and complete confidence in the integrity of the Enigma cipher machine. And in that misplaced confidence, the Germans were absolutely, completely, and fatally wrong.

NOTES

1. For example, after analysis of this very topic one German cryptographer wrote, "From a mathematical standpoint we cannot speak of a theoretically absolute unsolvability of a cryptogram, but due to the special procedures performed by the Enigma machine, the solvability is so far removed from practical possibility that the cipher system of the machine, when the distribution of keys is correctly handled, must be regarded as virtually incapable of solution."

2. Additional detailed descriptions on Enigma internals can be found in some of the references at the end of the article.

3. Subsequent naval Enigmas contained four rotors and up to two notches per ring.

4. If a letter's plugboard socket was left unconnected, eg, the letter A, then A on the keyboard was wired directly to the A input position feeding the rotors. On output a wire coming from the rotors' output A position was wired directly to the light bulb A. If, on the other hand, A was plugged to X, then on input the A key was fed to the rotors as X, the X key was fed to the rotors as A, and on output what would have normally illuminated the A light bulb now connected to the X light bulb, and what before would have gone to X instead lit up as A.

5. The boundary condition of $p = 0$ has one interconnection possibility.

6. The Germans used a variety of connections. In 1940, for example, keys were recovered that used from 6 to 11 plugboard cables. In 1941 they standardized on 10 plugboard cables for all traffic.

7. $26! = 403,291,461,126,605,635,584,000,000$. Since the rotor discs were hardwired, such a vast number would have been impossible to construct in practice. Indeed, only a very small handful of rotor discs was ever constructed since they were limited to what troops could physically carry with them. Also the Germans never changed the disc wirings during the war. They did, however, create several different groups of rotor disc wirings for special-purpose machines. (For example, the High Command had specially wired Enigmas to communicate with Hitler's headquarters.) Additionally, even if the practical rotor disc wirings were compromised, the rotor ordering was still an unknown, although of course the equation is much smaller under those conditions. Furthermore, German cryptographers knew attacking cryptanalysts would have to initially sift through all possible combinations. Finally, they could have deployed "pluggable rotor discs" which could have been changed by the operators in the field and thus would have restored the number of practical combinations back to the number of theoretical combinations. ("Pluggable reflectors" were in fact deployed later in the war.) See the final section of the paper for a practical and not a theoretical example.

8. It was known that the German troops carried individually numbered and unique sets of rotors. Hence selecting a rotor reduced the number of possibilities by one. So $26!^3$ is not the correct value.

9. The ring also held the A-Z indicators specified by the cryptographers as part of the key setting. The operators used this as a guide when setting the rotor in step 3. Moving the

notched ring against the wired disc also had the secondary effect of moving the A-Z indicators against the disc as well. This technically linked the rotational position in step 3 with the notch position in step 4. However, since it was possible to place the internal wired disc in any one of the twenty-six positions and the notched ring separately in any one of the twenty-six positions, these were, in fact, independent variables when counting initial cryptographic machine states.

10 In practice the operators did not frequently change the reflector in the Enigma. Only a handful of hardwired reflectors ever saw service. Additionally, reflectors were created that also had different internal wiring for the special purpose Enigmas. However, just as with the rotors, German cryptographers knew that initially Allied cryptanalysts would have to sift through all possible combinations. It was not until later that some four rotor naval machines gained easily selectable interchangeable reflectors. Even later, German cryptographers developed and deployed pluggable reflectors which could be rewired by the operators in the field. This restored the number of practical reflector combinations to the theoretical value.

11 The Germans did not want to retool their equipment and change the internal mechanics of the Enigma. Hence there was no fourth stepping lever to cause rotation of that rotor during a message. Since no stepping lever was present, the ratchets the lever interacted with were not added to the fourth rotor. This meant the fourth rotor (positioned on the extreme left next to the reflector) was incompatible and could not be used in the other three rotor locations.

12 In practice, the Navy initially deployed only one new fourth rotor disc. Later they added a second disc. But as before, Allied cryptanalysts were initially faced with determining which wiring configuration was used from all possible combinations.

13 This had a nice side effect, however. In practice, the fourth rotor and its new reflector had wiring chosen such that in one particular orientation the combination had exactly the same effective wiring as reflectors built for three rotor Enigmas. This gave the four rotor machines the ability to still communicate with the older three rotor machines.

14 In practice, the Navy introduced just one half-width reflector at the same time they introduced their first fourth rotor. A second half-width interchangeable reflector was released at the same time their second fourth rotor was released. Pluggable reflectors followed all of these events.

15 Some may choose to add another factor of 26 at this point, since the daily key was formally given by three positions for the rings (step 4) followed by rotational orientation of the three rotors (step 3). As previously stated, moving the rings containing the notches had the side effect of moving the indicators used as a guide by the operators used in step 3 . So although the notch was unimportant in the leftmost rotor due to the reflector, the ring position was very important to ensure the disc wiring was oriented correctly given an indicator for step 3. However, since there are twenty-six ways to specify the combination of ring position and indicator selection which will yield the exact same disc wiring orientation in the leftmost rotor, we can factor the twenty-six back out of the equation again.

16 Billion is to be understood in the American [thousand million] and not in the European sense.

REFERENCES

Erskine, Ralph, and Frode Weierud. "Naval Enigma: M4 and its Rotors." *Cryptologia*, Volume XI, Number 4, October 1987, 235-44.

Hinsley, F. H. *British Intelligence in the Second World War*. 2 volumes. London: Her Majesty's Stationery Office, 1979, 1981.

Kahn, David. *Seizing the Enigma*. Boston: Houghton Mifflin Company, 1991.

Kozaczuk, Wladyslaw. *Enigma: How the German Machine Cipher Was Broken, and How It Was Read by the Allies in World War Two*. Edited and Translated by Christopher Kasparek. Frederick, Maryland: University Publications of America, Inc, 1984.

Office of the Chief of Naval Operations CNC-OP-20. *Enigma Series: Volume 1. Click Process*. On file at the Smithsonian American History Museum. RIP 603, Reg. No. 9, Communications Intelligence Technical Paper TS-10/E-1, filed 2 December 1980.

Woytak, Richard. "A Conversation with Marian Rejewski." Transcribed and translated by Christopher Kasparek. *Cryptologia*, Volume 6, Number 1, January 1982, 50-60.

Dedicated to the memory of the Allied Polish cryptanalysts:
Marian Rejewski
Jerzy Rozycki
Henryk Zygalski

Chapter 5

Solving the Enigma

NOTES ABOUT HISTORICAL ACCURACY

The recorded history of the Second World War has been dramatically distorted by the fact that the deciphering of the German Enigma Messages was kept secret for thirty years! A great many WW2 history books were written during these thirty years and until 1974, none of them considered the fact that the Allies were regularly breaking the German Enigma codes. We now know that the breaking of the Enigma codes had a very significant impact on the course of the war and that the history books will all need to be rewritten. In fact, I have found that you can safely disregard any books written before about 1980 when the full story of the Enigma started to emerge. As late as 1982, British mathematician Gordon Welchman was threatened with lawsuits and censured by the security authorities for revealing too much information about the breaking of the Enigma codes. (Freedman, 2001)

Keeping secret the deciphering of the Enigma codes was probably the second most amazing achievement of the war, with the actual deciphering of the codes being the first. Between 7,000 and 10,000 people worked on breaking the Enigma-coded messages at Bletchley Park. Each person was sworn to life-long secrecy on penalty of death when they signed-up and *every* one of them kept the secret from family and friends for over thirty years!

When F W Winterbotham was given permission to write and publish *The Ultra Secret*, the first book on the deciphering of the Enigma and the use of 'Ultra' (deciphered Enigma information) in 1974, it was the first time that any military historians had heard of this incredible feat. His second book expanded on his revelations in 1978.

Since that time, many people who worked at Bletchley Park have written about their own work and that of others in the Enigma deciphering projects. Many of them criticize what they call the inaccuracies and distortions in the writings of Winterbotham and each other. Each of them claims to be telling the absolutely correct version of events and achievements. This leaves us with considerable uncertainty about the accuracy of the various reports. I suggest, therefore, that you keep this disagreement in mind as you study this and other accounts of the deciphering of the Enigma codes.

One example of the disagreement between Enigma historians concerns the report that Churchill intentionally allowed the English town of Coventry to be bombed without mounting a major fighter aircraft response. The report claims that since Churchill had learned about the impending raid through deciphering the German Luftwaffe (Air Force) Enigma messages, he did not want to launch a major fighter response because he feared that the Germans might suspect that he was reading their secret messages. Many historians now claim that this is absolutely false while others believe the story. The historians who claim that it is false cite a lack of hard evidence in support of the story. Those who support the story say that a lack of evidence does not prove that the event did not happen.

I have chosen to present what are currently the most widely-held opinions about events leading to the deciphering and use of the Enigma-coded information. However, I caution the reader that many of the reports are very contradictory and that I cannot be certain of their accuracy. Although the archives of the NSA/National Cryptologic Museum are open to study, the materials in the British Public Records Office (PRO) have only recently been declassified. The work of studying these archives in detail has only started and it will be many years before historians will be able to be relatively certain about what happened. Important and timely articles on this evolving topic can be found in journals such as *Cryptologia* (See the Appendix on further reading) which has been publishing very important articles since 1977, and other articles appear on the internet.

My CD, *The Story of the Enigma* (see page 6 of this book), includes the 2001 NSA / National Cryptologic Museum book by Jennifer E. Wilcox entitled *Solving the Enigma: History of the Cryptanalytic Bombe*. It is also available free on their website (http://www.nsa.gov/museum/index.cfm) and in printed form directly from the Museum. It is a very well researched and written summary of how the codes were broken.

Other books on the subject are listed in the Appendix to this book.

THE BEGINNINGS OF WW2 CODEBREAKING

(This material was distilled from most of the references cited in the Appendix to this book. It follows the general outline of Maurice Freedman's 2001 book: *Unravelling the Enigma*. It also includes information from the National Cryptologic Museum book by J Wilcox cited).

By using the methods outlined below, the Allies were able to read many of the German Enigma-enciphered messages throughout most of the war. From May, 1941 through October, 1941, the Allies were reading the German messages which used the 'Dolphin' key. From November, 1941 through January, 1942, and from December, 1942 through parts of May, 1943 'Shark' was being read. From September, 1943 through May, 1945, the 'Shark' messages were being read in less than 24 hours. In some cases, the Allies had deciphered and read the messages before the Germans received and deciphered them.

A pre-1952 timeline of cryptologic events is shown overleaf. It is from the website of the National Cryptologic Museum of NSA: http://www.nsa.gov/museum/index.cfm.

British codebreaking attempts directed at German military codes can be traced back to WW1 when the German cruiser *Magdeburg* ran aground in Finland. Although the Germans destroyed the wreck, Russian divers were able to recover the codebooks and give them to the British. With these codebooks and some recovered from another ship, the British Secret

US National Security Agency Pre-1952 Historical Timeline of Cryptological Events

DATE	EVENT
1912 Nov 16	Herbert O Yardley hired as Code Clerk, U.S. State Department
1916	Colonel Parker Hitt, USA published *Manual for Military Ciphers*
1916 Jul 28	US Navy Code and Signal Section established
1917	Gilbert Vernam, AT&T, invented one-time tape teleprinter
1917 Jan 16	Zimmermann Telegram sent
1917 Mar 1	Zimmermann Telegram released to the U.S. press
1917 Jun 10	Establishment of US Army Code and Cipher Section, MI-8
1917 Jun 29	Herbert O Yardley commissioned First Lieutenant in US Army
1917 Jul 28	Captain Frank Moorman detailed to form US Army Radio Intercept Section, AEF
1917 Oct 29	First US intercept in France in World War I
1917 Dec 12	US Army intercept station opened, Souilly, France
1918 Apr 15	Arthur Scherbius offered prototype Enigma machine to German Navy
1918 May	William Friedman commissioned First Lieutenant, assigned to Radio Intelligence Section, France
1919 May 19	Chief of the US Department of State approved creation of Cipher Bureau (AKA Black Chamber)
1919 Jul	Agnes Driscoll employed by US Navy
1919 Oct 1	The Cipher Bureau began operations.
1919 Nov 1	Great Britain: Government Code and Cipher School (GC&CS) established
1920	William Friedman published *The Index of Coincidence* at Riverbank Laboratories
1920 Dec 6	William Friedman hired as contract code compiler by US Army
1923	Chief of Naval Operations directed US Navy to undertake intercept of foreign communications
1924	US established COMINT site in Shanghai
1924 Jan 1	US Navy established Radio Intelligence Office
1924 Jan 1	Laurance Safford became Officer in Charge, Cryptographic Research, U.S. Navy.
1924 Sep 30	Edward Hebern received a patent for a rotor based electric code machine.
1926 Feb 9	German Navy introduced the Enigma machine as "Radio Key C" for communications security
1927	US intercept station established, Peking
1927	Swedish businessman Boris Hagelin introduced A-22 machine
1928	US Navy began Japanese kana intercept course
1928 Jul 15	German Army introduced the Enigma machine for communications security
1929	US intercept station established, Guam
1929 Mar	US intercept station in Shanghai decommissioned
1929 May 10	US Army decided to form Signal Intelligence Service; Friedman to be chief
1929 Oct 31	The Cipher Bureau, headed by Herbert Yardley, closed
1930 Apr 1	Frank B Rowlett hired by William Friedman as cryptologist for US Army Signal Intelligence Service
1930 Apr 10	Abraham Sinkov hired by William Friedman as cryptologist for US Army SIS
1930 Apr 21	Solomon Kullback hired by William Friedman as cryptologist for US Army SIS
1930 May	US intercept station established, Olongapo, Philippines
1930 May 13	John Hurt hired by William Friedman as Japanese linguist, US Army SIS
1931 Jan	Intercept site established, Bar Harbor, Maine.
1931 Jun	Herbert O Yardley published *The American Black Chamber*
1932 Mar	Intercept site established, Astoria, Oregon
1932 Dec	Polish Cipher Bureau began deciphering German Enigma-based messages
1935 Mar 11	US Navy intercept reorganized and redesignated as OP-20-G
1935 Apr	US Navy high frequency direction finding installed at Mare Island, California
1935 Jul	US intercept site moved from Peking to Shanghai
1937 Feb	US Army SIS produced first translation of Japanese diplomatic "RED" machine
1937 Feb	Great Britain: Air Ministry adopted TYPEX Mk 1 cipher machine
1938	Solomon Kullback published *Statistical Methods in Cryptanalysis*
1938 Jun	Japanese Ministry of Foreign Affairs introduced "PURPLE" cipher machine
1939 Jan 1	US Army Second Signal Service Company (later Battalion) created
1939 Jun	Japanese Navy introduced code system known to the US as JN-25
1939 Jul 24	UK-France-Poland tripartent meeting to discuss decryption of ENIGMA
1939 Aug	Astoria, Oregon intercept site relocated to Bainbridge Island, Washington
1939 Sep	US Army SIS produced first translation of Japanese "PURPLE" machine
1940 Aug	US Army approved exchange of cryptologic information with GC&CS
1940 Sep 11	US Army and Navy sign agreement on joint exploitation of Japanese "PURPLE" machine
1940 Oct	Cavite station moved to Corregidor
1940 Oct	Shanghai station decommissioned
1941 Feb	Sinkov-Currier mission to UK departed (in UK through March)
1941 Mar	Monitoring school established at Fort Monmouth
1941 Jun 11	Herbert O Yardley hired by Canada's National Research Council
1941 Aug	Commander Alistaire Denniston of GC&CS visited SIS
1941 Sep	DF station commission at Sitka, Alaska
1941 Nov 22	Herbert O Yardley dismissed by Canada's National Research Council

DATE	EVENT
1941 Dec 7	Japanese forces attack Pearl Harbor, Hawaii
1942	US Army Signal Intelligence Service redesignated Signal Security Service
1942	US - UK agreement on sharing naval communications intelligence
1942 Jan	First US - Canada cryptologic exchange (captured French code)
1942 Feb	US Navy Fleet Radio Unit, Melbourne (FRUMEL) established
1942 Feb 1	German Navy introduced four-rotor Enigma machine for U-boats
1942 Feb 5	First evacuation of Station CAST (Corregidor) personnel
1942 Mar 11	Second evacuation of Station CAST personnel
1942 Mar 15	US Navy began reading Japanese system JN-25
1942 Apr 15	Central Bureau established in Australia to support Southwest Pacific operations
1942 May	DF station established at Kodiak, Alaska
1942 Jun	US Army acquired Arlington Hall Station for the Signal Security Service
1942 Jul	Central Bureau moved to Brisbane
1942 Jul	Abraham Sinkov arrived at Central Bureau, Brisbane as Commander, 837th Detachment
1942 Jul 8	FDR limits COMINT activities to Army, Navy and FBI
1942 Oct 5	US Army SSA activated Vint Hill Farms
1942 Nov	COMINT station established on Guadalcanal
1943 Feb 7	US Navy OP-20-G moved to Nebraska Avenue
1943 Mar	German Navy adopted four-rotor Enigma machine
1943 Apr	First break into Japanese Water Transport System
1943 May	GC&CS activated Heath Robinson machine for cryptanalysis of German Tunny machine
1943 Aug	Strategic intercept station at Amchitka, Alaska
1943 Sep	Intercept site established at Adak, Alaska
1943 Dec	Strategic DF station established at Tarawa
1944	US Army Air Corps established independent intercept operations
1944 Feb	Intercept and DF stations established at Kwajalein
1944 Feb	GC&CS activated Colossus Mk I for cryptanalysis of Tunny; may be first computer
1944 Apr 18	Army-Navy COMINT Coordinating Committee - precursor of USIB - first met
1944 Nov	DF station Tarawa decommissioned
1944 Dec	DF station Guadalcanal decommissioned
1945 Feb	DF station Amchitka decommissioned
1945 Apr	Intercept and DF stations established at Iwo Jima
1945 Jul 3	Cryptographic Security Board established
1945 Aug	Strategic DF station established at Leyte
1945 Sep 15	US Army Signal Security Agency renamed Army Security Agency
1948 Jun 23	Air Force Security Group activated
1948 Oct 20	Air Force Security Group renamed Air Force Security Service
1949 May 20	Armed Forces Security Agency established
1952 Nove 4	National Security Agency established

Service and the codebreakers of Admiralty Room 40 and MI-1 were able to read the secret German Naval messages from 1914 through the end of the war.

After their successes in World War I, the British established a 'Government Code and Cipher School' (GC&CS) in 1919. It was staffed by WW1 codebreakers and it had some successes in reading Italian military codes but it was unable to read the German Military Enigma-coded messages despite the fact that it possessed a commercial version of the Enigma. The rotor wiring in the Military Enigma was different from the commercial version and GC&CS was unable to figure out the new wiring. The GC&CS was staffed with codebreakers but it did not employ any mathematicians with the theoretical knowledge to develop the complex calculations necessary to discover the wiring circuitry.

In 1938, Britain realized the threat of Hitler's growing power and ambition and increased their efforts to decipher the German Enigma codes. They continued to have no success until they received help from the mathematicians of the Polish Cipher Bureau that had been working on decoding the Enigma messages since the 1920s.

THE POLISH CIPHER BUREAU

The story of the successful decoding of the Enigma messages, therefore, must actually begin with the Polish Cipher Bureau which was formed in 1920 to keep track of the threat posed by the German Government. Polish spies had discovered that the Germans were using a secret code for all of their communications and the Polish Government established the Polish Cipher Bureau to try to keep track of what the Germans were planning. In 1928, the Polish Cipher Bureau noticed a change in the German coded messages and determined that the Germans must be using a machine to encode their messages.

Unable to read these new machine-encoded messages, the Polish Cipher Bureau brought in a brilliant young mathematician, Marian Rejewski (pronounced *MAR-yahn Rey-EFF- ski*). They soon added two other mathematicians, Jerzy Rozycki (*YEH-ih Roozh-IT-ski*), and Henryk Zygalski (*HEN-rik Zig-AHL-ski*). The Polish Cipher Bureau purchased a commercial German Enigma machine and learned the basic operation of the machine but the German military rotors were wired differently from those in the commercial version and they were unable to determine the wiring of the military rotors.

Through what many now consider the greatest feat of mathematical cryptanalysis ever performed, Rejewski managed to calculate the exact pattern of internal wiring in each of the German military Enigma rotors by 1932. My CD (see p6 of this book) includes the internal wiring data for all of the standard Enigma rotors (© 2004 Dr David Hamer).

Two factors helped Rejewski with his quest. The Cipher Bureau of French Intelligence had encouraged a German spy,

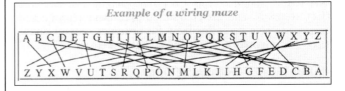

Example of a wiring maze

This diagram shows the complex maze of wires that connect the input side of a rotor to the output side. It was this wiring pattern that Rejewski had to discover. To make matters worse, each of the three rotors had a different wiring pattern. [From: Mowry, 2003]

Hans Thilo Schmidt, who worked in the German Military Cipher Office (*Chiffrierstelle*) to steal information from the German government. The spy had managed to steal an Enigma operation manual and several out-of-date Keys. These clues and the one described in the next paragraph helped Rejewski to work out the wiring of each of the rotors.

The second factor was an operational flaw in the Enigma machine itself. Because of the way it was designed, it was impossible for a typed-in letter to be encoded as the same letter. In other words, if you typed in a letter K, it would never light up the letter K in the light panel. This was a very useful piece of information in Rejewski's mathematical analysis.

Now that the Poles knew the wiring of the three rotors, they had to discover the rest of the wiring in the Enigma. Since it was unlike that of the commercial Enigma, it took considerable further work to discover the wiring between the keyboard and the input disk which fed voltages into the rotor stack. This puzzle had brought the British codebreaking attempts to a halt since there were so many ways that the 26 keyboard keys could connect to the 26 input disk positions. In the commercial version of the Enigma, the keyboard was wired directly to the input disk contacts so that the first (top left) key on the keyboard, Q was connected to the first contact on the input disk. The second key, W was connected to the second contact, the third key, E to the third contact, etc, as follows:

COMMERCIAL GERMAN ENIGMA

Input to Input Disk:
Q W E R T Z U I O P (The layout of the top row
                      of a German Keyboard)
Contacts of Input Disk:
A B C D E F G H I J (The Alphabet)

Rejewski simply took a guess that the input disk contacts: A, B, C, D, etc., were wired in plain alphabetical order as follows:

MILITARY GERMAN ENIGMA

Input to Input Disk:
A B C D E F G H I J (The Alphabet)
Contacts of Input Disk:
A B C D E F G H I J (The Alphabet)

With all of the complex possibilities to consider, the British codebreakers had not thought of such a simple wiring scheme [Sebag-Montefiore, 2000, p.38].

After he was confident that he had worked out all of the wiring of the Enigma, Rejewski asked the Polish Cipher Bureau to arrange to have several working replicas of the Enigma constructed. The company that built the replicas was AVA Radio Manufacturing Co (*Wytwornia Radiotechniczna AVA*). Rejewski and his group then used these reproduction Enigmas to help them find the Keys or Initial Settings and to decode the German messages which they intercepted.

FINDING THE KEY OR INITIAL SETTING

The actual reading of an Enigma-coded message depended on finding the key. The German Cipher Office changed the key four times a year up until 1936 when it went to monthly changes and then daily changes which led to the term, Day's Key. (Later in the war it was changing the keys twice a day and

Cover of the 2004 book: *ENIGMA* by Wladyslaw Kozaczuk and Jerzy Straszak showing the reproduction of the German Enigma that was made in Poland to assist in the codebreaking. Note that the two additional rotors have been mounted in the right side of the box where the battery compartment is normally located in the original German Enigmas.

Another Polish reproduction of the German Enigma. This view shows the reproduction plugboard (7) mounted in the rear of the machine. It is located on the front of the original German Enigmas. The spare rotors (3) are located on the right. The input wheel (4) is to the right of the 3 rotors (5) and the reflector (6) is to the left of the rotors. [from: Kozaczuk, 1979, p. 128]

in some cases every hour.) At first, then, the Poles had three months to figure out the key. Then it was only one month, and then only one day and finally, only one hour.

Fortunately, the Polish mathematicians developed techniques for determining the key when the changes were being made every three months and these techniques worked as the intervals between key changes shortened. Since, as we have seen, there was a nearly infinite number of possible keys, it was impossible to try each one until readable German text appeared. The Polish mathematicians were forced to use other techniques and clues to help them decipher the messages.

THE CLUE OF 'DOUBLE ENCIPHERMENT'

The Polish techniques for finding the key were based on an operational flaw in the way the Germans used the Enigma and not on a flaw in the Enigma itself. This flaw is called 'double encipherment of the first three letters' and it gave the Poles specific information, based on the first three letters of the text, that helped them work out the key for the entire message. Here is the way that this important clue works.

The German Enigma operator was instructed to set up the code-book-defined Initial Setting or Key for the machine. As we have mentioned, this key included the rotor position on the shaft, the ring setting of each rotor, the starting position of each rotor, and the plugboard jumper wires. A typical codebook page is shown below.

The Starting Position or Ground Setting (*Grundstellung*) referred to the three numbers (or letters for wheels with letters around their ring) that appeared in the three windows on top of the machine. The three rotors were set to show these three numbers (or letters) in their windows. Remember this as we continue.

After the entire Key was set up, the operator was instructed to Type "in any three letters *of his own choosing*" into the keyboard twice. (If the rotor had numbers instead of letters around its outer ring, the numbers were to be converted to their appropriate letters using the table inside the cover of the machine. ie, 1=A 2=B 3=C 4=D 5=E 6=F. etc.).

For instance, after setting up the Ground Setting, the operator had to type his choice of any 3 letters like A B C. Then he had to type the same three letters: A B C into the keyboard a second time. Let us say in this example that this plaintext: a b c a b c produced a CIPHERTEXT: X C D F G V.

The receiving Enigma operator set his Enigma to the codebook-defined KEY and then typed this received CIPHERTEXT: X C D F G V into his Enigma. His Enigma decoded this

Geheime Kommandosache!
Nicht ins Flugzeug mitnehmen!

Heeres-Stabs-Maschinenschlüssel Süd Nr. 70   Nr. ____

Datum		Walzenlage			Ringstellung			Steckerverbindungen	Kenngruppen
70	31.	III	I	IV	16	03	24	HZ YR IF QT JN GC AP UX BD KS	
70	30.	V	IV	I	26	22	25	BL AN GC IY VE MX SW QZ PO UK	vzw wbh nuf rev
70	29.	III	IV	V	14	18	05	CV WK MS UP OJ DZ XA LR IY HN	fze fug rdq bdo
70	28.	I	II	V	11	10	02	ZJ BP VK UG LN QX SA MT ED YH	hyy fso wxa whr
70	27.	V	I	III	20	07	15	KZ FD UP MG XS OC WR ZB YL IA	yor xcf axq ooz
70	26.	II	V	IV	01	02	21	GS VC IL HR JN XO TQ BD ·PP EU	lwc auq fvi lua
70	25.	I	V	II	07	08	19	BD WN CX TI KS MQ	cle myk ezl maq
70	24.	IV	II	I	17	19	08	GU OE XA CI MS RY	
70	23.	II	V	III	13	24	07	XP VB ZM HW QI DS	
70	22.	III	II	I	18	16	01	QI HE BP MU AR YL	
70	21.	V	II	IV	23	09	26	VQ IN EB PY ZX GJ	
70	20.	V	I	II	25	25	14	PV EY HN US KJ IM	
70	19.	I	III	II	06	20	23	JZ FW XK OC PQ MH	
70	18.	I	IV	III	22	26	22	XK ZS QU WA TV IE	
70	17.	III	I	II	24	21	18	JN GP CB KS WU ZL	
70	16.	V	IV	II	19	06	06	UQ BG EI MG HP OT	
70	15.	III	V	IV	04	13	13	XV KF YS PI UE LJ	
70	14.	I	II	IV	09	11	17	EY UR IQ ZK CP WM	
70	13.	V	III	II	05	25	09	LY XU VN OM RC PD	
70	12.	I	V	IV	03	06	12	XW KB IZ UN DA MP	
70	11.	V	I	IV	10	02	20	DA IC SY GL OE XN	
70	10.	II	IV	V	08	05	16	QT AZ UY JS DW CN	
70	9.	IV	II	III	26	09	11	ZU PD KR XT BM AC	
70	8.	I	V	III	20	10	10	ZD YQ AK IE RB VS	
70	7.	III	IV	I	01	19	24	AH GM OV RP BF EJ	
70	6.	III	II	V	07	14	10	VN AY CM ZG XU RT	
70	5.	II	III	IV	04	12	18	CA YW HO ZB KP ID	
70	4.	II	I	V	14	08	19	HD PY XM FU IG LK	
70	3.	IV	V	II	25	07	14	CM QS BT KJ FY VN	
70	2.	II	I	III	06	23	03	KV FA NT UW ZD OM	
70	1.	IV	III	V	19	22	17	GZ UD TY KN PW RH	

Nr. 731
Nur für den Dienstgebrauch (N.f.D.)!
Darf im Flugzeug mitgeführt werden!

Signaltafel
für
Flak-Übungen

(Flak-S.Ta.)

Berlin 1938

M. Dv. Nr. 81
L. Dv. Nr. 411b

This German Enigma Codebook page shows the Daily Keys to be used on different dates. The columns from Left to Right are: The date; the order of the three rotors on the shaft; the ring setting for each of the three rotors; the plugboard jumper cable settings; and the letters to appear in the windows for each rotor (The Starting Position or Groundsetting). (Inset) A typical Codebook front cover. [NSA/National Cryptologic Museum]

CIPHERTEXT back into the original plaintext: a b c a b c. The fact that the first three letters were the same as the second three letters told the receiving Enigma operator that the system was working properly and that he could decode the rest of the message correctly. In other words, the appearance of three letters, followed by the same three letters confirmed the proper operation of the Enigma system.

After confirming that the first three letters were the same as the second three letters, *both* the sending and the receiving Enigma operators then set the first three letters of this repeated plaintext into their Enigmas as the Ground Setting. They then sent and received the secret messages. As a result of this technique, even if the enemy had captured the codebook, they would have no way of knowing the Ground Setting since it had been made up or created by the sending Enigma operator's mind.

For Rejewski, this was a genuine gift! He knew that in the plaintext sequence (a b c a b c) the 1st and 4th letters were the same. Similarly, the 2nd and 5th were the same and the 3rd and 6th were the same. Knowing the wiring of the rotors and recognizing that the rotors rotated one step with every key press so that the rotor had rotated three steps between the first letter A and the second letter A, Rejewski was able to mathematically determine the initial Ground Setting and ultimately the key.

With the key, it was a simple matter to use their Polish reproduction Enigma machines to convert the intercepted CIPHERTEXT into the original plaintext.

When the German Army added the plugboard to the Enigma, with its 532,985,208,200,576 possible Key settings, Rejewski found that the clue of 'double-encipherment' still worked fine since the plugboard settings were constant through all of the entire text including the important initial double-encipherment of the first three letters.

Always looking for ways to make their messages more secure, The German Cipher Bureau made other changes in

The world's only Enigma Stamp. It was issued in Poland to commemorate the work of their mathematicians. You will also see how you can obtain one of these stamps.

procedure and in the machine which made it difficult for the Polish codebreakers to decipher the messages.

One change was the addition of two additional rotors to the three in the Enigma. Now, instead of three rotors and six possible sequences along the rotor shaft, they could pick three rotors from a total of five. This gave 60 possible sequences of three rotors along the shaft. This added complexity to the decoding process since the poles did not know the wiring of the two new rotors. After a great deal of effort, Rejewski and his team worked out the wiring of the additional two rotors. Luckily, the Poles had intercepted some German messages with the three original rotors in place and some with one of the new rotors in place and this helped Rejewski to figure out the wiring in the two new rotors.

A second change involved eliminating the entire Ground Setting from the codebooks. Instead of setting up the Ground Setting from the codebook-defined tables, the sending Enigma Operator had to think of "*any* 3 letters" and send these letters in the clear by radio to the receiving Enigma operator. They would each set these three letters into their Enigma as the Ground Setting.

Then, the sending Enigma operator would type another three letters of "his own choosing" into the Enigma (twice) and send the CIPHERTEXT of these six letters to the receiving Enigma operator who would type the CIPHERTEXT into his Keyboard and read the original three plaintext letters (twice). The first three of these

Dyplom
ENIGMA

Przyznany **Tom Perera W1TP** za udział w obchodach Jubileuszu 60-lecia przekazania przez wywiad polski wywiadowi angielskiemu i francuskiemu tajemnicy niemieckiej maszyny szyfrującej ENIGMA.

Kazimierz Drzewiecki SP2FAX
kierownik radiostacji 3Z0ENI

Krzysztof Jasiński MOAXH
kierownik radiostacji GB6OENI

Sylwester Jarkiewicz SP2FAP
redaktor naczelny MK QTC

25 lipca 1999 roku

Marian Rejewski

Jerzy Różycki

Henryk Zygalski

The three Polish mathematicians are honored on this special card by the appreciative Polish people. [http://w1tp.com/enigma Museum]

plaintext letters were now used by each Enigma Operator as the Ground Setting for the secret message.

For example, If the sending operator decided that the first three letters would be H I T, he would simply send them to the receiving Enigma operator in the clear (by radio or telephone). Both Enigma operators would then set the letters H I T as their Ground Settings. The sending Enigma operator would then think of another three random letters like: L E R and type them Twice into the keyboard and get CIPHERTEXT: K O S M X P. He would then transmit the CIPHERTEXT: K O S M X P to the receiving Enigma operator who would type them into his keyboard and read the plaintext: l e r l e r from his light panel. As long as the first three letters matched the second three letters, this would confirm that the system was working and the secret messages would be sent using the Ground Setting: L E R.

Rejewski and his fellow mathematicians discovered that, although the German Enigma operators had been instructed to chose the three letters *at random,* they were often lazy and used a recognizable word made from the first three and second three letters. In the example above, you can see that the first three letters: H I T combined with the second three letters: L E R, spell HITLER. One German Enigma operator consistently used the name of his girlfriend, C I L L I E for every message. The codebreakers named this kind of procedural error on the part of the Germans: CILLIES. Whenever they found CILLIES, it made their job much easier!

Another closely related technique for finding the Ground Setting was to make an educated 'guess' about what the last three letters might be when they intercepted the first three letters sent in plaintext. For instance, the Germans were fond of using names like: G R E T T A or G U D R U N, and they even used words like E N I G M A ! Sometimes they chose the first six letters of a line of keys in the keyboard: A S D F G H. I spent some time in Germany talking with an Enigma operator. He admitted that he and his friends had been very lazy about choosing these three letters and that, although they were forbidden to do so, they often used common six-letter words.

Several other techniques helped the Polish codebreakers to identify the Key and to decipher the messages. As an aid in finding the Key more rapidly, Rejewski and his group designed several machines which helped them in their work.

The Poles designed a machine that used electric motors to electrically step the rotors of six interconnected Enigma

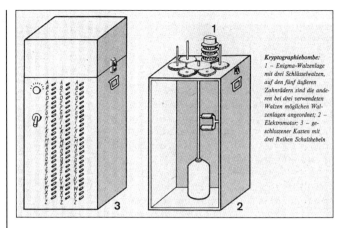

The Polish Bombe which electrically tried many positions of Enigma rotors searching for the Key. [Kozaczuk, 1979, p 82]

machines. It was built by the same company that had constructed the Enigma replicas. The machine would signal when it encountered three matching pairs of letters. This machine helped the Polish Cipher Bureau to rapidly try many different possible Days Keys or Initial Settings in an attempt to speed the deciphering of messages. They called this machine a Bomba and this name and its French version, 'Bombe' has been used to describe the many similar machines developed later by the British and Americans to electrically assist in the decoding process.

There are several explanations of the derivation of the word Bombe. One suggests that Bomba was the name of a popular Polish ice-cream dessert favored by the codebreakers. Another suggests that it came from the clicking sound (like that of a ticking bomb) that the machine made as it rotated the wheels in search of a solution. The French word for Bomb is Bombe. Still another suggestion is that it was simply an abbreviation of a word or set of words.

Another helpful deciphering technique was developed by Polish mathematician Henryk Zygalski who constructed a series of sheets of paper with holes punched in them which he could slide back and forth looking for light to pass through the holes. When he found the proper spot, it would indicate a matching pair of letters in the CIPHERTEXT first six letters and this in turn helped to derive the original Ground Setting. These sheets were called Zygalski sheets and, although slow and cumbersome, they helped speed the codebreaking.

As it became more and more apparent that Hitler intended to invade Poland, the Poles put increasing amounts of time and energy and money into decoding the German Enigma messages.

When the invasion of Poland was clearly imminent, the Poles called a meeting of the French and British codebreaking agencies near Warsaw on 24 July, 1939. The British had been trying to discover the coding techniques and technology of the German Enigmas but they had been unable to work out the wiring connection between the keyboard and the input disk. The French had been passing along all of the information from their spies to Poland but they had not been able to decode any messages. They came to the meeting without much hope of further progress.

The Polish mathematicians surprised and amazed the British and French codebreakers at the meeting by explaining how they had been regularly reading the German Enigma messages. Not only did the Polish mathematicians give them an

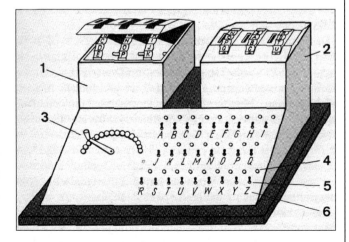

A Polish Cyclometer which helped with the decoding operations. [Kozaczuk, 1979, p 57]

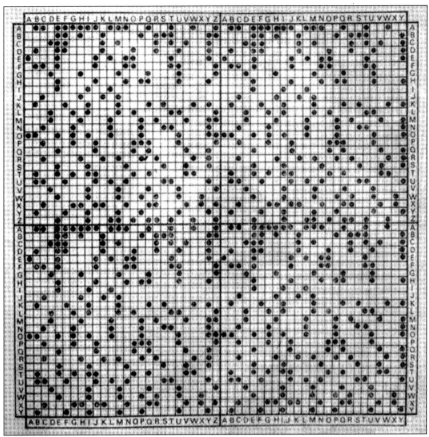

explanation of their codebreaking work, but they further amazed the British and French by presenting them each with a fully-operational Enigma machine replica, and descriptions and plans for the Zygalski Sheets, and for building the Bombe.

About a month later as the Germans invaded Poland, the three Polish mathematicians made a desperate and dangerous escape to France and ultimately to England. They somehow managed to bring their papers and Enigma replica with them.

BLETCHLEY PARK: HOME OF BRITISH CODEBREAKING

The British now finally realized that they needed expert mathematicians to help the Government Code and Cipher School (GC&CS). They hired Cambridge mathematicians Alan Turing, Gordon Welchman, and John Jeffreys and gave them all of the information that the Poles had provided at the Warsaw meeting. They were to take over where the Poles had been forced to stop and find faster and better ways of determining the Key.

The GC&CS moved into an old Victorian manor called Bletchley Park. It was located an equal distance from Cambridge and Oxford Universities and 50 miles NW of London in a village called Bletchley. The mathematicians and staff were housed in rooms in nearby private homes and rooming houses. The British GC&CS codebreakers set up headquarters there and built temporary 'huts' to house the various offices and divisions.

With the vastly expanded facilities at Bletchley Park, work progressed rapidly. Zygalski Sheets were punched and used and the mathematicians worked on more efficient ways of determining Keys. Copies of the Zygalski Sheets were sent to the French at the Chateau de Vignolles near Paris where the first wartime breaking of a German Enigma Key was performed on 29 October, 1939 using Bletchley Park Zygalski Sheets. The British were motivated to work even harder by the French success. In October, 1939, the British found the key for another message and in January of 1940, they broke the German Air Force (Luftwaffe) general key which allowed them to read most Luftwaffe traffic.

By August, 1940, Turing had designed a vastly improved version of the Polish Bombe and the British Tabulating Company had delivered the first of these machines to Bletchley Park. (They would eventually build 210 Bombes throughout the war.) The rotors on this British Bombe spun at speeds as fast as 100RPM trying 100 possible settings every minute until a solution was found.

Even at this speed, it would have taken the Bombe many years to find even one key if it had not been for the techniques developed by the Polish mathematicians. These techniques allowed the Bombe to be programmed to examine only the most likely solutions. This reduced the number of possibilities that a

Bombe had to iterate through by many orders of magnitude and brought the solution of keys into a reasonable time frame.

I think it is important, at this point, to emphasize that the Enigma machine itself was indeed unbreakable at that time and that it was only the carelessness of the Germans in the procedures for making the initial settings and their carelessness in operating the machine that allowed the wiring and the key to be found and the CIPHERTEXT to be deciphered. Perhaps it is this fact that explains why the same general technology is still being used in the most sophisticated computerized coding machines of today.

CRIBS

Unlike the Polish Bombe, Turing's Bombe did not search for clues in the first six letters of a message. Instead, this Bombe searched for 'assumed text'; letters, words, and phrases that cryptologists thought were likely to appear in a message. These assumed words were called Cribs and many of them were the radio call letters of a particular German unit, an officer's name, a known weather report, or a frequently used phrase. When the spinning wheels encountered a match with a crib, they indicated a solution leading to a key. This key was set up in a replica Enigma and checked to see whether it decoded the entire message.

TRAFFIC ANALYSIS HELPS FIND CRIBS

Bletchley Park eventually expanded to include many functions. Each was housed in a separate building or 'hut'. The huts were interconnected with a system of pneumatic tubes that allowed written messages, radio intercepts, and Ultra decodes to be sent rapidly from one hut to another.

Replica of one of the radio intercept rooms, called 'Y' Stations located all over England, where German radio transmissions were monitored and recorded. Five National HRO receivers may be seen. Their power supplies were stored under the tables. [Photo taken recently at the Bletchley Park Museum]

German radio messages were intercepted at various 'Y' Stations. (The 'Y' was a codename standing for 'Wireless') Banks of radio receivers (mostly National HRO models) were installed, and trained radio operators (many of whom had been "ham" or amateur radio operators before the war) wrote down the exact letters in each CIPHERTEXT message. Mistakes could not be tolerated so the operators were under a great deal of pressure to copy the Morse Code messages perfectly. Early recorders which recorded sound on moving wires or tapes were used to capture critical messages.

Much critical information was recovered from simply studying the volume and timing of the radio intercepts. This information was called 'Traffic Analysis' and it provided considerable knowledge about the enemy military operations. For instance, an increase in the volume of traffic between two stations whose locations were known by radio direction finding and/or by their callsigns indicated that some change was taking place in those military groups. If they were planning on relocating or making a raid, the traffic increased and the British paid extra attention to these groups even if they were not able to decode the actual messages.

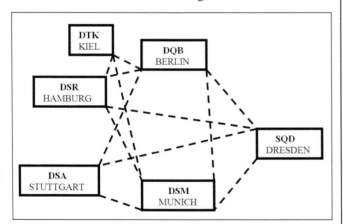

Diagram that shows the communication links between German military stations at different locations. Berlin (Callsign DQB) is in the upper center of the diagram and Munich (Callsign DSM) is in the lower center. Note that Stuttgart (DSA) did not communicate directly with either Hamburg (DSR) or Kiel (DTK). This type of information helped the Allies to understand German radio communications even if they could not read all of the the Enigma-coded messages. [Adapted by the author from a British Public Records Office diagram]

Bletchley Park codebreakers at work. [British Public Records Office]

The 'Y' Stations were aided by a network of direction finding stations throughout England. This network allowed the intercepted information to be linked to a specific German military radio station located at a specific geographic point. For example, a CIPHERTEXT message might be intercepted at a 'Y' Station. Simultaneous messages telephoned or teletyped in from the direction finding stations would inform Bletchley Park that the message had come from Berlin. Previous traffic analysis and radio intercepts had determined that the callsign for the Berlin station was 'DQB' so the callsign 'DQB' could be used as a Crib for these CIPHERTEXT messages.

The codebreakers at Bletchley Park discovered other useful Cribs such as the callsigns of special weather reporting ships located in the North Sea. Whenever direction finding revealed that a message was coming from one of these ships, Bletchley Park codebreakers used the callsign of this ship as a Crib.

Still another technique helped the codebreakers find Cribs. Different branches of the German military used unique keys and transmitted their messages on unique frequencies. The coded messages sent by the different branches were assigned names of colors. For instance, the German Luftwaffe (Air Force) Key was named Red and other Keys were named Green and Blue with Yellow being the Key used for combined operations. When the codebreakers heard these codes being transmitted on a particular frequency, they knew the military service that was doing the transmitting and they could use the previously determined callsigns of that service as Cribs.

GARDENING
When Cribs could not be found, the British sometimes resorted to what they called 'Gardening'. This involved literally planting things that the Germans would need to report in Enigma-coded messages sent by radio. For example, the British might lay mines in a specific ship channel. They would then search intercepted messages using as a Crib, the name of the ship channel, knowing that the Germans would need to use the name to identify where the mines had been laid. This technique worked well when no other cribs could be located.

CAPTURED CODEBOOKS AND KEYS:
Starting with the information from the German spy Hans Thilo Schmidt which was forwarded by the French to the Polish

codebreakers, the allied codebreakers received a long stream of information that helped their work. Much of this information was captured from the Germans in one-way or another. Capturing a codebook with tables showing the Day's Keys for a month or more gave the codebreakers a great deal of information. Not only did it allow them to read all German Enigma messages during the month covered by the book, but it also gave clues as to how the Enigma coding for that military service worked. When the Germans made a change in the Enigma coding, a captured codebook could help the codebreakers to understand that change and change their deciphering techniques accordingly. The long list of captures of German codes and Enigmas have been chronicled in many books so I will just list a few here.

The British Minesweeper *HMS Gleamer* captured German submarine *U-33* in January, 1941. Although the submarine sank rapidly, two of the three new rotors that the German Navy had started using were discovered in the pockets of a German submariner who had forgotten to drop them overboard. The third rotor was captured from the *U-13* in May of 1941.

The Enigma Home Waters Key was recovered from the damaged German Trawler *Krebs* in March, 1941. The Enigma settings and keys for June, 1941 were recovered from the weather ship *Munchen*. The British were still unable to read the German Naval Enigma even with the three recovered rotors until they captured *U-110* with all of its codebooks and its Enigma. This capture allowed the British to read all of the German Naval messages for two months.

After such a capture, the British took extraordinary measures to ensure that the Germans would not discover that they had recovered the codebooks. These measures included either keeping the entire crew in confinement to prevent them from letting anyone know that the ship had been searched, or hurrying the submarine crew below decks and then constructing an elaborate story about how quickly the U-boat had sunk.

When German ships and codebooks had not been captured for a long time, the British were tempted to try to capture them by extraordinary means. Realizing the critical importance of keeping the capture secret from the Germans, elaborate plots were developed to obtain German Enigma codes. The pictures

---

OPERATION RUTHLESS

(by C. Morgan)

During the last days of August and early September a plot began to be hatched for the capture of a German enigma-cypher machine. There were earlier projects vaguely and verbally discussed but the first concrete proposal was made in an informal note by Fleming to D.N.I.

"D.N.I.

I suggest we obtain the loot by the following means:

1. Obtain from Air Ministry an air-worthy German bomber.

2. Pick a tough crew of five, including a pilot, W/T operator and word-perfect German speaker. Dress them in German Air Force uniform, add blood and bandages to suit.

3. Crash plane in the Channel after making S.O.S. to rescue service in P/L.

4. Once aboard rescue boat, shoot German crew, dump overboard, bring rescue boat back to English port.

In order to increase the chances of capturing an R. or M. with its richer booty, the crash might be staged in mid-Channel. The Germans would presumably employ one of this type for the longer and more hazardous journey.

F. 12.9.40"

Captain Clayton, in a note of the same date, saw in this "a chance to get what we much want", and, as Captain Clayton was not given to unreasoned enthusiasm, his support at once gave solidity to the project. Fleming produced a more detailed plan. The bomber was to take off shortly before dawn on the tail of one of the big London raids. As the German rescue-boats worked in fixed grid squares, they were unlikely to be in company, and the bomber would seek an isolated R. or S.boat as far out from the French coast as possible, cut out one engine, make a distress signal if necessary, lose height fast with smoke pouring from a candle in the tail, and pancake. The crew would then put off in a rubber-boat, having arranged for the bomber to sink as soon as possible so that the rescue-boat should be delivered from all temptation to summon help in an attempt to salvage the machine. The rescue boat would then take the crew on board and be overpowered. To this hopeful plan, Fleming added an ingenious note of caution: "N.B. Since attackers will be wearing enemy uniform, they will be liable to be shot as franc-tireurs if captured, and incident might be fruitful for propaganda. Attackers' story will therefore be "that it was done for a lark by a group of young hot-heads who thought the war was too tame and wanted to have a go at the Germans. They had stolen plane and equipment and had expected to get into trouble when they got back". This will prevent suspicions that party was after more valuable booty than a rescue boat." Fleming also drew up a detailed list of "Material and Personnel Required". The pilot was to be "tough, bachelor, able to swim"; the German speaker was to be "as for pilot" and was further earmarked, with a touch of autobiographical genius, as "Fleming".

Frank Birch, on behalf of Naval Section of G.C. & C.S., described this as a "very ingenious plot". It had, for him, "the enormous advantage of not giving anything away if it fails". He went into details of the German signals and markings and attached a three-page memorandum (Z. No. 191) from the German Naval Section of G.C. & C.S. on the "Activities of German Naval Units in the Channel". Arrangements then went forward. D.N.I. obtained the necessary bomber from Lord Beaverbrook, Fleming brought his party together and went off to Dover to await his chance, and the Air Ministry co-operated. But his chance did not come. No birds were rising and V.A. Dover suggested looking for them elsewhere:

"From: V.A. Dover   To: Admiralty for D.N.I. for C.S.O.
                              to 1st S.L.

1029/16 October.   Naval Cypher D at ATX

Important. Personal.

Operation RUTHLESS postponed. Two reconnaissance flights by Coastal Command revealed no suitable craft operating at night and evidence from W/T is also negative. Suggest material and organisation should not be dispersed. Possibly Portsmouth area may be more fruitful. Lieutenant Commander Fleming returns to Admiralty 1800 today Wednesday."

How much importance was attached to the operation may be judged from these extracts from a letter by Frank Birch to Callaghan, dated 20th October:

"Turing and Twinn came to me like undertakers cheated of a nice corpse two days ago, all in a stew about the cancellation of operation Ruthless. The burden of their song was the importance of a pinch. Did the authorities realise that, since the Germans did the dirt on their machine on June 1st, there was very little hope, if any, of their deciphering current, or even approximately current, enigma for months and months and months - if ever? Contrariwise, if they got a pinch - even enough to give a clue to deciphering one day's material, they could be pretty sure, after an initial delay, of keeping going from day to day from then on; nearly up-to-date if not quite, because the level of traffic now is so much higher and because the machinery has been so much improved. The 'initial delay' would be in proportion to the pinch. If the whole bag of tricks was pinched, there'd be no delay at all. They asked me to add - what is self-evident - that they couldn't guarantee that at some future date, near or remote, the Germans mightn't muck their machine about again and necessitate another pinch. There are alternative operations possible. I put up one suggestion myself, and there are probably lots better. Is there anything in the wind? I feel there ought to be."

Fleming replied that Birch needed to have no fear that the value of a pinch was underestimated. Ruthless was still fully laid on and the Air Ministry (21st October) had issued elaborate operation orders. Favourable circumstances were awaited. But they never arose.

Detailed proposal to capture German Enigma codes, devised by Ian Fleming who went on to write the James Bond books. [British Public Records Office]

on this page describe a very risky plan to crash a German bomber with British agents onboard near a German patrol boat. The British were to quickly take over the patrol boat and recover the Enigma codes before the Germans could radio a report to headquarters. This plan was developed by Ian Fleming who went on to write the James Bond novels after the war.

The British had to be exceptionally careful not to let the German Navy know that they had captured the keys because the Navy would have immediately changed their codes if they had known the British had the keys. The delicate balance between using the captured material to hunt down and sink the U-boats which were attacking the British convoys and possibly giving away the fact that they were reading the codes caused great concern.

A combination of four factors helped keep the Germans from suspecting that their codes had been broken:

1 The British maintained extreme secrecy about the Enigma messages codenamed "Ultra" they deciphered.
2 The British let the Germans think that Ultra information was coming from spies.
3 The British arranged for 'accidental' flyby sightings of the German submarines so that the Germans thought they had been spotted from the air by accident.
4 And finally, the absolute conviction on the part of the German Cipher Bureau that the Enigma CIPHERTEXT was undecipherable convinced the Germans that their messages were secure.

THE FOUR-ROTOR GERMAN NAVY ENIGMA
However, Admiral Donitz, the German U-boat Commander, remained suspicious that the Enigma codes were being read and he encouraged the development of a new Naval model Enigma for his U-boats. This model was to have four rotors but, by locking the thin leftmost rotor in the 'A' position, it could be used as a three-rotor machine and therefore retain its compatibility with

the rest of the German military Enigma machines. There was no drive mechanism for the leftmost rotor so it did not rotate with keypresses. This was to be a considerable help to the Allied efforts to decode Naval Enigma messages.

There are many pictures of the four-rotor German Navy Enigma in an earlier chapter of this book.

The British knew through reading the Enigma messages that the new Navy four-rotor Enigma was to be used soon by the German U-boats. By an incredible stroke of luck, the British intercepted a message that was enciphered with the new four-rotor Enigma *and* then they intercepted the same message which was retransmitted using the three-rotor Enigma. This allowed them to compare the two codes and get an early start at deciphering the new Navy four-rotor Enigma messages. Even with this critical information, Bletchley Park was not able to read the four-rotor Naval Enigma until October, 1942.

In October, 1942, German Submarine *U-559* was damaged and the Enigma codebooks for the Short Weather Cipher and the Short Signal Book were retrieved before the sub sank. These codes helped the British decipher the four-rotor Naval Enigma messages. The British also recovered a secret 'Bigram Table' or 'Grid' system which divided the ocean into squares identified by two letters and pairs of numbers. The U-Boats had been reporting that they were in square 'AZ6847' for example and now the British could tell exactly where they were operating.

THE AMERICAN NAVY BOMBES
In 1943, The National Cash Register Company in Dayton, Ohio began manufacturing a four-rotor version of the Bombe for the American Navy. (Alan Turing also designed a four-rotor version of the Bombe for Bletchley Park.) By 1944, the Navy had 96 Bombes which were regularly breaking the U-boat messages with an average delay of only 12 hours. The ability to read these messages is credited with having saved hundreds of ships and shortening the war by several years.

The American Navy Bombe. [On display in the NSA/National Cryptologic Museum]

A closer view of the American Navy Bombe rotors. [on display in the NSA/National Cryptologic Museum]

A back view of the American Navy Bombe. [On display in the NSA/National Cryptologic Museum]

(bottom left) A much closer view of the American Navy Bombe rotors. [On display in the NSA/National Cryptologic Museum]

Wired Bombe Rotor

ULTRA

The information decoded from Enigma Messages was given the codename 'ULTRA'. The codename was used to try to keep the Germans from discovering that the information had come from their Enigma messages. Churchill realized that if the Germans were to discover that their Enigma messages were being deciphered, they would have changed the enciphering system and this would have cut off any possibility of continuing to decode and read German CIPHERTEXT messages. Churchill, therefore, used great caution in the dissemination of ULTRA and always covered it by saying that a spy or a scheduled aircraft overflight was the source of the ULTRA. He hoped that if the Germans intercepted any ULTRA, they would believe that it had come from a spy or an aircraft overflight. With the exception of Admiral Donitz who was in charge of the U-boats, the Germans did indeed believe that the information had come from these sources and that their Enigma-enciphered messages were secure.

The story that Churchill allowed the bombing of Coventry to proceed despite his ULTRA knowledge of the exact timing of the raid in order to maintain the secrecy of the ULTRA has now been questioned by several historians. However, it is clear that Churchill did work hard to disguise the ULTRA information at every opportunity (see letter below from Prime Minister Churchill).

For thorough descriptions of the ULTRA messages that were intercepted and how the information was used, I suggest that you read some of the books on the topic listed in the references section at the end of this book. I present here a few representative documents that have been made available by the British Public Records Office through the Bletchley Park Trust to give an idea of the scope of the information.

MOST SECRET

This is a very interesting document written on 24 June, 1941, describing Churchill's hesitancy about sharing ULTRA information about U-boats with the Americans for fear of the Germans discovering where the information came from. [British Public Records Office]

C/6863.

LONDON,

24th June, 1941.

PRIME MINISTER.
- - - - - - - - - - - -

After considering, from all angles, the possibility of divulging to the President the information regarding U.S. Naval Units being chased by U. Boats, I find myself unable to devise any safe means of wrapping up the information in a manner which would not imperil this source, which should, without fail, play a vital part in the Battle of the Atlantic.

The fact that the message in question was passed by the Admiral Commanding U. Boats to submarines actually operating, renders it well nigh impossible that the information could have been secured by an agent, and however much we insist that it came from a highly placed source, I greatly doubt the enemy being for a moment deceived, should there be any indiscretion in the U.S.A. That this might occur, cannot be ruled out, as the Americans are not in any sense as security minded as one would wish, and I need only draw your attention to the attached cutting from to-day's "Daily Express", on a matter which, in my opinion, should not have been made public if the two Secret Services are to work together as closely as is imperative.

It is true that the American experts who visited the United Kingdom gave us a very valuable insight into Japanese cryptographic methods, but they, themselves, impressed upon me how cautious they were in passing any of the results to the State Department.

At a recent Meeting of the Chiefs of Staff, it was agreed that information derived from this Most Secret source should only be communicated to the U.S. Naval and Military Authorities when we were satisfied that the source was not endangered. I believe that any other decision as regards weakening the veil of secrecy would cause the greatest regret at a later date, and I similarly hold the view that it would be fatal to divulge to the Russians immediate information which we are securing about German operational intentions on the Eastern Front. To be of any value, it would mean that the information would be immediately transmitted to the Commanders

in the Field, and as the Russian Military cyphers are compromised, it would only be a matter of days before the Germans would know of our success, and operations in the future would almost certainly be hidden in an unbreakable way.

PRIME MINISTER TO GENERAL WAVELL.

1.   It seems clear from our information that a heavy Air-borne attack by German troops and bombers will soon be made on Crete.(Stop) Let me know what forces you have in the Island and what your plans are.(Stop) It ought to be a fine opportunity for killing the parachute troops. (Stop)   The island must be stubbornly defended. (Ends)

(right) This ULTRA information describes an impending raid on Crete. Note that Churchill simply says "It seems clear from our information", never mentioning ULTRA or Enigma decoding. [British Public Records Office]

This translated and summarized German ULTRA describes executions in concentration camps in April, 1942. Note that the Germans called these executions 'natural deaths'. The number of 'natural deaths' is reported as: NIEDERHAGEN: 21; FLOSSENBURG: 88; AUSCHWITZ: 6829 men, 1525 women; and BUCHENWALD: 74. [British Public Records Office]

MOST SECRET

40/42. 2.

10. Reports on deaths in German prison camps during August reveal the following figures:-

      NIEDERHAGEN: 21;   AUSCHWITZ: 6829 men, 1525 women;
      FLOSSENBURG: 88;   BUCHENWALD: 74. (1/9).

A message of 4/9, in reply to a request for 1000 prisoners for building the DANUBE railway, states that AUSCHWITZ cannot provide them until the "ban" (Lagersperre) on the AUSCHWITZ camp has been lifted. It appears that although typhus is still rife at AUSCHWITZ, new arrivals continue to come in.

11. As from 1/9/42, "natural deaths" among prisoners in Concentration Camps are to be reported apparently only in writing (durch Formblatt).

12. The Norwegian Police Battalions are to send in wireless report every day if anything of note occurs in their areas. For example, the discovery of underground organisations, sabotage, serious accidents, attempted murder, revolts of prisoners, suicide among the Orpo, etc. (15/9).

13. The Germans are making plans for building light railways in UKRAINE. A list of all places in UKRAINE of importance in the harvesting and exploitation of fruit and vegetables, which are not served by a railway, and which require light railway connection with the main line, is to be sent in with sketch maps to the Hauptostsentrale, KIEV. (11/9)

A.C.T.
25/9/42.

Most Secret.   1.4.44.

Mr. Bonsall,
Block F.

AT 750 of 22.3.44.

WARSAW CQ.

In the night of ??.3.44 from P/W camp No. ??? of the Luftwaffe in SAGAN British Flying Officers escaped. Apparently they had on over their uniforms overcoats smeared with sand and are pretending ot be French civilian workers. Probable direction of flight BERLIN and/or BRESLAU but it is also quite possible that they are making for the General Gouvernement. Please send out an alarm. addrssed to Kripo and Grenzpolizeistellen: to be passed on to all.
From Sipo WARSAW.

N.B. See also AT 767 of 31.3.44.

MOST SECRET

Mr. Bonsall,   5 Apr 44.
Room 71,
Block 'F'.
- - - - - -

AT. No. 785 of 29.3.44.

To Kripo, WORMS, OFFENBACH, GIESSEN.

70 British officers recaptured. Extraordinary state of search to be reduced to strengthened state of search (war-time). Search and guard over railways and borders to be continued in full force. Wehrmacht must continue search with adequate forces.
From Kripo DARMSTADT.

(Cf. AT 774, 767. Refers to mass flight of 80 British flying officers from SAGAN).

This translated German ULTRA describes an escape from a German prison camp and the subsequent recapture of 70 British flying officers. [British Public Records Office]

UNDECIPHERED WW2 ENIGMA MESSAGES DECIPHERED IN 2006

Hundreds of Enigma-enciphered U-boat messages were never deciphered during the war. There were not enough people at Bletchley Park to decipher every message so they were stored in archives that were gradually opened in recent years.

With the help of many hundreds of people who loaded and ran special deciphering programs on their home computers, the power of distributed processing was turned loose on these undeciphered messages. Home computers simply tried every possible combination of settings hoping for a breakthrough into the Day's Key and hoping to be able to decipher the messages.

After many months, the first two messages yielded to this brute-force approach and they are shown below.

If you would like to try competing in a contest that will test your understanding of the Enigma and the deciphering process by giving you some original Enigma messages and most but not all of the Day's Key, connect to the internet and go to: http://users.telenet.be/d.rijmenants/en/challenge.htm.

MESSAGE #1

Original Enigma-encoded CIPHERTEXT that had not previously been deciphered:

```
NCZW VUSX PNYM INHZ XMQX SFWX WLKJ AHSH NMCO CCAK
UQPM KCSM HKSE INJU SBLK IOSX CKUB HMLL XCSJ USRR
DVKO HULX WCCB GVLI YXEO AHXR HKKF VDRE WEZL XOBA
FGYU JQUK GRTV UKAM EURB VEKS UHHV OYHA BCJW MAKL
FKLM YFVN RIZR VVRT KOFD ANJM OLBG FFLE OPRG TFLV
RHOW OPBE KVWM UQFM PWPA RMFH AGKX IIBG
```

The above Enigma-encoded CIPHERTEXT deciphered in 2006:

```
VONV ONJL OOKS JHFF TTTE INSE INSD REIZ WOYY QNNS
NEUN INHA LTXX BEIA NGRI FFUN TERW ASSE RGED RUEC
KTYW ABOS XLET ZTER GEGN ERST ANDN ULAC HTDR EINU
LUHR MARQ UANT ONJO TANE UNAC HTSE YHSD REIY ZWOZ
WONU LGRA DYAC HTSM YSTO SSEN ACHX EKNS VIER MBFA
ELLT YNNN NNNO OOVI ERYS ICHT EINS NULL
```

The above Enigma-encoded CIPHERTEXT deciphered in 2006 - and broken up into German words:

Von Looks: Funktelegramm 1132/19

Inhalt: Bei Angriff unter Wasser Gedrueckt, Wasserbomben.

Letzter Gegnerstandort 08:30 Uhr, Marqu AJ 9863, 220 Grad, 8 Seemeilen, stosse nach. 14 Millibar faellt, NNO 4, Sicht 10.

The above Enigma-encoded CIPHERTEXT deciphered in 2006 - and translated from German into English:

From Looks: Radio signal 1132/19

Contents: Forced to submerge during attack, depth charges.

Last enemy location 08:30h, Grid Square AJ 9863, 220 degrees, 8 nautical miles,

(I am) following (the enemy). (Barometer) 1014 Millibar (tendency) Falling, (Wind) North North East 4, Visibility 10.

Research in the U-boat Archives (see http://www.u-boot-archiv.de/dieboote/u0264.html and http://ubootwaffe.net/ops/boat.cgi? boat=264) reveals the following fascinating historical information about Captain Looks and his *U-264* submarine:

7 Patrols: Sank 3 major ships.
February 19, 1944 Spotted by destroyers.
Sent position of American convoy by radio before submerging.
5 destroyers joined in trying to sink U-264.
250 Depth Charges dropped near the submarine!
Out-of-control submarine sank to 230 meters.
Kapitanleutnant Looks gave the order to blow tanks and surface.
All 5 chase ships opened fire while crew abandoned ship.
All 52 men were picked up safely !!! ...while the submarine sank.

MESSAGE # 2

Original Enigma-encoded CIPHERTEXT that had not previously been deciphered:

```
TMKFN WZXFF IIYxU TIHWM DHXIF ZEQVK DVMQS
WBQND YOZFT IWMJH XHYRP ACZUG RREMV PANWX
GTKTH NRLVH KZPGM NMVSE CVCKH OINPL HHPVP
XKMBH OKCCP DPEVX VVHOZ ZQBIY IEOUS EZNHJ
KWHYD AGTXD JDJKJ PKCSD SUZTQ CXJDV LPAMG
QKKSH PHVKS VPCBU WZFIZ PFUUP
```

Distributed processing deciphered text - converted into German words:

0425 Ausgang FT. 0246/21/203:

Auf Geleitkurs 55 grad, nichts gefunden, marschiere befohlenes quadrat. Standort marquandt. AJ 3995.

SO 4, See 3, 10/10 bedeckt, 28 mb steigend, Nebel, Sicht 1 sm.

Schroeder

The above Enigma-encoded CIPHERTEXT deciphered in 2006 - and translated from German into English:

0425 Outgoing Radio Signal 0246/21/203:

Found nothing on convoy's course 55 degrees,

[I am] moving to the ordered [naval] square. Position naval square AJ 3995.

[wind] south-east [force] 4, sea [state] 3, 10/10 cloudy, [barometer] [10]28 mb [tendency] rising, fog, visibility 1 nautical mile.

Schroeder

The front of the Bletchley Park Mansion appears exactly as it did seventy years ago. High in the attic above the arched entrance is a secret wireless radio station called Station "X".

BLETCHLEY PARK TODAY

For a frighteningly long time the mere survival of Bletchley Park was in doubt as commercial interests striving to convert the grounds into profitable developments battled with groups of historians and scholars who wanted to preserve it as a National Monument.

In 2010, a large grant from Hewlett-Packard underwrote the digitizing of all of the stored documents. This and other sources of funding assured the continuance of the buildings and grounds. Not only will Bletchley Park continue to be a repository of WW2 codebreaking but the digitized documents will provide tremendous insights into the history and underlying psychology of the war as they become accessible to everyone on the internet.

Bletchley Park, in itself a museum, also hosts extraordinary exhibits of codebreaking, wireless, photographic and computer equipment. Codebreaking exhibits include a great deal of historical equipment, timelines of codebreaking mileposts, wartime displays, wireless and communications exhibits and a working model of the three-rotor Bombe.

The National Computer Museum is housed in one of the former codebreaker's buildings and displays an extraordinary variety of computers from the earliest models to the present. A highlight is the working rebuild of the Colossus computer from WW2. Please see: http://www.bletchleypark.org.uk for opening hours and special events.

Every September, in addition to its long list of special events and exhibits, Bletchley Park opens its doors to the surviving veteran codebreakers who worked there during the war. The veterans walk around their old workplace and give talks and answer questions from the thousands of people who attend the event.

The photographs reproduced here were taken at the annual Bletchley Park reunion in 2009 where the author constructed an Enigma display, met and interviewed some of the returning veterans and gave a lecture entitled: 'The U-boat Menace and the Enigma'. The first photograph shows the front entrance to Bletchley Park Mansion. It is virtually unchanged in the 70 years since the war.

A tiny room located in the attic far above the arched entrance port housed a top secret wireless station called Station "X". Although the stairway is now too unsafe for public showing, I was allowed special admission to the room. When I entered the secret room, I found a sign that reads as follows:

STATION "X"

In August, 1939 was set up a secret Foreign Office covert radio station run by MI6. It was commanded by Charles Emary. The two Morse code wireless transmitters were made at Barnes in West London and ran at a power of 35 watts. They were type MK1 and MK3. The receivers were made by Hallicrafters, Hammerlund, and Philips. The Aerial was used for transmission and reception and was attached to a large tree on the green in front of the mansion and it is still there today, 60 years later. All messages were encoded using book

Some of the equipment in Station "X" in the attic of the mansion is original and some is more recent. Dedicated volunteer radio amateurs put the station back on the air in 1999.

cipher. Two way working was to MI6 agents in Berne, Madrid, Stockholm, Tangiers, Paris, Lisbon, and Istanbul. The agents took on the name of "Passport Control Officers" to protect their identity. By early 1940 the system had outgrown itself and MI6 was building a special radio station at the nearby village of Whadden. Station "X" was then used for monthly testing as an emergency standby radio station until 1945. All staff were transferred to Wadden Hall at the end of February, 1940.

As you enter the main cipher machine exhibit rooms, a statue of Alan Turing dominates the room as his intellect dominated the codebreaking efforts in wartime.

Continuing into the main exhibits you find a small section of a Bombe that has been set up as an operating display to allow people to see how the mechanism worked.

This statue honouring mathematician Alan Turing dominates the cipher machine exhibit rooms.

This small section of the three-rotor Bombe is set up as a working display to demonstrate the principle of the Bombe.

Further into the display room you find yourself in front of the fully-operational Bombe itself. The Bombe is periodically demonstrated by some of the people who actually worked on the Bombes during the war.

In another section of the Bletchley Park complex where the National Computer Museum is located, the Colossus rebuild project is on display.

The front of the fully-operational three-rotor Bombe with one of the veterans demonstrating the settings of the wheels.

Other cipher machines are also on display at Bletchley Park. They include the American M-209 and the Russian "FIALKA" (see the pictures opposite).

(below) The rear of the Colossus rebuild project showing the complex wiring.

(above) The front of the Colossus rebuild project showing the printer in the foreground and the 'bedstead' or paper tape reader mechanism in the background.

(below) The back of the fully-operational three-rotor Bombe showing the incredibly complex set of relays and motorized drive mechanisms.

(above) An American M-209 cipher machine and (below) a Russian Cold-War era FIALKA cipher machine on display at Bletchley Park.

The author interviews and records the reminiscences of three of the veterans who came to Bletchley Park for the reunion in 2009.

BP REUNION
The 2009 Bletchley Park Reunion attracted veterans from all over the world who had worked there during the war. The reunion also attracted historians, collectors and interested visitors. The photographs on this page were taken during the reunion.

SHORT-WAVE RADIO AT BLETCHLEY PARK AGAIN
The Radio Society of Great Britain has set up an operating amateur radio station at Bletchley Park. This station will communicate with 'ham' radio operators all over the world. Visitors will be able to see a radio station in operation and participate in communications. For further information, please visit the RSGB site at www.rsgb.org.

A fly-over by a Lancaster bomber brought everyone outside to watch the huge plane circle over Bletchley Park.

This photograph shows the historians and collectors who came to the reunion. Many of them brought their own Enigma machines to display, demonstrate and explain.

Chapter 6
Hunting for Enigmas

WHERE ARE THE GERMAN ENIGMAS TODAY?

German WW2 Enigma cipher machines are exceptionally hard to find since, at the end of the war, the Allied forces were ordered to destroy every Enigma machine that they could find. There are several possible reasons for this destroy-on-sight order. It is possible that the Allies did not want other countries to have these machines and to work out methods of breaking the code since the fact that the codes had been broken was a highly classified secret that was not revealed for an incredible 30 years after the end of the war. It is also possible that the Americans and British did not want the Enigma machines to fall into the hands of the Russians whom they did not trust.

The destruction orders were very explicit and required that the machines have a hand grenade detonated in the mechanism to ensure that they were totally destroyed. Consequently, most of the Enigma machines ended up being discarded as trash.

They were forgotten and gradually sank into the ground. Some of the twisted and rusted pieces were later dug up by trophy hunters and occasionally appear on auction sites like ebay. Not only do these Enigma parts show extreme damage from the explosions but also from being buried underground for 50-60 years.

A few Germans heard about the "destroy-on-sight" order and thought that there must be some good reason for it. With this thought in mind, some soldiers and officers decided to grab an Enigma or two and hide them from the Allies in their home or barn - often quickly forgetting that they were there. Now, sixty years later, these few "hidden" machines are owned by very old men or their families and many have forgotten that they even have them. They have been stored in attics and basements alongside tons of household articles and may have been thrown out as useless garbage.

To build and expand my telegraph museum: www.w1tp.com, I frequently travel to Europe to try to locate early European telegraph instruments.

At one of the antique shows I found a person who owned an Enigma machine from WW2. After a great deal of discussion, he agreed to sell it to me and I have been researching the history and hunting for these machines ever since.

The thrill of the hunt is the most exciting part of collecting Enigmas for me. There are very few of them around and the hunt is therefore extremely challenging and interesting. I have had a wonderful time hunting for these forgotten machines over the years and I have been fairly successful in finding them.

I typically ask antique dealers and individuals about antique telegraph keys and scientific instruments. If there is any chance to visit them to look at what they have for sale, I keep a sharp lookout for the telltale wooden boxes of Enigma machines. I have found that it is a waste of time to ask about Enigmas directly since most people do not know that they have them and many do not even know what Enigma machines are.

Below is a photograph taken in the attic of a house in Germany. If you look carefully, you will see an Enigma box with its leather carrying handle peeking out from under some plastic packing material. You can imagine how exciting it is to see something like this surface after all these years! Despite the excitement of finding one of these rare machines, it is still extremely important to find out as much as you can about the history of its use and who used it. Each of these machines has a fascinating story to tell and if you walk out of the house with your Enigma tucked proudly under your arm and forget to write

It often feels as though I am hunting for some rare species of animal. Pictured above is the successful end of an Enigma hunt in the German Alps. My wife looks as happy as I am.

The attic of a German house showing a partially hidden Enigma machine amongst a pile of other discarded material.

The attic of a home containing several Enigmas: Look closely and see how many Enigma machines you can find.

down or record its history, you will have lost an important link between your machine and world history.

After several years of hunting, the author met a man who had several Enigma machines tucked away in different places in his attic. It was quite a thrill to stand in the middle of such a collection of historic machines, and even more exciting was the fact that the owner was willing to talk about the histories of each of the machines.

A few years ago, the author met a man named Karl Hille who had been an Enigma repairman. He talked at length about his job of repairing the machines in the field. He said that most of the problems were with dirty contacts between the rotors.

He said that there were very clear instructions about cleaning the contacts right inside the lid of the machine but that very few people paid any attention to the instructions.

It seemed as though the complex bundles of wires connecting the various components would have given the most problems but he emphasized that they were very well bundled and seldom caused problems.

The author (left) and Karl Hille, who had been a German Enigma repairman.

RECOVERING GERMAN NAVY ENIGMAS FROM THE OCEAN

Most of the German WW2 Navy *Kriegsmarine* Enigmas went down with their ships and are now in rather poor condition after more than sixty years on the bottom of the ocean.

Here is an example of a marine Enigma that was recovered from a submarine off the East coast of the United States in 2001.

ENIGMA MACHINES RECOVERED FROM SUNKEN U-BOAT U-85

Dr David Hamer's website (see box) gives the following account of the recovery of the Enigmas:

On 3 July 2001 Enigma M2946 and parts of Enigma M3131 were recovered from *U-85* together with a printing device - a modified typewriter - which appears to have been connected to M2946. This feat was accomplished by divers Jim Bunch and brothers Rich and Roger Hunting - all three of whom have been diving on the wreck of *U-85* for a number of years. Also recovered were a number of pages of a codebook used for flag signal communications with merchant vessels and a pad used for preparing radio messages for transmission.

The following description is in the words of diver Roger Hunting.

"We found the Enigma on 3 July, 2001. We began running an air-lift dredge operation inside the *U-85* during the summer of 2000. This past summer we concentrated our efforts in the Radio Room [A] and the Sound [sonar] Room [B].

"In June we spent a week emptying out the Sound Room (we did that first since it was easier to reach). It took three divers about six days to pump out the Sound Room at two to three dives each per day, 30-35 minutes per dive (about 20 hours of continuous dredging). We found lots of little artifacts in the Sound Room, probably the most significant was a large brass compass, a wooden box of phonograph records and the stack of Enigma log sheets.

"We then moved to the Radio Room, which was considerably more difficult to dredge because of its location and the volume of debris to be removed. On the third day of dredging,

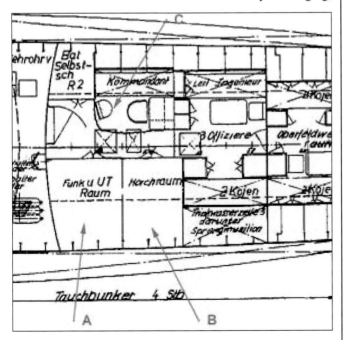

Plan view of the *U-85* U-boat. The letters A, B and C are referred to in Roger Hunting's account.

All photographs of these recovered artifacts are copyright 2001-2003 courtesy of Jim Bunch, Rich Hunting and Roger Hunting.

The dive expeditions during which these artifacts were recovered were underwritten by Seascan Dive Centre of Nags Head, North Carolina, USA.

Many of the items recovered from *U-85* are now on display in the Graveyard of the Atlantic Museum, Hatteras, NC (www.graveyardoftheatlantic.com).

Many more photographs - colour and monochrome - can be found in a book by Jim Bunch: *A Shadow in the Sea*, published in 2003 by Deep Sea Press, Nags Head, North Carolina, U.S.A. ISBN 0-939591-00-6. The book tells the story of *U-85* and her crew and includes details of many of the dives carried out upon the wreck during various expeditions.

This and much other Enigma material may be found on Dr David Hamer's website: http://home.eclipse.net/~dhamer /u-85gal.htm

Enigma M2946 is recovered from the radio room of *U-85* after 60 years under the ocean.

The History of *U-85*

German U-boat *U-85* was first put into service on 7 June, 1941. On her fourth war patrol she torpedoed a Norwegian freighter off the East coast of the United States. Four days later, on 14 April, 1942 she was hunting for ships at midnight near Nag's Head along the coast of North Carolina when she was spotted by the American destroyer *Roper*. The 90ft depth of the water made it suicidal to submerge so she fired a torpedo at the destroyer. It missed and she was sunk by the destroyer. All hands were lost in the intense depth charge attack.

Initial plans to salvage the submarine from the relatively shallow depths were abandoned due to the effective job that her crew had done in scuttling her. 33 years later, the first sport divers reached the sub. Many artifacts were removed during subsequent years but no serious hunt for the Enigma machines was attempted until 2001, nearly 60 years after her sinking. This historical information was derived from the excellent book: *Dive into History* by Keatts and Farr, ISBN 0-936849-00-2.

we uncovered the Enigma (M2946) laying on the floor about in the center of the room. The wooden lid was not on the box when we found it. We found the printer contraption on the same day, about in the same location.

"Two days later, we found the lid of the box and the wheels for what appears to be the second machine (M3131). We spent another week or so cleaning out the Radio Room and found a couple of coffee cups, a Perrier water bottle, a flashlight, two ceramic insulators used on the external radio antenna and other miscellaneous junk.

"If you are familiar with the configuration of the interior of a Type VII U-boat, you know that the captain's quarters [C] were on the port side just across the aisle from the Radio Room. Since the *U-85* is sitting in the bottom with about a 30 degree heel to starboard, all the lockers in the captain's quarters have broken loose and fallen into the debris in the aisle. A lot of this is still buried under mud and sand, and it is an area of future opportunity."

Photographs of the recovery of Enigma M2946 are shown below. The story and photographs of the recovery of Enigma M3131 are shown later in this chapter.

A year later - on 22 August 2002 - the rest of Enigma M3131 was recovered. Again - as described by diver Roger Hunting:

"The second Enigma was located in the Radio Room, just like M2946. As you recall, we had recovered the rotors and wooden lid of M3131 shortly after recovering M2946 on July 3, 2001, but the rest of the machine was not found during the summer of 2001.

"At that time we were using a four-inch diameter dredge and we had removed about as much as we could out of the Radio Room. The only remaining mud was at the very low side of the room, remembering that the submarine has a 40 degree list to starboard.

Three views of Enigma M2946 after some of the mud had been washed away.

The rotor stack of Enigma M2946.

Rotor number IV from Enigma M2946.

All four rotors after they were removed.

The other side of the four rotors from Enigma M2946.

(left) This is the special typewriter attachment used with Enigma M2946. It was apparently attached to the contact block that was mounted over and in place of the light bulbs. It was attached by means of the cable that can be seen to the left of its keyboard. It is believed that the keys of this typewriter contained light bulbs and that these bulbs were illuminated by voltages from the light panel on the Enigma. By pressing each illuminated key, the operator would type the correct message onto a piece of paper.

The box of six additional rotors that were used with Enigma M2946.

The additional rotor set for Enigma M3131.

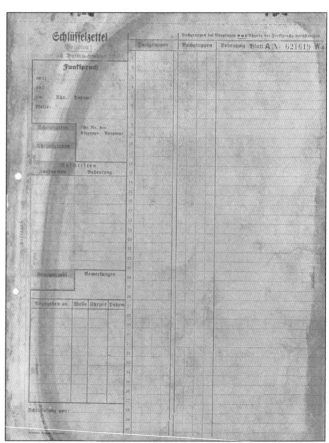

This is a page of a pad used for preparing radio messages for Enigma encoding and transmisison.

Damit — Datieren — 610 — Teil III

K F N	Damit (i. S. v. In der Absicht, daß)	K H I	Dampforderei
N R D	Damit (i. S. v. zu dem Zweck)	Q M V	Dampfpfeife(n)
F M M	Damm (Dämme) von	Z L	Lassen Sie die Dampfpfeife oder Sirene in Zwischenräumen ertönen!
O B U	Dampf (i. techn. S.)	N M X	Geben Sie Signale mit der Dampfpfeife oder Sirene!
O B Z	Dampf aufhaben	N M Y	Signalisieren Sie bei Nebel mit Dampfpfeife oder Sirene!
O C A	Hab... Dampf aufgehabt	Z K	Ich will/werde bei Nebel mit der Dampfpfeife oder Sirene signalisieren!
W N	Haben Sie Dampf auf	N M H	Ich werde mit der Dampfpfeife oder Sirene signalisieren
W M	Zu welcher Zeit werden Sie Dampf aufhaben	Q M W	Dampfpfeife unbrauchbar
W I	Behalten Sie Dampf auf!	M F V	Wiederholen Sie Ihre Mitteilung(en) mit Dampfpfeife oder Sirene!
O C B	Dampf aufmachen	K Z I	Dampfrohr(e)
O C J	Hab... Dampf aufgemacht	K Z L	Dampfrohr ist beschädigt
O C K	Werden, Wird Dampf aufmachen	K Z K	Dampfrohr ist geplatzt
O C U	Machen Sie Dampf auf!	K Z J	Dampfrohrleitung
O C C	Ich kann keinen Dampf aufmachen	O D O	Dampfrudergeschirre
W J	Machen Sie Dampf auf, und melden Sie, wenn/sobald Sie bereit sind!	R M N	Dampfschiff
O C F	Machen Sie sofort Dampf auf, und melden Sie, sobald Sie fahrbereit sind!	I S G	Dampfschiff-Compagnie(n) / Dampfschiffahrt-Gesellschaft(en)
W K	Machen Sie so schnell wie möglich Dampf auf!	N O G	Dampfsirene(n)
O C G	Können Sie Dampf aufmachen	Q R M	Dampfwinde(n)
O C H	Können Sie sofort Dampf aufmachen		Dampfwinsch(en)
W L	Machen Sie aus Sicherheitsgründen Dampf auf!	V V W	Danach (i. S. v. nachher)
W O	Soll ich Dampf aufmachen	O V F	Dank
O C D	Ich werde, um Dampf aufzumachen, (Zahl angegeben) Stunden benötigen		Dankbar
O C I	Innerhalb welcher Zeit können Sie Dampf aufmachen	J Y C	Ich würde dankbar sein, wenn
W G	Ich habe Dampf auf und Maschinen klar	V F E	Ich würde Ihnen sehr dankbar sein, wenn... Sie würden
W H	Dampf wird nicht klar sein für (Zahl angegeben) Minuten	O V F	Danken
R Z E	Kein/Ohne Dampf	O V H	Hab... gedankt
O B V	Unter Dampf	O V G	Danke, n) Ihnen für
O B W	Unter eigenem Dampf	V V E	Dann
O B U	Dampf- (i. techn. S.)	N R O	Dann und wann
I G Q	Dampfbarkasse(n)		Darauf siehe unter "Danach" (i. S. v. nachher)
L J Y	Dampfstrahl		Dargelegt
O B U	Dampfen	O A G	Wie dargelegt in
O B Y	Hab... gedampft	V H C	Darüber (i. S. v. über das Erwähnte)
O B X	Dampfen Sie langsamer, Sie überanstrengen mein Spill	O W A	Darum (i. S. v. deshalb)
R M N	Dampfer	V W O	Das/Den/Der/Die (Einzahl des bestimmten Geschlechtsworts, 1. und 4. Fall)
O C O	Dampfer mit Decksholzladung	R Z J	Das/Der/Die (Rückbezügliches Fürwort, 1. Fall)
O C Q	Durch/Mit/Der Dampfer	R Z K	Das/Der/Die (Rückbezügliches Fürwort, 4. Fall)
I O D	Dampferlicht	V V D	Daß
I O L	Dampferlicht	E L F	Datieren
I O B	2. Dampferlicht	E L S	Hab... datiert

This page of a codebook that was used for flag signal communications with merchant vessels is amazingly well preserved after 60 years underwater.

"We had reached a cabinet along the hull and assumed that the cabinet went all the way to the floor. It was difficult getting down in that portion of the room since you almost had to be standing on your head to reach the far corner. It is interesting that on the outside of the submarine the sand bottom registers 100 feet, yet when we were at the low side of the Radio Room we were reaching 107 feet.

"In addition to being difficult to reach, the low pocket in the Radio Room contained lots of debris (remains of cabinetry, electrical parts, wiring, etc.) that kept plugging up the 4-inch dredge pipe. So we left the last remaining mud and gave up on finding the second Enigma.

"We moved our dredge pipe from the Radio Room to the Galley area towards the end of the summer of 2001 and recovered several pieces of silverware and a few coffee cups and saucers. At the beginning of the 2002 dive season we

Enigma M3131 immediately after recovery from *U-85*. It had been under water for more than 60 years and is covered with mud.

The rotor stack removed from Enigma M3131 after some of the mud had been cleaned off.

Rotor number Beta from Enigma M3131.

increased the dredge pipe diameter to six inches and were able to handle much larger pieces of debris without plugging. We did more dredging in the Galley and then moved to the Forward Torpedo Room.

"We felt fairly certain that the M3131 was still in the last remaining pile of mud in the Radio Room. In July we moved our dredge back to the Radio Room for one last shot at the remaining mud. The 6-inch pipe worked well and in no time, we discovered that what we thought was a cabinet was a counter top. Down under that counter, at the very lowest part of the room, was the second machine. It took only three dives to finish the job that we gave up on the previous summer".

RESTORATION OF THE U-85S ENIGMAS

The recovered Enigma M-2946 is being restored by Jim Oram of www.enigma-replica.com. In addition to expert work on Enigmas, Jim makes and sells a wide range of replica parts for Enigmas and maintains a very interesting website. Here are several photographs showing his progress on this Enigma.

A closer view of the partially restored Enigma M3131.

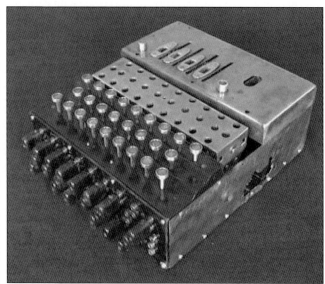

Enigma M3131 after thorough cleaning and partial restoration.

Details of the recovery are also given in a paper: 'The Enigmas - and Other Recovered Artefacts - of U-85', Hamer, David H., *Cryptologia*, Vol. XXVII(2), April 2003, pp. 97-110. Copyright 2001- 2005, David Hamer.

The restoration of Enigma M2946 from U-boat U-85 as it appeared in 2010. The restoration is being performed by Jim Oram of www.enigma-replica.com for the Graveyard of the Atlantic Museum (www.graveyardoftheatlanticmuseum.com).

Another view of the restoration of Enigma M2946 from German U-Boat U-85 for the www.graveyardoftheatlanticmuseum.com as it appeared in 2010. [Jim Oram of www.enigma-replica.com]

HOW MANY ENIGMA MACHINES EXIST & WHAT IS THEIR VALUE?

It is not known how many Enigmas were originally made. All records were destroyed in the war. Estimates range from 2000 up to 20,000. I have seen a great number of Enigma machines but I have personally never seen one with a serial number over 20,500. Therefore, I tend toward accepting this figure as a reasonable estimate of the total number that were made.

The question of how many Enigmas have actually survived destruction is also difficult to answer.

Comparing the frequency with which I find an Enigma with the frequency with which I find a very rare telegraph key, suggests that about 300 Enigmas survive worldwide with perhaps 60-80 of them in America. It is clear that many more of the three-rotor German Army Enigmas have survived than the four-rotor Navy Enigmas. The early model K and the commercial models of the Enigma are found much less frequently than the Army or Navy models.

The fact that so few German Military Enigmas have survived coupled with their great historical significance helps to explain why they sell for very high prices if one happens to appear on the market. Their value appears to reflect their scarcity, with the Navy Enigma typically bringing twice the price of the Army Enigma. The commercial models are scarcer but have somewhat less historical significance than the military models so their prices typically fall between the Army and the Navy price extremes.

Chapter 7
Making your own Enigma

HOW TO MAKE A SIMPLIFIED VERSION OF THE ENIGMA

Obviously making a complete replica of an Enigma is beyond most people (though see later in this chapter for details of some people who have done just that). However, a coding machine based on the same techniques as an Enigma is easy to construct using simple materials.

Code wheels have been in use at least as far back as the fifteenth century. They offer interesting examples of a Caesar-like coding strategy (see the chapter on cipher machines). Pictured below is an accurate replica of a code wheel used by the CSA (Confederate States of America) during the American Civil War.

With this wheel, the plaintext is inscribed around the outside of the wheel and the CIPHERTEXT is inscribed on the rotating centre disk.

You can easily make an accurate reproduction of this type of historic code wheel in the following way:

1. Use your computer printer to print TWO pictures of one of the code wheels shown on this or the next page. (A printable copy of the picture is available on my CD: *The Story of the Enigma*, or you can scan from this book). You may need to use a photograph viewing or processing program if you wish to change the size of the printed pictures.
2. Carefully cut out the central wheel from one of your printouts.
3. Push a pin or tack through the exact centre of the cut-out wheel and into the exact centre of the complete photograph.
4. You will now have a replica of an historic code wheel which can be used for display or as the basis for a school science project.

Code wheels were widely used throughout history and some were even used as toys and prizes for buying certain breakfast cereals in the pre-WW2 period, as shown by the 1930s "Captain Midnight" code wheels pictured in Chapter 1.

Confederate States of America Civil War cipher wheel. A brass replica is available from the museum shop of the NSA/National Cryptologic Museum.

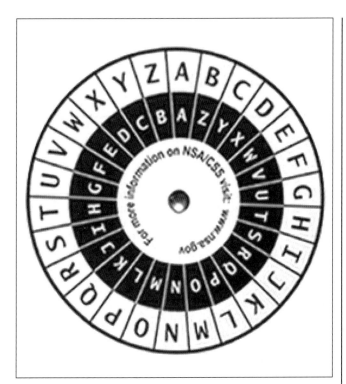

Copy this picture to make your own Enigma-style code wheel. Note that on this wheel the alphabet is reversed on the inner wheel.

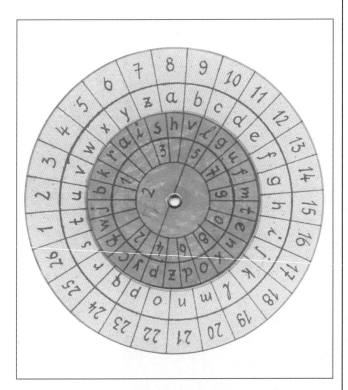

The German WW2 spy codenamed 'TATE' carried this homemade code wheel on his person to allow him to encode messages into CIPHERTEXT for safe transmission back to Germany. TATE was eventually convinced to work for the British as a double-agent and he continued transmitting code wheel encoded messages back to Germany under the direct control of the British. [British Public Records Office]

HOW THE CODE WHEEL IS SIMILAR TO THE ENIGMA

The German Enigma machine uses precisely the same basic principle as the code wheel but, as we will see, it effectively rotates the inner wheel to a new position with each letter to be enciphered.

It decides how much to rotate the inner wheel according to a rather complex set of mechanical and electrical settings and rules.

Since it rotates the inner wheel with each character, it is the initial starting position of the inner wheel which forms the key for the Enigma. We will learn about the Enigma settings and rules shortly.

HOW YOUR CODE WHEEL REPLICA CAN BECOME A SIMPLIFIED VERSION OF THE ENIGMA MACHINE

If you have constructed a working model of the code wheel using the techniques described above, you can make it work like an Enigma machine in the following way:

Let's say you want to use your code wheel to send a coded CIPHERTEXT version of the plaintext message: 'help' to a friend who has the same kind of wheel.

You must start out by selecting a KEY or STARTING POSITION.

Pick an easy KEY and set the inner wheel to exactly the same letters as the outer wheel. This means that the letter 'a' on the outer wheel lines up with the letter 'A' on the inner wheel.

Your friend must also be told what the KEY or STARTING POSITION is.

You must also determine exactly how many letters the inner wheel must rotate past each time you convert a letter into CIPHERTEXT. This amount can vary with each plaintext letter inputted.

Let's say we are going to rotate the inner wheel RIGHT by:

2 letters before inputting the plaintext letter 'h'.
4 letters before inputting the plaintext letter 'e'.
3 letters before inputting the plaintext letter 'l'.
2 letters before inputting the plaintext letter 'p'.

Remember this sequence of rotations: 2, 4, 3, and 2, and be sure your friend knows the sequence.

Now, convert the plaintext message 'help' into CIPHERTEXT as follows:

- Turn the inner wheel two letters to the right (clockwise). Now, the plaintext letter 'h' on the outer wheel becomes the CIPHERTEXT letter 'V' on the inner wheel. write this letter down.
- Turn the inner wheel four letters to the right (clockwise). Now, the plaintext letter 'e' on the outer wheel becomes the CIPHERTEXT letter 'C' on the inner wheel. Write this letter down.
- Turn the inner wheel three letters to the right (clockwise). Now, the plaintext letter 'l' on the outer wheel becomes the CIPHERTEXT letter 'Y' on the inner wheel. Write this letter down.
- Turn the inner wheel two letters to the right (clockwise). Now, the plaintext letter 'p' on the outer wheel becomes the CIPHERTEXT letter 'W' on the inner wheel. Write this letter down.
- This gives the CIPHERTEXT letters: 'V', 'C', 'Y', 'W'

Now transmit this CIPHERTEXT message to your friend - perhaps by sending an email or text message. Make sure your friend has a similar code wheel that is set to the same KEY or STARTING POSITION with 'a' on the outer wheel lined up with 'A' on the inner wheel. Be certain that your friend knows the sequence of rotations of the inner wheel: 2, 4, 3, and 2

Your friend can now decode the CIPHERTEXT message 'FYCE' as follows:

- Turn the inner wheel two letters to the right (clockwise). Now, the CIPHERTEXT letter 'V' on the inner wheel becomes the plaintext letter 'h' on the outer wheel.
- Turn the Inner wheel four letters to the right (clockwise). Now, the CIPHERTEXT letter 'C' on the inner wheel becomes the plaintext letter 'e' on the outer wheel.
- Turn the inner wheel three letters to the right (clockwise). Now, the CIPHERTEXT letter 'Y' on the inner wheel becomes the plaintext letter 'l' on the outer wheel.
- Turn the Inner wheel two letters to the right (clockwise). Now, the CIPHERTEXT letter 'W' on the inner wheel becomes the plaintext letter 'p' on the outer wheel.
- This gives the recovered plaintext letters: 'h', 'e', 'l', 'p' which is the original plaintext message 'help'.

This analogy is quite close to the way the Enigma machine works with the main difference being in the more complex 'rules' that determine how much the inner wheel is rotated with each subsequent letter.

KITS FOR CIPHER MACHINES

Several people are developing and offering more complex kits to allow you to build working models of the Enigma that range from simple analogies to nearly exact electronic and electro-mechanical replicas. You will find some of these kits on the internet.

Many people have decided that they want to make their own Enigmas. The results range from simple code-wheel derived models through strip-cipher models through electronic models, and all the way up to exceptionally complex electro-mechanical versions. A number of these will be seen and referenced below:

In addition, numerous fine software simulators allow computers to emulate all of the different Enigma models as well as a number of other cipher machines. A search of the internet will locate software that will run on a PC or Mac and that will transform the computer into the appropriate Enigma model complete with graphics and sound effects that will make you think you are sitting in front of a genuine Enigma. Most of them are freeware.

Michael C Koss has put a very nice paper model of the Enigma on the internet at: http://mckoss.com/Crypto/Enigma.htm. His website also has several other Enigma simulators.

BUILDING ENIGMA MACHINES

Enigma-E-Kit
Paul Reuvers and Marc Simons have designed the most elaborate and widely used electronic model of the Enigma which they call the Enigma-E kit. It is easy to build and extremely versatile with its ability to emulate virtually every model of the Enigma.

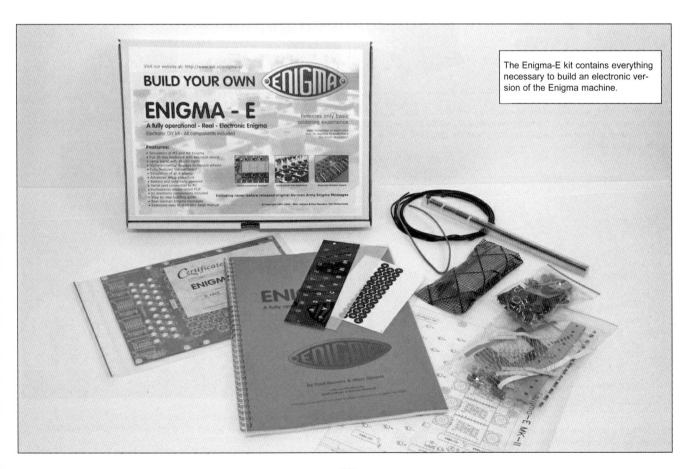

The Enigma-E kit contains everything necessary to build an electronic version of the Enigma machine.

Over 1300 of these kits have sold, perhaps in part because the price is so low at less than $200. Ordering information is at: http://cryptomuseum.com/kits/order.htm and they are sold directly by the Bletchley Park store.

The Enigma-E works just like a real Enigma machine and is compatible with the standard Service Machine used by the German *Wehrmacht* and *Luftwaffe*. It is also compatible with the three-wheel naval M3 Enigma machine and the four-wheel M4 machine that was used exclusively by the U-boat section of the German *Kriegsmarine*. A message encrypted on, say, a real Enigma M4 can be read on the Enigma-E and vice versa.

The wheels have been replaced by four alphanumerical displays, each capable of displaying the entire alphabet. Above and below the displays are up and down buttons allowing the initial settings to be changed. Just below the displays are 26 LEDs, replacing the 26 lamps of the original machine. Each LED represents one letter of the alphabet. Below the lamp section is the keyboard, with 26 push-buttons. Again, each button represents one letter of the alphabet and the keyboard features the original German layout (QWERTZ).

Finally, the lower part of the PCB contains the *Steckerbrett*, that was used by the German Army to swap pairs of letters, in addition to the coding wheels. The *Steckerbrett* part of the PCB can be separated from the rest to allow it to be mounted vertically, just like on the real machine.

The kit contains everything needed to build a working Enigma machine, including the PCB, all electronic components and a manual with detailed building instructions. All that is needed to complete the project is a soldering iron, solder, a power supply and some soldering experience. It should be possible to complete the kit in a few hours or a few nights. Once it is completed, the kit can be put to test by trying one of messages supplied in the manual.

Also available from the same supplier is the UhrBox-E kit, an add-on to the Enigma-E. It is the electronic equivalent of the famous Enigma *Uhr* that was introduced by the German *Luftwaffe* in 1944 in an attempt to make the Enigma safer. At the centre of the PCB is a so-called rotary encoder which simulates the large 40-step dial of the original *Uhr*.

Full information about Enigma-E can be found at: www.cryptomuseum.com/kits/enigma/desc.htm.

Jim Oram's Replica Enigma

Jim Oram has made what is probably the most accurate replica of an Enigma ever constructed. His company http://enigma-replica.com sells a wide variety of parts and pieces for people who want to repair and rebuild Enigma machines and his website is a must-view for people interested in the Enigma.

Rather than building an Enigma replica, which is a tedious task, you can build an electronic alternative, using modern components to replace the mechanical parts of the original Enigma. The picture shows both the Enigma-E and an original Enigma side by side.

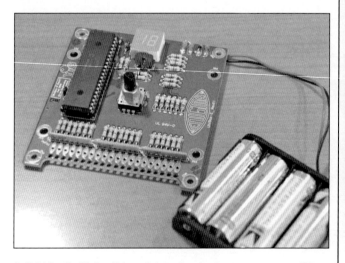

(left) Adding the UhrBox-E to an Enigma-E makes it even more secure. This simulates the *Uhr* employed by the *Luftwaffe*.

The four-rotor German Navy Enigma Replica created by Jim Oram of www.enigma-replica.com is shown along with a number of the AutoCAD figures from which the parts were created.

Jim Oram of www.enigma-replica.com sits next to his extremely accurate and fully functional replica of a German WW2 Navy four-rotor Enigma.

(shown below) The completed "Scrapbox Enigma" constructed by Melvin L Kalb starting in 2001.

The machine tools at www.enigma-replica.com show Jim Oram's dedication to exceptional precision in making Enigma parts.

Below is photo of Jim Oram's replica Enigma showing some of the AutoCAD-created rotors. Jim disassembled and measured every part of a Marine Enigma and created a complex set of AutoCAD files. He has used these to create the actual pieces of his enigma through a complex computerized process in which the computer reads the Autocad files and creates the objects. Jim Oram's machine shop at www.enigma-replica.com is designed to allow him to produce extremely accurate reproductions of Enigma parts.

Scrapbox Enigma

Melvin L Kalb of Scottsdale, Arizona was fascinated by the relatively simple construction of a machine that produced such an enormous complexity of codes. In 2001 he decided to build what he called a "Scrapbox Enigma" (pictured right) using primarily parts that came from materials that he had in his shop.

A top view of Melvin Kalb's "Scrapbox Enigma".

One of the rotors of Melvin Kalb's "Scrapbox Enigma". You can clearly see the wiring maze that connects the pin contacts on one side of the rotor to the flat contacts on the other side.

The interior of Melvin Kalb's "Scrapbox Enigma". You can see that he has replaced the leaf-switches of the keyboard with microswitches and designed a special rotor moving mechanism that is not powered by the force of pushing down on the keyboard keys.

A view into the left side of the "Scrapbox Enigma". It shows how the keyboard keys are mounted so that they press down on the microswitches.

Photographs and articles on the internet served as his primary sources of information. He discussed his project at length with Jim Oram of www.enigma-replica.com (see above) and finally decided to go ahead and build it.

HOME MADE CIPHER MACHINE OF TATJA VAN VARK

At least one individual has designed and built a cipher machine as complex as an Enigma. Her name is Tatja Van Vark and she lives in the Netherlands.

Tatja has always been interested in all kinds of mechanical and electronic devices. She was particularly fascinated by the Enigma machine and wanted to own one but an original was

The machine's designer and builder Tatja Van Vark from the Netherlands.

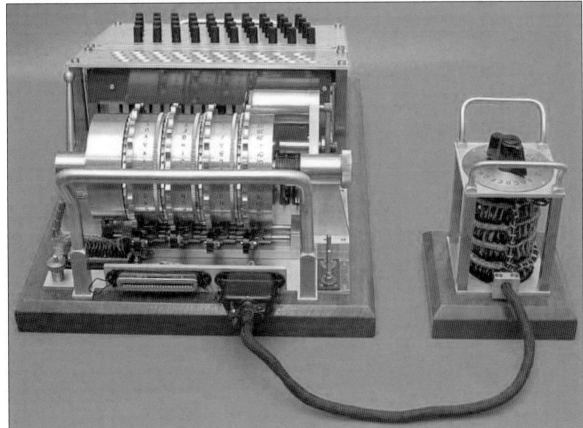

Tatja Van Vark's absolutely incredible enhanced Enigma-inspired cipher machine has thousands of home made components.

An internal View of Tatja's Enigma-inspired cipher machine.

out of reach and she decided to build her own. After studying a short description of the principles of the Enigma, she decided to design and build an improved cipher machine and a printer similar to the German *Schreibmax* printer which worked with the Enigma.

Tatja has no formal education in electronics or mechanics. As she puts it: "I wanted to own a coding machine and now I do." Building it took about eight months. No wonder when you see how many parts are inside, and everything had to be home made. For example, each of the rotors has 509 individual parts.

She is particularly proud of the helical gearing in both the cipher machine and the printer. Tatja makes everything herself including the varnish which is made from all natural ingredients.

A nearby museum has asked Tatja to restore their Enigma machine and to give a lecture and demonstration of both machines. She is now working to restore the museum's automatic telephone exchanges and carrier wave equipment.

The machine has the looks and uses many of the principles of the original Enigma but it has much stronger coding capabilities. She says: "I will bet that nobody in the next hundred years will be able to decipher the short message I created with my machine:

GUK59 XBOFJ -AFF1 SGU65 0-KME YKCL7 76PRO LIKNY /WVSZ X-JYI OS6GN 9GLYL CTOSE -UBO6 OFD7P I+M3J

This chapter features a collection of photographs of Tatja's fascinating cipher machine and of some of the other amazing instruments that she has built.

Take a look at Tatja's website: http://www.tatjavanvark.nl where you will find much more detailed descriptions of her work and more photographs of her various projects.

More pictures of Tatja van Vark's home-made cipher machine follow >>>>>>>>>

The four rotors of Tatja's Enigma-inspired cipher machine.

Two views of the four rotors designed and built by Tatja van Vark for her cipher machine.

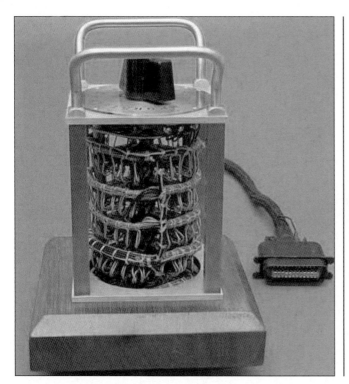
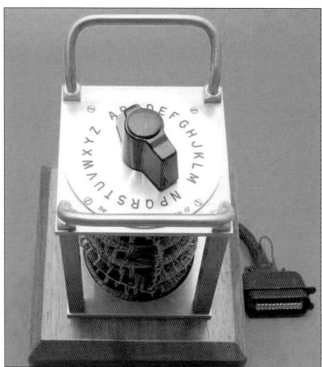

The switch that Tatja designed to replace the plugboard typically found on the German Enigma machines.

Two views of Tatja van Vark's amazing and beautiful home made printer for her Enigma-inspired cipher machine.

Another view of Tatja van Vark's home made printer for her Enigma-inspired cipher machine.

Chapter 8
Japanese, American, Swiss Machines

Much of this chapter is based on the research of F L Bauer in 1997.

Machines similar to the Enigma were produced both before and after World War 2. Countries developing them included the United Kingdom, the United States, Italy, Japan, Switzerland and Russia.

Russian machines used during the Cold War are the subject of the next chapter. The bulk of this chapter deals with equipment developed by the Japanese, Americans and Swiss.

BRITISH CIPHER MACHINES

The British cipher machine, the Type-X had two rotors instead of a plug board. Built by Creed, it was used during and after WW2 and had several enhancements leading to improved security. Security was further improved by limiting the number of machines and restricting their use. It is believed that the messages from these machines were never cracked during the War. Quite a number of Type-X machines were modified to emulate German Enigma machines and used to decipher messages once the 'key' had been discovered. Type-X was in use until the 1970s.

ITALIAN CIPHER MACHINES

Ottico Meccanica Italiana (OMI) of Rome produced an Italian seven-rotor, fixed reflector cipher machine. Each rotor had two sections which could be interchanged, resulting in a large number of permutations.

JAPANESE CIPHER MACHINES

Many German Enigma machines were sold to Japan and carried there in submarines and other vessels. In addition to the German Enigmas, the Japanese developed their own version. One of these rare machines is on display in the NSA / National Cryptologic Museum:

Shown here are several historically important Japanese Cipher machines.

Japanese version of the Enigma Machine. You can see the keyboard, rotors, and the light panel with Japanese letters. [NSA / National Cryptologic Museum]

Japanese analog cipher machine codenamed PURPLE. [NSA/National Cryptologic Museum]

AMERICAN CIPHER MACHINES

Several machines were designed by US Army cryptographer William Frederick Friedman, based on the early designs by Edward Hebern which used rotors. Friedman analysed Hebern's machine and produced his own which avoided the flaws in the basic design.

The machines designed by Friedman included:

- M-94 (1922) 25 thin aluminum cylinders,
- M-134-T2 (1933),
- M-134-A (SIGMYC),
- M-134-C (SIGABA) (1936) SCP889 (ECM Mark II),
- M-138 (1934) Strip version. Improved 138-A (1938),
- M-209 (1943) Widely used during WW2, and
- M-138-T4: (1944) (SIGTOT).

The following pages contain photographs of American Cipher Machines taken in 2004 at the National Security Agency / National Cryptologic Museum, Maryland.

The largest recovered piece of the Japanese digital cipher machine code-named PURPLE. [NSA/National Cryptologic Museum]

Japanese cipher machine codenamed JADE. [NSA/National Cryptologic Museum]

(below) American WW2 SIGCUM cipher machine. [NSA/National Cryptologic Museum]

American WW2 SIGCUM cipher machine rotors. [NSA/National Cryptologic Museum]

American WW2 M-325 SIGFOY cipher machine. [NSA/National Cryptologic Museum]

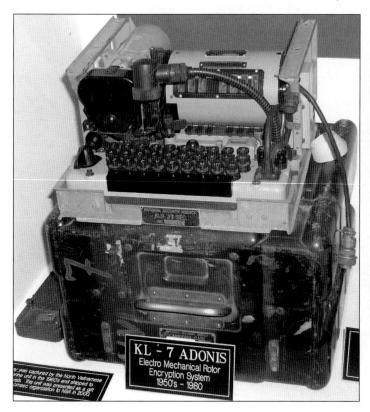

American KL-7 cipher machine from the 1950s (left) with (right) a box of rotors. [NSA/National Cryptologic Museum]

Two views of the American World War 2 M-209 cipher machine. [NSA / National Cryptologic Museum]

M-209
Tactical Cipher Machine
Mechanical Rotor/Pin System
WW-I I - 1970's

AMERICAN WW2 M-209 CIPHER MACHINE

The M-209 was in use for the entire duration of WW2 and later in the Korean War. It was phased out after the Korean War ended in the mid 1960s. Three different versions of the M-209 are known: M-209, M-209-A, and M-209-B. Apart from some manufacturing differences, these machines are all identical.

This machine was originally developed in 1938 as the C-38. In 1940 it was adopted by the US Army who renamed it M-209. The design was simplified and the mechanics were made more robust before the machine went into mass production in the United States in 1942. It was first used during the invasion of Africa in November, 1942. Licensee Smith Corona built about 125,000 units before it was discontinued in the early 1960s. The US Navy designator for this machine is CSP-1500. (Information from www.cryptomuseum.com)

The M-209 uses an entirely mechanical mechanism with a simple Encode/Decode lever. It has six rotors with 26 individually-adjustable rotation advance pins. It also has a complex set of internal settings to control the ultimate rotation of a print wheel that prints the text onto glue-backed paper tape that can be stuck onto paper message blanks.

The following description of the operation of the M-209 cipher machine is from the book: *German Cipher Machines of World War II*, by David P Mowry. It was written in 2003 and published by the Center for Cryptologic History of the National Security Agency.

"There are six wheels whose lengths are mutually prime. These lengths are indicated by different lengths of letter

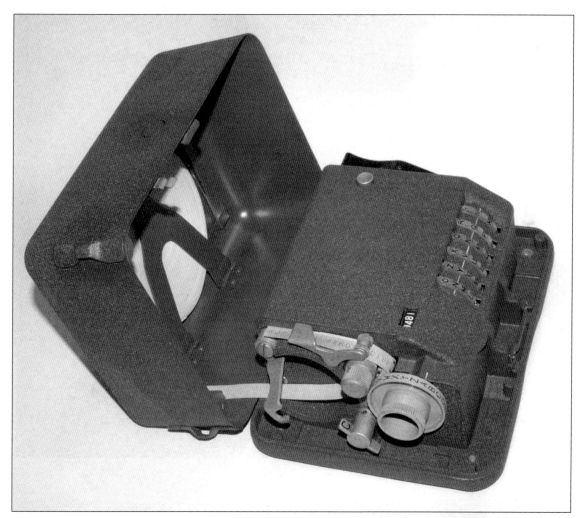

A closer view of the M-209. Note the paper tape printing mechanism on the left side. The lowest knob can be set to "C" for "Cipher" the input or "D" for "Decipher" the input.

sequences (26, 25, 23, 21, 19 and 17) on the wheels. Each key wheel steps once with each encipherment, returning to its starting position after its period. These wheel lengths give a cycle length of 26 x 25 x 23 x 21 x 19 x 17 = 101,405,850.

"On each key wheel there are 'pins' corresponding to the letters (on that wheel). Each pin can be set as 'active' (ie pushed to the left so it can engage a lug on the cage) or 'inactive'.

"The 'cage' is a cylinder composed of twenty-seven bars bearing projections known as 'lugs', which are positioned to correspond to the key wheels. The cage rotates once with every encipherment. If a lug encounters an active pin, the bar is slid to the left so that its end projects past the end plate. In each case, this effectively creates a gear 'tooth'. These 'teeth' engage another gear and turn it in accordance with the total number of 'teeth' projecting from the cage. The number of lugs for each key wheel governs the number of teeth and thus the 'kick' for that wheel.

"To set the device up for encryption, the pins and lugs must be set according to a keylist giving the settings for the day. The key wheels are then turned by hand to position six letters in the starting window. These letters constitute the message indicator, which must be included in the message in some way to inform the decipherer where to set the wheels for decryption.

"In operation, the encipherer sets the machine to 'encipher' and turns a knurled knob on the left side of the machine to align the desired letter on the plaintext wheel with an index

A much closer view of the paper tape printing mechanism. You can see some enciphered letters that have been printed on the tape. Note also the lettered wheel that is used to input letters into the cipher machine. Turning the wheel so the desired letter ("U" in this case) is adjacent to the white index mark and then turning the big black handle on the other side of the machine operates the mechanism and prints the ciphertext on the paper tape.

A view of the M-209 with the cover opened to allow access to the programming mechanism. The "Cipher/Decipher" knob is set to "C", the "Cipher" mode, which enciphers the input letters and prints the ciphertext on the paper tape.

A closer view of the internal programming mechanism. The input wheel and printer are on the left. The character counter is also on the left. The six code wheels are in front and the programming wheel is in the background.

A closer view of the six code wheels. If you look closely, you can see the individual pins that can be moved from side to side at each of the 26 letter positions of each of the six wheels to control the rotation of each wheel.

mark. A low-frequency letter such as 'X' is used as the word separator. The operating lever on the right side of the machine is then rotated. The cage rotates, the gear is turned and turns the print wheel, which is fixed to the plaintext wheel, the number of places determined by the projecting teeth on the cage. A counter keeps track of the number of characters enciphered.

"With the completion of the movement of the operating lever and its return to its normal position, the paper tape advances one position, the print wheel prints the ciphertext character on the paper tape, the bars in the cage return to their normal position, the key wheels step one position, and the machine is ready for its next input. The ciphertext characters are printed on gummed paper tape in five-letter groups.

"The decipherer in turn sets his machine up in accordance with the key list. When the message is received he sets the key wheels to the message indicator, sets the machine to 'decipher' and follows the same procedure as was used in enciphering. The plaintext is then printed on the gummed paper tape." (Mowry, 2003).

A great deal of additional technical information on the M-209 is available on the web at sites like www.cryptomuseum.com and some very fine simulators with excellent graphics allow your computer to accurately emulate the M-209 operation.

The operation is described in *War Department Technical Manual TM11-380*, parts of which are reproduced in the appendix to this book .

The original 30-minute film used to train soldiers in the proper use of the M-209 has been digitized by Bill Burns and can be found on Bob Lord's wonderful Cipher Machine web site: http://ilord.com. The video is very detailed and even includes an appropriate musical background. A simple descriptive video lasting six minutes is available via the

The pins on the left side of the programming matrix in the background have been set to the "1" position. The pins on the right side have been set to the "0" position.

This shows how the individual pins are set using the specially notched screwdriver. If they are not set carefully so that they click into position, the machine may jam.

A closer view of the pins that determine the rotation of the leftmost programming wheel on the M-209. The pin adjacent to the letter "M" is being pushed to the left position.

author's web site http://w1tp.com/enigma/. This shows how the M-209 is used to encode and decode a message. Both videos are on the CD *The Story of the ENIGMA*.

SWISS 'NEMA' CIPHER MACHINE

The Swiss had some model K Enigmas which they had obtained from the Germans before the war. They modified these Enigmas and used the resulting so-called Swiss K machine throughout the war. When they discovered that their machines were being deciphered by both the Germans and the Allied forces, they developed their own cipher machine. Starting in 1946, the Swiss manufactured a machine called the NEMA. The name derives from "NEue MAschine" (New Machine). It was made by Zellweger AG in Uster.

The machine was developed between 1941 and 1943 by a team led by Captain Arthur Alder (a professor of mathematics at Berne University.) and the first prototype was ready in early 1944. After a few modifications and improvements, the machine was finally approved in 1945.

The first of the total of 640 NEMAs did not enter service until 1947. Three variants were made and identified by their serial numbers that start with TD (Tasten Drucke Maschine) (Key Press Machine):

A complete Swiss NEMA cipher machine.

TD-100 to199	Foreign Office Service
TD-200 to 419	Training Machines
TD-420 to 740	Operational Military Machines

Typing a letter causes another letter to light up . . .

View of the inside of the cover showing the power cord, data cables, power adapters, cleaning brush and spare code wheels: Also shown is the remote light panel which could be used to prevent the keyboard operator from seeing the decoded messages.

. . . and typing the same letter again causes a different letter to light up.

A close-up view of the code wheels.

A close-up view of the ten code wheels in place in the NEMA machine.

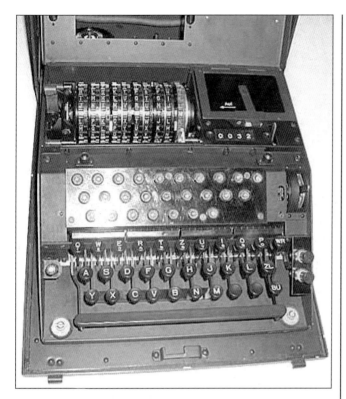

A front view with the cover over the entire mechanism and light bulbs open. This view shows the four rotors surrounded by the rotatable reflector on the left and a red rotatable counter-incrementing wheel around the fixed position input disk on the right. Note that each rotor has its rotatable setting thumb-wheel on the right and its rotatable ring setting wheel on the left.

A close-up view of the mechanism which rotates and reads the code wheels.

A close-up view of the NEMA's code wheels, spare wheels, and covers out of the machine.

An overall view of the NEMA with cover closed showing the two original keys. The serial number: TD-600 shows that this is a NEMA made for use by the Swiss Military. The label says that it is only to be used in case of war.

They were declassified in 1992 and sold on the surplus market beginning on 4 May, 1994. (Information from: www.cryptomuseum.com)

The NEMA which had four active rotors, a rotatable reflector on the left, and a rotatable counter-incrementing wheel around the fixed position input disk on the right. It also had a remote light panel.

NEMA worked on the same principles as the Enigma. The four active rotors each had an easily adjustable ring-setting wheel that could be changed as though it was one of the rotor thumbwheels. All these thumbwheels gave the erroneous impression that the NEMA had ten rotors.

An eight-minute descriptive video, *The Swiss NEMA Cipher Machine*, showing how the NEMA is set up to encode and decode a message is included in the CD *The Story of the Enigma* (see page 4).

The photographs in this book show the NEMA in more detail. Since it was not until 1970 that it became known that the Enigma code had been broken, the Swiss thought that this machine was immune to deciphering.

It has several advanced features including a full ten code wheels which could be mounted in any position and set to any

A Swiss Hagelin CD-57 pocket cipher machine.

letter. It was also supplied with additional code wheel sets which are stored inside the top cover.

An interesting feature of this machine is the remote light panel which can be positioned in such a way that the person typing in the coded letters cannot see the message as it is decoded.

This machine is also capable of feeding its output into a printer.

SWISS HAGELIN CD-57 MECHANICAL POCKET CIPHER MACHINE

This pocket cipher machine was manufactured by the Crypto-AG company in Switzerland and first produced in 1957. It shows a level of complexity and superb machining that is similar to that seen in the CURTA series of pocket calculators. It is entirely mechanical and uses no electricity in its operation. This machine was very popular with the French Secret Service during the Cold War (www.cryptomuseum.com).

A closer view of the mechanism of the Hagelin cipher machine.

A closer view of the mechanism of the Hagelin cipher machine showing the rotors and the character counter.

A closer view of several rotors showing their internally adjustable pins.

The Hagelin cipher machine hinged open and with the six rotors removed to show the top side of each rotor.

It employs six interchangeable and internally adjustable rotors similar to those of an Enigma. First, the Day's Key must be set up in the machine.

To encipher a message, a plaintext letter is first set at the top of the dial using the manually rotatable outer black ring. The finger operated lever is then squeezed and the resulting cipher-text letter is read on the inner dial. To decipher a message, process is reversed.

The Hagelin design was incorporated in the World War 2 US M-209 Cipher Machine.

The photographs here are of an early model of the Hagelin cipher machine.

Chapter 9
Cipher Machines in the Cold War

RUSSIAN COLD WAR ERA M-125 FIALKA CIPHER MACHINE

The Russian cipher machine codenamed "FIALKA" is of particular importance for several reasons. First, it has been in use from the mid 1960s to the present and second, it embodies a number of very sophisticated techniques for overcoming most of the weaknesses of earlier cipher machines like the Enigma. The following descriptions and photographs will attempt to explain the unique features of this machine.

Very little was known about this machine until 2005 when a few Fialkas began appearing for sale. The author managed to purchase one at that time and began the process of documenting and trying to understand it. After taking a great many photographs, studying and disassembling the machine, and measuring the wiring of the rotors, he provided all of his information as well as some Fialka modules and parts to Paul Reuvers and Marc Simons in the Netherlands who methodically researched the history and systematically reverse-engineered the machine and wrote a complete reference manual that explains every aspect of this complex machine and even offers information on servicing and maintenance.

M-125-MN Fialka cipher machine used by the Russians during the Cold War. It shows the slot for inserting a punched paper programming card.

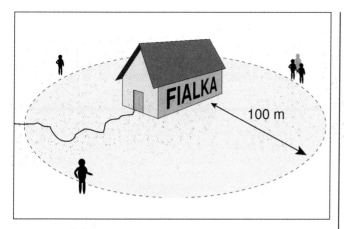

Extreme security precautions and safety zones were placed in effect wherever a Fialka was used. [Reuvers and Simons, 2009]

This reference manual is now available for sale. You can find purchase details in their website at: http://cryptomuseum.com. Some of the following information comes from their manual.

The codename "Fialka" is the Russian word for "violet" (Both the color violet and the flower named violet). Reuvers and Simons (2009) point out that the codename "Fialka" is technically the name of the ciphering procedure and the actual name of the machine is M-125. However, the machine itself is now commonly called the "Fialka".

The first version of the Fialka, the M-100 was produced in the 1930s and it was followed by the M-105 and then the several M-125 models described here.

The M-125 models include the M-125-xx and the much more complicated M-125-3xx. The M-125-xx machines were developed for use by the Russians and have Cyrillic and later Cyrillic and Latin keyboards and character sets. The model M-125-3xx Fialkas were developed later with expanded character sets to allow the machines to be used by other countries

in the Warsaw Pact including Poland, Czechoslovakia and East Germany (the former DDR). The xx in the model number is replaced by letters that indicate the country where the Fialka was used. The author has encountered Fialkas with these model numbers: M-125-MN, M-125-3MN, M-125-3MP2 and M-125-3MP3.

Extreme security precautions were set up to protect Fialka installations. Information about the Fialka was on a need-to-know basis with only a few maintenance personnel in addition to the operator able to access the machine. Even the person who originated or received a Fialka message was not given access to the machine room.

SIMILARITIES BETWEEN THE FIALKA AND THE ENIGMA

Since the Fialka was initially developed in the era when the German Enigma machine was being used, it embodies most of the design features of the Enigma. However, unlike the Enigma which remained basically unchanged, the Fialka was improved and modified to try to eliminate the weak points of the Enigma design.

- The Fialka has a set of rotors that can be placed at any position along the rotor shaft.
- The rotors have Enigma-like ring settings that affect the stepping sequences of the rotors.
- The rotors can be rotated to establish a specific starting position.
- The Fialka has a programming matrix like the plugboard on an Enigma.

It is clear from this list that setting up the Day's Key on a Fialka is generally similar to setting it up on an Enigma. The rotor position on the shaft, the ring setting on each rotor, the starting positions of each rotor, and the Card Reader (the Fialka analogy of the Enigma Plugboard) all need to be set up in order to establish a Day's Key.

It is also clear from this list that the overall design of the Fialka follows that of the Enigma. The following flow diagrams from the *Fialka Reference Manual* by Reuvers and Simons (2009) further clarify the similarities and show the added complexity of the Fialka design.

The Fialka was often used in The GAZ-66 Command Vehicle shown here. [Photograph copyright: http://www.nva-ddr.co.uk]

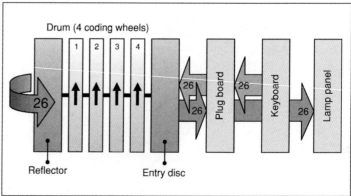

Information Flow Diagram for the German Enigma: This diagram is presented to remind the reader of the flow of information through the German Enigma machine. The Keyboard generates one of the 26 letters of the alphabet and sends this letter through scrambling components in a sequence that includes: the Plugboard, Entry Disc, Rotors, Reflector, Rotors, Entry Disc, Plugboard and finally the Lamp Panel. [Reuvers and Simons, 2009]

Information Flow Diagram for the Russian M-125-xx Fialka: This flow diagram helps to clarify the similarities and differences between this Fialka model M-125-xx and the German Enigma whose diagram appears on the previous page. Again, trace the information as it flows as one of 30 characters from the Keyboard through the Card Reader (the Fialka version of the Enigma's plugboard). Continue to follow it through the Entry Disc, the ten Rotors, the Reflector, the ten Rotors again, the Card Reader again, and finally the Printing Mechanism. Also note the Magic Circuit that compensates for problems presented by the circuitry that allows self-encipherment of letters. It is described later. [Reuvers and Simons, 2009]

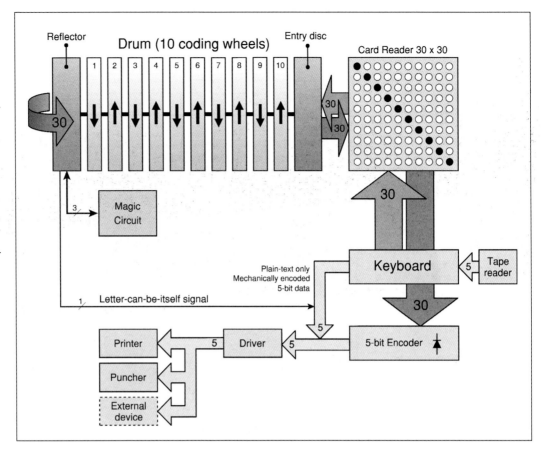

Information Flow Diagram for the Russian M-125-3xx Fialka: This flow diagram helps to clarify similarities and differences between this M-125-3xx model Fialka, the M-125-xx model and the German Enigma whose diagrams appear above. Again, trace the information as it flows as one of 30 characters from the Keyboard through the Card Reader (the Fialka version of the Enigma's plugboard). Continue to follow it through the Entry Disc, the ten Rotors, the Reflector, the ten Rotors again, the Card Reader again, and finally the Printing Mechanism. Also note the Magic Circuit that compensates for problems presented by the circuitry that allows self-encipherment of letters (described later) and also note the 30-10 reduction circuit that is not present in the M-125-xx model Fialka. It allows ten or all 30 keyboard keys to be connected to the Card Reader. [Reuvers and Simons, 2009]

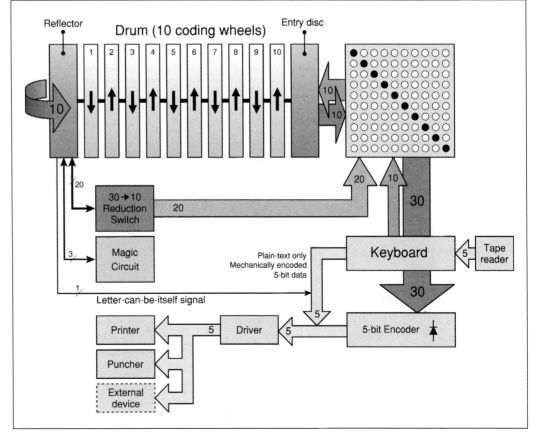

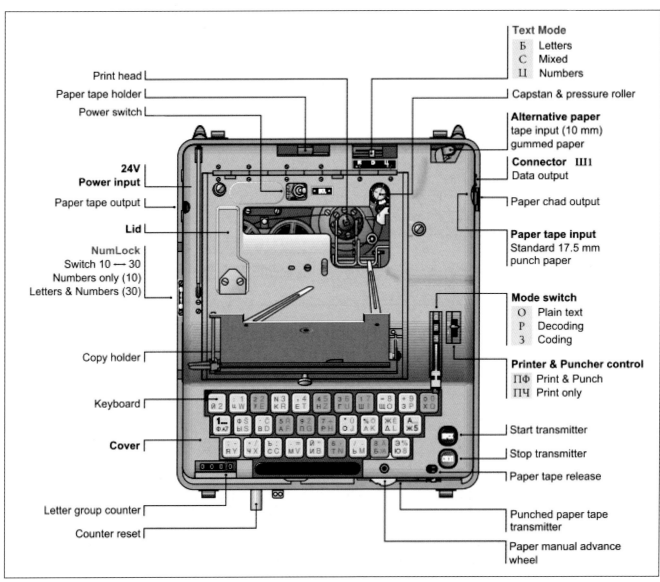

Text Mode
Б Letters
С Mixed
Ц Numbers

Print head
Paper tape holder
Power switch

Capstan & pressure roller

Alternative paper
tape input (10 mm)
gummed paper

24V
Power input

Paper tape output

Lid

Connector Ш1
Data output

Paper chad output

Paper tape input
Standard 17.5 mm
punch paper

NumLock
Switch 10 — 30
Numbers only (10)
Letters & Numbers (30)

Mode switch
О Plain text
Р Decoding
З Coding

Copy holder

Printer & Puncher control
ПФ Print & Punch
ПЧ Print only

Keyboard

Cover

Start transmitter

Stop transmitter

Paper tape release

Letter group counter

Counter reset

Punched paper tape
transmitter

Paper manual advance
wheel

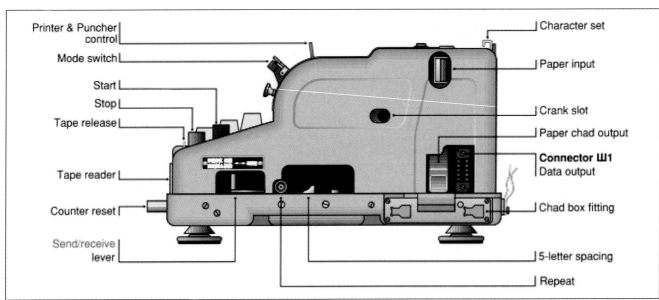

Printer & Puncher
control

Mode switch

Start

Stop

Tape release

Tape reader

Counter reset

Send/receive
lever

Character set

Paper input

Crank slot

Paper chad output

Connector Ш1
Data output

Chad box fitting

5-letter spacing

Repeat

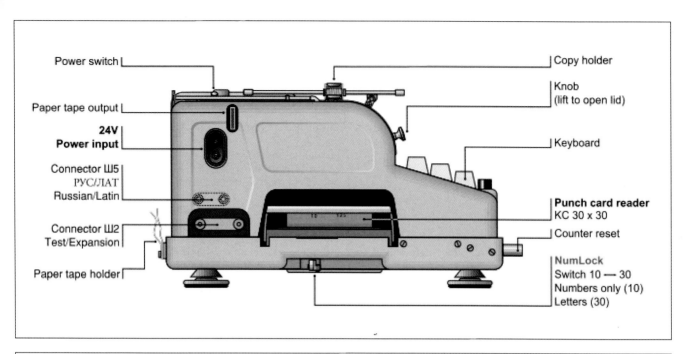

Power switch

Copy holder

Paper tape output

Knob
(lift to open lid)

**24V
Power input**

Connector Ш5
РУС/ЛАТ
Russian/Latin

Keyboard

Connector Ш2
Test/Expansion

Punch card reader
KC 30 x 30

Counter reset

Paper tape holder

NumLock
Switch 10 — 30
Numbers only (10)
Letters (30)

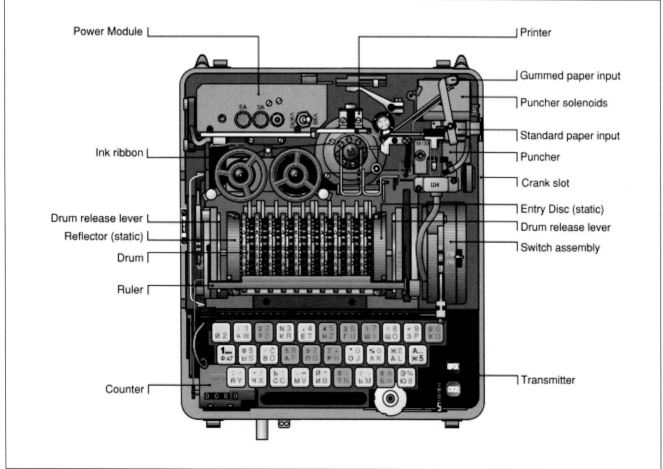

Power Module

Printer

Gummed paper input

Puncher solenoids

Ink ribbon

Standard paper input

Puncher

Crank slot

Drum release lever

Entry Disc (static)

Reflector (static)

Drum release lever

Drum

Switch assembly

Ruler

Counter

Transmitter

(opposite page) Top view and right side of the M-125-3xx Fialka showing the controls. [Reuvers and Simons, 2009]

(this page) Left side and inside view of the M-125-3xx Fialka showing the components and controls. [Reuvers and Simons, 2009]

The drawings on these pages, made by Reuvers and Simons (2009), show the top and side views of the M-125-3xx Fialka and describe some of its controls:

DIFFERENCES BETWEEN THE FIALKA AND ENIGMA

The Fialka is generally similar in design to the German Enigma cipher machine but there are several very important differences. The differences are listed below and detailed explanations follow. On the assumption that you are familiar with the operation of the German Enigma cipher machine (see Chapter 3), these explanations will focus on the unique features of the Fialka in comparison to the Enigma. The photographs and diagrams in this section should help to clarify the comments and descriptions below:

FIALKA FEATURES IN COMPARISON TO THE ENIGMA

- Ten rotors instead of the three or four of an Enigma.
- Alternately counter-rotating rotors.
- Complex rotors, some with internally adjustable wiring mazes.
- More frequent rotor turn-overs than the single one in an Enigma.
- A punched paper card replaces the plugboard on an Enigma.
- Punched paper tape input and output capabilities replace light bulbs.
- Multi-lingual operation.
- A Magic Circuit that allows letters to be enciphered as the same letter (a problem that made original Enigmas more vulnerable to breaking).
- A Tempest compensating power supply.

Ten Rotors
The fact that the Fialka uses a total of ten rotors dramatically increases the complexity of deciphering it's output.

Rotor Rotation Direction
The Fialka mechanism turns each of its ten rotors in a direction that is opposite to that of each neighboring rotor. Almost all other cipher machines have rotors that all turn in the same direction. This counter-rotation coupled with the large number of potential turn-over points dramatically increases the complexity of Fialka encoding.

Unique Rotors
The Fialka can use both a simple, non-adjustable set of rotors or an unique and extremely complex set of multi-adjustable modular-wiring-matrix rotors that allow a very large number of internal wiring variations.

The rotors in the non-adjustable set are very simple. Each of these rotors has a fixed wiring maze connecting the thirty input connections to the thirty output connections.

The other set is exceptionally cleverly designed in that it allows for both the normal changes in ring settings coupled with the ability to actually remove the internal wiring maze

module from each rotor. Once the wiring maze is removed, it may be reinserted into the rotor in any of the thirty possible positions and/or flipped upside down and inserted in any of the thirty positions. In addition, the wiring maze module itself may be removed from the rotor and inserted into a different rotor. This modular wiring matrix allows the rotors to have a total of sixty unique and different internal wiring layouts. Much more information on rotors will be found later in this chapter:

There are at least two series of rotors. Each series has unique wiring and rotation blocking pin locations. One wiring and rotation option is found in the series of rotors with the numerical prefix '3K'. At least some of these rotors are known to have come from Poland. A second wiring and rotation option is found in the series of rotors with the numerical prefix '6K'. Some of these rotors are known to have come from the former Czechoslovakia. It is possible, therefore, that the different series were used in different countries and/or by different military entities. Rotor photographs and wiring data are given later. A complete spare set of rotors is carried in a metal cylinder under the cover of a Fialka.

Rotor Turn-overs
The Fialka has a total of 30 turn-over control positions on each rotor. Each position may have a pin in place to control the stepping of adjacent rotors. Thus, the turn-overs depend on the number and placement of these pins. This increases the possible number of turn-overs of adjacent rotors dramatically when compared to the single turn-over spot on an Enigma rotor.

Card Reader
Another difference is that the Fialka incorporates a card reader which allows punched paper cards to be used to set internal coding parameters. These cards replaced the clumsy, difficult to set, and therefore error prone plugboards of the German Enigmas.

Paper Tape
One of the major differences is that the Fialka prints and punches its output on five-level paper tape. This punched paper tape can be read by eye, read into a radioteletype transmitter, or read into another Fialka machine via its internal tape reader. The Enigma and NEMA cipher machines (see the previous chapter for more on NEMA) used light bulbs to illuminate letters that had to be written down by hand and then manually sent and received by Morse code or manually typed into another cipher machine. The Fialka eliminates the need for a human operator to read and write down the illuminated letters by punching them on a paper tape. It does not use the standard Baudot five-bit code but instead it uses a code that is unique to Fialkas. Reuvers and Simons (2009) have discovered this code and it is shown below.

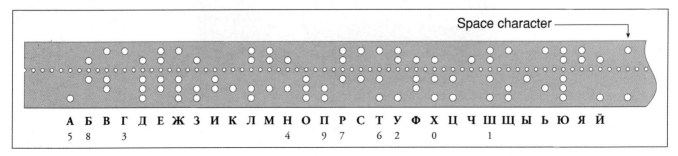

The special code used by the Fialka to punch data holes into the moving paper tape. [Reuvers and Simons, 2009]

Comparison between the M-125-xx keyboard (top) and the M-125-3xx keyboard (bottom) shows how the M-125-3xx can be used with several languages. [Reuvers and Simons, 2009]

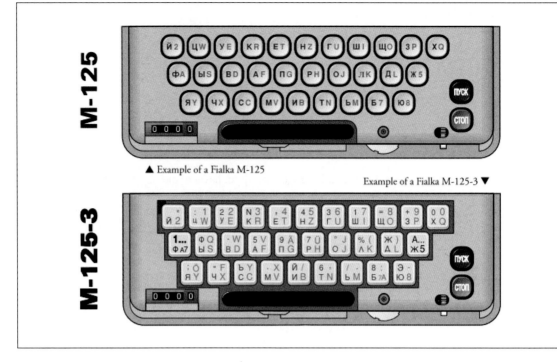

▲ Example of a Fialka M-125

Example of a Fialka M-125-3 ▼

Multi-lingual Operation

The M-125-3MN and M-125-3MP3 models differ from the M-125-MN models in that they incorporate multi-lingual keyboards and typewheels and some unique and complex switches that allow the machine to function with several languages.

Different keyboard letter layouts and switching systems were issued to specific countries. This figure compares the M-125-xx and the M-125-3xx keyboards. Clear and detailed descriptions of each keyboard layout are given in Reuvers and Simons (2009).

The "Magic Circuit"

Perhaps the most difficult task performed by Paul Reuvers and Marc Simons was determining the function of the Magic Circuit. It is a tiny little circuit tucked into the end of what appears to be simply the Entry Disc. Their book provides a

The author's CD *The Story of the Enigma* (see page 4 of this book for ordering information) includes extra information on the Fialka:

- **A Fialka simulator software program:** A versatile simulator program with excellent graphics that allows the user to simulate all three models of the Fialka. It was written by Chernov Vyacheslav Vyacheslavovitch. He is an engineer who works on radio communications and lives in Ukraine. He was kind enough to allow me to include his program in the CD.

- **The Fialka in Action video:** This eleven-minute video shows the Fialka being set up and used. The components are described, the Day's Key is set up, and the motor is run in order to encode a message and then play back the punched paper tape.

detailed explanation of how it compensates for a technical problem produced when a plaintext letter produces the same ciphertext letter. A weakness of the design of the Enigma was that no plaintext letter could produce the same ciphertext letter. The Fialka overcomes this problem and allows a plaintext letter to produce the same ciphertext letter but it also creates a problem with reciprocity that must be overcome by the Magic Circuit. Their book explains this circuit in detail.

"Tempest" Compensating Circuits

Tempest refers to the auditory or electromagnetic information that radiates from a cipher machine as it is being operated. This information may be picked up by enemy monitoring stations and used to read secret message traffic. Different sounds coming from the operation of different mechanisms in a cipher machine may give off enough information to be of use to a monitoring station. As electrical components in a cipher machine such as solenoids are activated, they very slightly pull down the power supply voltages. These tiny dips in voltage may be carried along the AC power lines and detected by monitoring stations at a considerable distance from the machine. The Fialka compensates for these transients dips in voltage by sending data to its special power supply which orders the power supply to put out a compensating increase in voltage to hide the dip in voltage caused by the solenoid operation. This makes it virtually impossible to use Tempest with a Fialka. Nevertheless, extreme security precautions and wide safety zones were still established around any Fialka installation. [Reuvers and Simons, 2009]

Unique Input Wheels

The input wheel on the right side of the German Enigma rotor stack carries voltages into and out of the rotor stack. The Fialka input wheel has two levers that activate internal contact switches and allow the connections to be changed. The position of these levers must be included in the overall initial setting key.

THE MODEL M-125-MN FIALKA

Right side view of a Model M-125-MN Fialka showing the emergency hand crank and the slot for activating a mechanical switch under the rotors.

A closer view of the keyboard showing the character counter and paper tape reader.

View of the ten rotors after opening the cover. The paper tape printer and punch are also visible behind the rotor stack.

The right side of the Fialka with the cover removed. The round plastic box to the right of the rotors houses the Magic Circuit.

The left side of the Fialka with the cover removed.

A top view of the Fialka after the cover has been removed (three screws). The paper tape printer and punch are visible behind the rotor stack.

A view of the ten rotors with the outer levers in the released position. The reflector on the left and input wheel on the right have been moved out and the index bar has been raised to facilitate rotor removal.

The ten rotors have a fixed internal wiring maze connecting the input contacts to the output contacts. It may be uncovered as shown but it is not designed to be modified.

(left) Removing the rotors reveals the complex drive cog mechanism that causes each rotor to revolve in a different direction from the adjacent rotor. The lower horizontal bar activates cogs that pull forward on the bottoms of rotors 2, 4, 6, 8 and 10 (counting from left to right) and rotate them so that the tops of the rotors move away from the keyboard. The upper horizontal bar activates cogs that pull back on the bottoms of rotors 1, 3, 5, 7 and 9 (counting from left to right) and rotate them so that the tops of the rotors move towards the keyboard. A set of ten spring-loaded arms with rollers holds the ten rotors in their detent positions.

A view of the ten rotor stack after removal from the Fialka. The rotors may be removed from their shaft and moved to different positions.

THE MODEL M-125-3MN FIALKA

This model is *much* more complex than the M-125-MN model. It has the following additional features:

- A multilingual keyboard and typewheel.
- A mechanical switch along the right side of the keyboard that modifies keyboard function.
- A three-position lever on the back of the Fialka that modifies paper tape punch operation.
- A large matrix switch that alters the wiring of the programming matrix and therefore the effect of the programming cards.
- A rotary switch located under the base of the Fialka.
- A position on the switch located to the right of the input wheel that stops rotation of the rotors and character counting as characters are typed in.
- An extended copyholder.

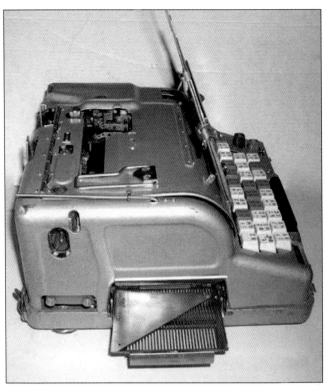

The carrier for the paper programming card being pulled out of the left side of the Fialka to allow insertion of the card.

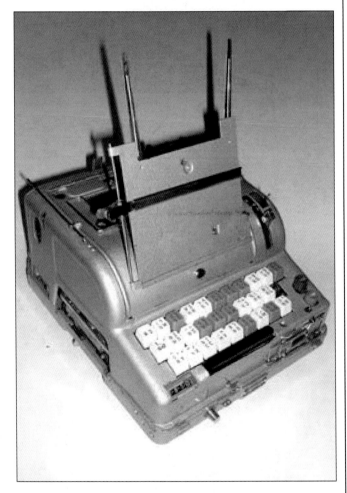

The left side view of the M-125-3MN Fialka shows the copy holder with its extensions, the character counter, the multilingual keyboard, and the slot on the left side for the paper programming card.

(picture right) The right side of the Fialka showing the copy holder and input wheel levers. The switches under the keyboard and rotors, and the hole for the hand crank that allows manual operation of the Fialka are just barely visible.

The complicated multi-contact switch located under the punched paper programming card that switches many of its contacts. This switch is not found in the M-125-MN model.

The ten rotors after the cover door is opened. The index bar has been lowered in place in front of the rotors to allow accurate setting of their starting positions.

A top view of the Fialka with cover removed (three screws). The power switch and fuses are in the left rear. The paper tape printer ribbon reels, the printer and the paper tape punch are behind the ten rotors. The brown reflector is on the left end of the rotor stack. The input wheel is on the right end of the rotor stack. The keyboard and paper tape reader with its manual paper tape feed wheel are in front.

DETAILED PHOTOGRAPHS OF FIALKAS

Some of the following pictures show parts of a model M-125-3MP2 Fialka which is very similar to a model M-125-3MN, and the model M-125-3MP3. The only differences appear to be slight variations in the keyboards.

Close view of the carrier for the paper programming card opening to allow insertion of the card.

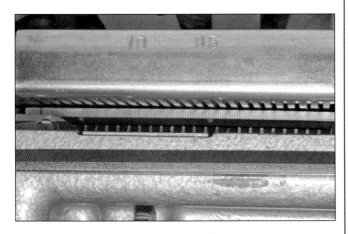

Close view of the contacts that are activated by the programming card.

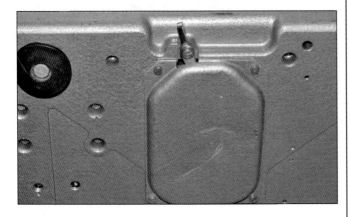

The underside of the M-125-3MN showing the unique chromed programming card matrix switch lever that changes the contacts in the card reader. This switch is not found in the M-125-MN model.

Another unique feature of the M-125-3MN model is this rotary switch that is located near the center of the bottom of the base of the Fialka. This switch is not found in the M-125-MN model. It controls the operating mode of the printer and tape punch.

The switch (left) and paper tape control lever (right) are part of the switch assembly that is located on the right side of the Fialka adjacent to the input wheel. In this M-125-3MN model, the switch in the 0 position as shown disables rotation of the rotors and incrementing of the character counter. In the M-125-MN model, this position of the switch has no effect.

The rear of the Fialka showing the three position lever that is not found on the M-125-MN model. It is located half way between the centre and the left corner. The lever must be pushed downwards to unlock it and allow it to be set to one of the three positions that select the text mode of the printer.

This mechanical switch located under the right side of the keyboard modifies the function of the keyboard. This switch is not found on the Model M-125-MN. It selects the automatic five-letter spacing option.

This picture shows the mechanical switch under the right side of the keyboard with the cover removed. The knurled and slotted activating pin is positioned between the left and right positions. It modifies the function of the keyboard. This switch is not found on the Model M-125-MN Fialka.

The left side of the Fialka connected to its 24 volt DC power supply. This is the power supply that compensates for "Tempest" radiations by detecting solenoid transients in the Fialka through a data cable and making appropriate compensatory voltage changes.

The right side of the Fialka connected to its 24 volt DC power supply.

Close view of the power switch, fuses, the paper tape printer ribbon spools, the printer and the punch mechanism. The unique three position text mode selection lever is seen extending upwards from the rear of the mechanism.

The left side view of the Fialka with the cover removed showing the programming card holder under the rotors and the reflector.

View of the back of the Fialka after removal of the cover. Note the three-position text mode selection lever to the left of the center of the machine. This lever is not found on the model M-125-MN Fialka. Note the metal box on the left corner of the mechanism. It houses the paper tape punch solenoids as shown in the next photograph.

A very close view of one of the cogs that move towards the back of the Fialka causing the rotor to rotate its top towards the keyboard. The cog mechanism and the advance blocking feeler for the second rotor to the right of this one are also visible in the foreground.

The five paper tape punch operating solenoids are located under a metal cover in the back right corner of the Fialka. Note also the three-position switch lever with the three detent positions located in back of and below the colored wires. It is located in front of the manual mechanism drive wheel with its arrow indicating the correct direction of rotation.

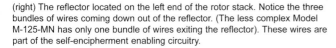

(right) The reflector located on the left end of the rotor stack. Notice the three bundles of wires coming down out of the reflector. (The less complex Model M-125-MN has only one bundle of wires exiting the reflector). These wires are part of the self-encipherment enabling circuitry.

The input wheel located on the right end of the rotor stack. If you look closely, you can see a bundle of wires coming up into the input wheel.

Pulling the circuit board outwards reveals the seven power diodes and other components of the "Magic Circuit" which compensates for problems produced by self-encipherment of characters.

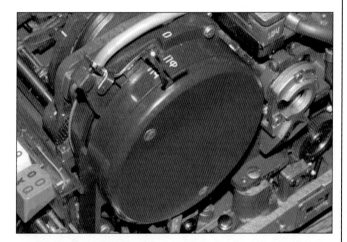

A closer view of the switch assembly adjacent to the input wheel shows the three position switch lever on the left and the paper tape control lever on the right. Notice that the three-position switch is in the uppermost position. In this position, it disables rotation of the rotors and incrementing of the character counter. The switch does not appear to have any function in the top position in the M-125-MN Fialka. The "Magic Circuit" is located under the plastic cover on the right of the switches.

Pulling the circuit board further out of the way reveals the switching mechanism that is activated by the lower two positions of the three position switch adjacent to the input wheel. The uppermost position ("O") of the switch lever completely disables rotor rotation and character counter activation in the M-125-3MN Fialka. It has no effect at all on the functioning of the M-125-MN Fialka.

Removing the cover of switch assembly that is adjacent to the input wheel shows the internal circuitry and paper tape punch control lever mechanism of the "Magic Circuit", and the paper tape punch control switch lever mechanism.

DISASSEMBLY OF THE MODEL M-125-3MN / -3MP3 FIALKA

The following section describes and displays the disassembly of the Model M-125-3MN / -3MP3 Fialka.

The picture below is a top view of the Fialka showing all five of the modular components after disassembly.

They are:

- The Electric Motor in the top left.
- The Paper Tape Punch and Printer top right.
- The Base Plate in the middle of the picture.
- The Rotor Mechanism below the base plate.
- The Keyboard below the rotor mechanism.

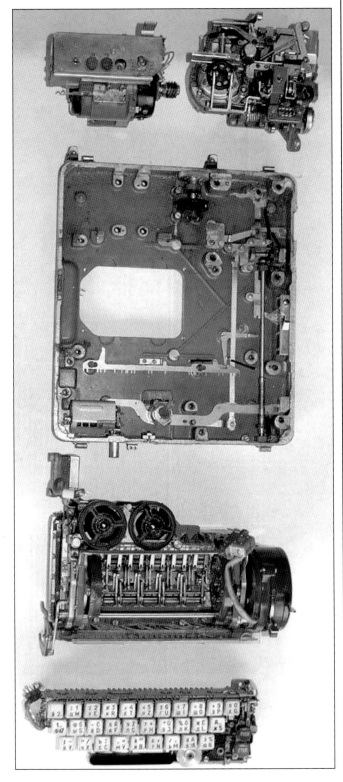

An overall view of the M-125-3MN Fialka with cover open showing accessories.

The left side (top) and right side (bottom) of the M-125-3MN Fialka.

The back of the M-125-3MN Fialka after the motor mechanism has been unscrewed and removed.

Close view of the front of the motor mechanism.

Close view of the back of the M-125-3MN Fialka showing the mounting position and mounting screw locations of the motor mechanism.

Closer view of the right side of the motor mechanism.

Closer view of the left side of the motor mechanism.

Close view of the back of the motor mechanism.

The keyboard after it has been unscrewed and moved forward from the base of the M-125-3MN Fialka. The brown rocker switches on the rotor assembly are mechanically activated by small pins that extend from the keyboard whenever a character is typed.

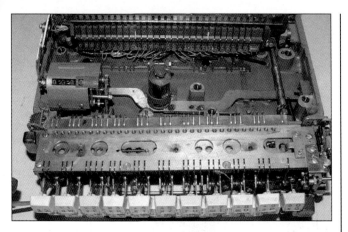

The keyboard after it has been unscrewed from the base of the M-125-3MN Fialka and rotated forward. The row of small round holes along the edge of the keyboard contain the small pins that extend from the keyboard whenever a character is typed. These pins press against the rocker switches on the rotor assembly that can be seen in the background.

The keyboard being rotated backwards away from the viewer. The paper tape reader mechanism can be seen on the lower right.

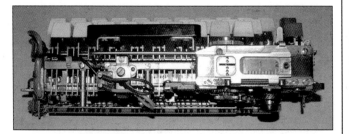

The keyboard rotated backwards away from the viewer. The paper tape reader mechanism is on the right.

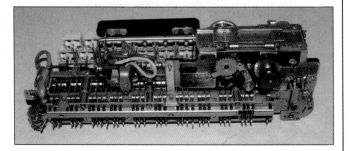

The keyboard rotated backwards away from the viewer. The gears that drive the paper tape reader mechanism can be seen on the right. They engage a motor-driven gear on the base of the Fialka.

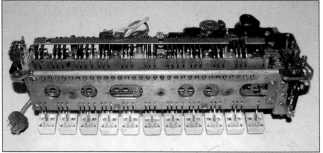

The keyboard rotated backwards away from the viewer. In this view you can see the row of small round holes that contain the pins that activate the rocker switches on the rotor assembly when a keyboard key is pressed.

The base plate after removal of the keyboard, showing the sealed secure character counter and the rocker switches that are mechanically activated when a keyboard key is pressed.

A closer view of the rocker switches that are mechanically activated when a keyboard key is pressed.

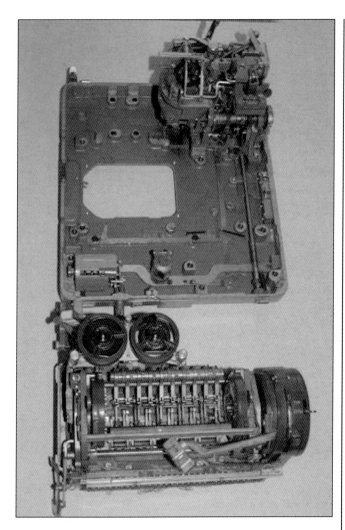

The base plate of the M-125-3MN Fialka after removal of the motor module, the keyboard, and the rotor mechanism. This view also shows the bottom of the rotor mechanism where the punched card reader is located.

The base plate of the M-125-3MN Fialka after removal of the motor module, the keyboard, and the rotor mechanism. This view also shows the top of the rotor mechanism .

The base plate of the M-125-3MN Fialka before removal of the paper tape printer and punch mechanism located in the right rear corner.

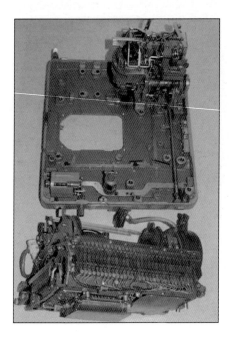

The base plate of the M-125-3MN Fialka after removal of the motor module, the keyboard, and the rotor mechanism. This view also shows the keyboard activated switches on the front of the rotor mechanism.

The base plate of the M-125-3MN Fialka after removal of the paper tape printer and punch mechanism. It is shown in the right rear corner of this photograph. The previously removed electric motor mechanism is in the left rear corner of the picture.

A right side view of the paper tape printer and punch mechanism.

A left side view of the paper tape printer and punch mechanism.

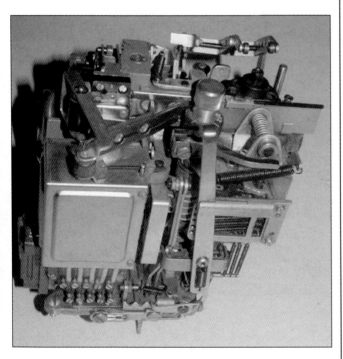

A back view of the paper tape printer and punch mechanism.

A front view of the paper tape printer and punch mechanism.

A top view of the base plate with all modules removed.

Top view of the front of the base plate showing a close view of the sealed secure character counter.

A top view of the rotor mechanism showing the brown reflector on the left and the brown input wheel on the right.

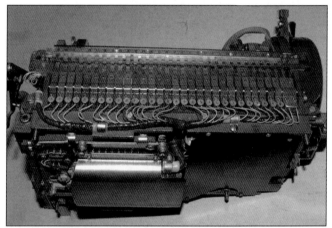

A front view of the rotor mechanism showing the keyboard activated rocker switches.

In this view, the keyboard activated rocker switch module has been unscrewed and moved away from the rotor mechanism to show the normally-closed rocker switch connections and the partly unbundled wiring.

A close view of the rocker switches showing the normally-open contacts on the top and the normally-closed contacts on the bottom.

A bottom view of the rotor mechanism showing the black plastic cover over the internal circuits on the right and the metal cover over the slide switch on the left. The two position slide switch lies under the metal cover and switches many circuits simultaneously. This switch is part of the circuit that changes languages, and most of the input wiring to this switch comes from the keyboard and goes to the card reader mechanism that lies under it.

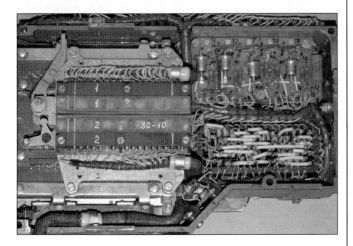

A closer view of the two position multi-contact slide switch on the bottom of the rotor mechanism that switches many circuits simultaneously.

A still closer view of the two position multi-contact slide switch on the bottom of the rotor mechanism that switches many circuits simultaneously. It has been unscrewed from the card reader mechanism that lies under it.

The two position multi-contact slide switch on the bottom of the rotor mechanism that switches many circuits simultaneously has now been disassembled on one side to show its internal contacts. Most of the pins on the white plastic sliding contact bar (marked '1') are connected to one adjacent pin. When the bar moves, these contacts slide along the contacts on the stationary brown bar (marked '1') and connect adjacent pins on this bar which are connected to the wiring. Note that much of the wiring has been unbundled to help in tracing the connections.

A bottom view of the rotor mechanism after the the multi-position slide switch has been swung back to reveal the connections on the punched card reader mechanism.

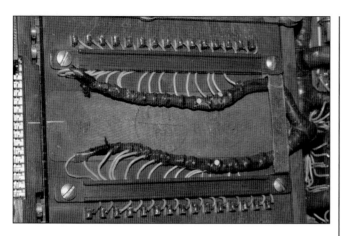

A bottom view of the rotor mechanism showing a closer view of the connections on the punched card reader mechanism. This view shows the contacts numbered 1-30 that are connected directly to the 'common' or 'rocker' connections of the keyboard-activated rocker switches numbered 1-30. If you look closely, you can see the numbers. The order of the connections is not simple so it is explained in the box below.

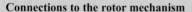

Connections to the rotor mechanism

If you count the thirty keyboard-activated rocker switches from left to right as being numbers 1 - 30, the following is the sequence of numbered contacts on this punched card reader that are connected to the normally-open contacts of the rocker switches.

The first number is the keyboard-activated rocker switch number and the second number is the number on the punched card reader mechanism:

1-17, 2-25, 3-30, 4-14, 5-26, 6-21, 7-6, 8-19, 9-1, 10-15, 11-29, 12-20, 13-4, 14-28, 15-24, 16-2, 17-22, 18-23, 19-18, 20-12, 21-7, 22-5, 23-27, 24-8, 25- 10, 26-9, 27-16, 28-13, 29-11, 30-3.

For example: The leftmost rocker switch (number 1) has its common connection connected to contact 17 of the punched card reader mechanism. The next rocker switch to the right (number 2) is connected to contact 25 on the punched card reader mechanism, and so on.

As you can see, no wiring is color-coded and it is all bundled and wrapped together making tracing the circuit very difficult. As the disassembly progresses, you will see that the author has removed the bundling and wrapping and freed the individual wires for visual tracing. After this disassembly was completed, Reuvers and Simons (2008) managed to completely trace and explain all of the wiring in their book which also includes a complete schematic wiring diagram.

In this view, the bottom of the punched card reader mechanism that contains the thirty connections described above has been unscrewed and swung to to the right to show all of the individual contact pins. These pins on the right are each connected to a contact bar that runs from top to bottom of this picture. These bars are perpendicular to the bars on the lower part of the card reader mechanism. Each of these perpendicular bars is therefore connected to the thirty horizontal bars shown on the left by the sliding contacts that are mounted on each of the bars on the left. These sliding contacts are slid along the bars to a predetermined position as the punched card is slid into the mechanism by the punched card carrier. In this picture, the sliding bars on the left are shown in the default position that is created by the use of the triangular metal insert that is contained in the punched card mechanism and that positions the sliding contacts when no punched card is used.

A closer view of the punched card reader mechanism showing the sliding contacts that are mounted on each of the bars on the left. These sliding contacts are slid along the bars to a predetermined position as the punched card is slid into the mechanism by the punched card carrier. In this picture, the sliding bars on the left are shown in the default position that is created by the use of the triangular metal insert that is contained in the punched card mechanism and that positions the sliding contacts when no punched card is used.

(left) A closer view of the bottom of the punched card reader mechanism that contains the 30 connections described above with wires that come from the keyboard and the switch. These 30 connections go to the 30 bars that run up and down in this picture. Each of these bars provides 30 pins that are seen in this view. These pins are connected to the horizontal 30 bars shown on the left by the sliding contacts that are mounted on each of the bars on the left. These sliding contacts are slid along the bars to a predetermined position as the punched card is slid into the mechanism by the punched card carrier. In this picture, the sliding bars on the left are shown in the default position created by the use of the triangular metal insert that is contained in the punched card mechanism and that positions the sliding contacts when no punched card is used.

In this view the punched card reader mechanism has been unscrewed from the bottom of the rotor mechanism and the wiring has been unbundled and unwrapped to allow visual tracing of the wiring. This view shows the sliding contacts that are connected to and slide along each of the 30 bars. They have been slid along the bars as the punched card carrier was slid into the mechanism. In this picture, the punched card carrier was slid only part way into the card reader.

The entire punched card reader mechanism has been swung to the right to reveal the wiring coming from the reflector and from a switch. The three light purple wires contain bundles of wires coming from the reflector. The dark purple wire contains a bundle of wires coming from a rotary switch that closes every time the rotor mechanism is activated to rotate the rotors. The cover over the swing-up door of the punched card reader mechanism on the right can be seen in the closed position. This door opens when the punched card carrier is slid out of the Fialka and it allows the punched cards to be inserted. It can be seen in the open position in the next picture.

A very close view of the sliding contacts that are connected to and slide along each of the thirty bars. The bars can be seen on the bottom of the picture and the pins that the sliding contacts make contact with are in the top of the picture.

In this view the cover over the swing-up door of the punched card reader mechanism has been removed to show the door in the open position. This door opens when the punched card carrier is slid out of the Fialka and it allows the punched cards to be inserted. The default triangular metal insert is shown in place that allows positioning of the sliders into a default diagonal pattern when no punched card is inserted.

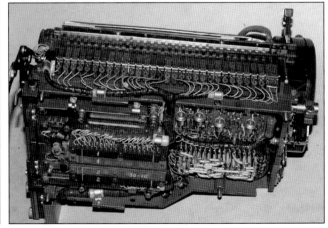

(pictured right:) Bottom view of the rotor mechanism after the cover over the paper tape punch driver circuits (top right) and the diode matrix (bottom right) has been removed.

A view of the paper tape punch driver circuits. The driver circuit board has been unscrewed and tipped forward to allow viewing of the other side of the circuit board.

A closer view of the underside of the diode matrix.

A closer view of the diode matrix showing the very complex wiring and partially hidden diodes. The diodes can be seen as the black cylinders towards the right of this picture.

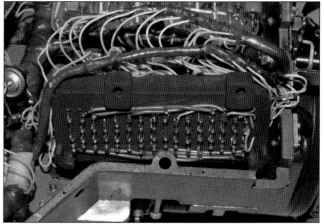

A view of the bottom of the diode matrix showing the very complex wiring.

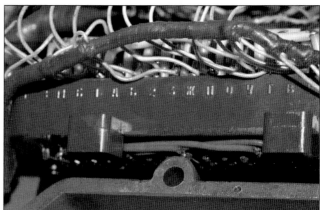

A closer view of the bottom of the diode matrix showing the very complex wiring.

An overview of the switch and card reader on the left and the diode matrix and printer driver circuit board on the right with the bundling and wrapping of the wires removed to facilitate tracing the individual wires.

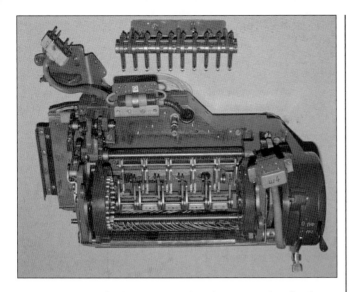

The rotor assembly after the detent levers have been removed to allow the brown reflector on the left and the brown input wheel on the right to be slid inward and removed from their shafts for disassembly.

The reflector assembly after being slid off its axle. The easily removable cover has been removed from its position over the wiring.

A close view of the three bundles of wires that are connected to the reflector.

A close view of the wiring of the reflector. Every connection is numbered from 1 to 30. The number 1 is straight up and numbers 2, 3, 4, etc. run back and around the reflector.

A close view of the input wheel and switch assembly on the right end of the rotor stack. Note that the serial number of the Fialka is stamped into the frame of the rotor mechanism.

The input wheel assembly after being slid off its axle. Note the easily removable cover over the wiring.

A close view of the wiring of the input wheel with the cover removed to allow access to the wiring. Note that each connection has a number from 1 to 30 adjacent to it. These numbers start with 1 at the top and increase as you move back and around the wheel.

Another view of the switch assembly on the right end of the rotor stack after the cover has been removed. The mechanical switch lever and Magic Circuit board are now visible.

This is the axle and rotor locking lever for the input wheel. Moving the lever forward moves the metal pins against the cams on the brown input wheel. This moves the input wheel inwards to compress the rotor stack.

Another view of the switch assembly after the cover and mechanical switch lever have been removed. The Magic Circuit board and part of the internal switching circuits are now visible.

A view of the switch assembly on the right end of the rotor stack. The cover protects the Magic Circuit.

The switch assembly. The Magic Circuit board has been unscrewed and pulled out to show the circuit components.

The other side (left side) of the switch assembly on the right end of the rotor stack. Note the metal plate that covers the switch connections.

A closer view of the switch connnections on the left side of the switch assembly on the right end of the rotor stack. The metal plate has been removed to show the connections.

A closer view of the switch contacts on the left side of the switch assembly on the right end of the rotor stack after the switch mechanism has been dis-assembled to show the internal wiper contacts. The Magic Circuit is on the right.

THE ROTORS

The Fialka can use both a simple, non-adjustable set of rotors or a unique and extremely complex set of multi-adjustable modular-wiring-matrix rotors that allow a very large number of internal wiring variations.

A closer view of the ten rotors with the index bar raised to permit removal of the rotor stack. The two rounded levers that push the reflector on the left and the input wheel on the right inward have been pulled forward so that the reflector and input wheel may be pushed outwards to allow the rotor stack to be removed. These are the non-adjustable rotors. The multi-adjustable rotors are described later under accessories and in the special detailed section on rotors and rotor movement.

The drive mechanisms that produce the rotation of alternate rotors. The lower horizontal bar activates cogs that pull forward on the bottoms of rotors 2, 4, 6, 8 and 10 (counting from left to right) and rotate them so that the tops of the rotors move *away* from the keyboard. The upper horizontal bar activates cogs that pull back on the bottoms of rotors 1, 3, 5, 7 and 9 (counting from left to right) and rotate them so that the tops of the rotors move *toward* the keyboard. A set of 10 spring-loaded arms with rollers holds the 10 rotors in their detent positions.

The ten-rotor stack of non-adjustable rotors is shown here after removal from the Fialka. The rotors may be removed from the shaft and reinserted in any order.

The internal hand-wired set of connections between the input contacts and output contacts of this non-adjustable rotor is called a wiring maze. It can be inspected or repaired by removing a metal disc as shown here. The wiring of these non-adjustable rotors is not designed to be changed.

The multi-adjustable rotors can have their modular wiring maze removed and reinserted in sixty different ways. Their outer ring setting can also be changed in thirty ways.

DIFFERENCES BETWEEN THE FIALKA ROTORS AND THOSE OF OTHER CIPHER MACHINES

There are two main differences: the direction of rotation of the rotors, and the unique adjustable rotors.

The Fialka rotates each of its ten rotors in a direction that is opposite to that of each neighboring rotor. Other cipher machines have rotors that all turn in the same direction. Later in this section the rotor advance blocking pins that control the rotation of individual rotors are described.

DETAILED DESCRIPTIONS OF THE ROTORS AND ROTOR WIRING

As mentioned above, there are two different sets of ten rotors that fit into the Fialka. The rotors in one set are very simple and they are non-adjustable. Each rotor has a fixed wiring maze connecting the thirty input connections to the thirty output connections.

The other ten-rotor set consists of multi-adjustable rotors. Each rotor in this set has both an adjustable external ring setting with thirty possible positions and a modular wiring matrix that can be removed and reinserted in sixty different orientations. This modular wiring matrix allows the rotors to have a total of sixty unique and different internal wiring layouts.

These simple and complex rotors are described in detail below, and their internal wiring data is presented in a comprehensive table.

Non-adjustable Rotor Set

This set consists of ten brown-colored rotors that are identified by the first ten letters of the Russian Cyrillic Alphabet.

Each rotor has thirty contacts that are identified by thirty letters of the Cyrillic Alphabet that are stamped around the outer ring of the rotor. The contacts receive electrical voltages from the input wheel on the right side of the Fialka and are therefore called the input contacts. These contacts are on the right side of the rotors when they are inserted into the Fialka. The right side of the rotors face the input wheel which on the far

The thirty input contacts for the non-adjustable Rotor "A". The heavy grease lubricates the contacts and eases rotation.

The thirty output contacts for the non-adjustable rotor "A".

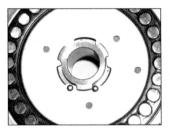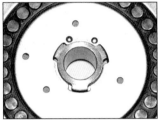

The non-adjustable rotors can be disassembled to allow access to the wiring maze but no changes can be made to the maze. To access the wiring, this metal disc is rotated until it releases the brass central shaft as shown in the right hand photograph.

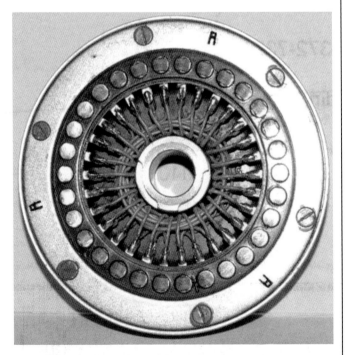

The metal disc and the insulating fiber washer (see picture on previous page) have been removed to reveal the hand-wired wiring maze. Access to the wiring maze makes it easier to repair any cold-soldered joints.

right side of the Fialka and which carries the voltages from the keyboard to the rotor stack.

The other side of the rotor contains the thirty output contacts that pass the electrical voltage out of the rotor and left to the next rotor in the stack or to the reflector at the far left. Each of these output contacts is identified by a letter from the Russian Cyrillic Alphabet stamped on the outer ring of the rotor.

Specific Wiring Data for all Non-adjustable Rotors
The wired connections between the thirty input contacts and the thirty output contacts are fixed and cannot be changed. The Cyrillic letter stamped on the outer ring and associated with each contact is also fixed and cannot be changed. The exact wiring between the input and output connections is given for each of the ten rotors in the table overleaf. The table shows the Cyrillic and the corresponding numerical identifier for each of the input contacts in a column on the left side of the table. The output contact that is fixed-wired to each of the input contacts is given by the number in the table under the Cyrillic letter identifying each of the ten rotors. To convert this number back into its corresponding Cyrillic letter, just use the column on the left.

Rotor Rotation Advance Blocking Pins
The actual rotation of the rotors is controlled by the placement of the metal pins adjacent to each of the contacts. These pins block or lock-out the drive mechanism and determine which rotors will not rotate. The photograph below shows several of the pins and several of the un-pinned locations. A detailed table showing the locations of all of the pins in all of the rotors can be found on page 151.

Although all known Fialka rotors have exactly the same rotor advance blocking pin placements it is possible, with a considerable amount of effort, to change the placements. These pins can be removed from the rotors and inserted into other holes but it is quite difficult to do this. It does not appear to be a real adjustment of the rotor but rather an assembly convenience and perhaps a provision for a major engineering revision.

To remove the pins, the six screws holding the outer ring plate must be unscrewed. Each screw is covered with red paint that both makes it difficult to unscrew, and also reveals any attempts to do so. After the outer ring plate is removed, the pins drop out of their cylindrical holes and can be repositioned. This

A close view of the rotation advance blocking pins for one of the rotors.

Internal Wiring Data for Non-adjustable and Multi-adjustable Modular-wiring-maze Rotors for Russian M-125-MN and M-12-3MN Fialka cipher machines

Copyright 2005: Tom Perera PhD and David Hamer PhD

This table gives the output contact number that is wired to each of the thirty input contacts on all ten rotors. The input contacts (which are on the right side of the rotors facing the input wheel when mounted in the Fialka) are specified by both their Cyrillic letter and number in the left column. You may convert the output contact numbers given in the table back into Cyrillic output letters by using the column on the left The wiring data in this table applies to the brown-colored non-adjustable rotors. The multi-adjustable modular-wiring-maze rotors are black in color and can be set to 30 different ring settings and 60 different internal wiring layouts. When they are set to their overall BASE setting, however, they exactly follow the wiring maze layout in the non-adjustable rotors as presented in this table. In the overall BASE setting, the outer lettered ring is set so that the Cyrillic letter A is adjacent to the Cyrillic letter A on the main rotor frame. Then the internal modular wiring maze is removed and placed back into the rotor so that its index mark points to the Cyrillic letter A and so that its side 1 is facing outward. Please see the accompanying text and pictures for a detailed explanation of the special multi-adjustable modular-wiring-maze rotors and their ring settings.

Rotor Input Contact Letter	No	ROTOR IDENTIFICATION LETTER										(Reversed maze K)
		А	Б	В	Г	Д	Е	Ж	З	И	К	
А	1	23	3	20	16	18	9	7	29	5	20	26
Б	2	22	24	5	21	15	14	9	27	19	24	14
В	3	3	20	7	28	1	13	5	15	2	8	7
Г	4	7	2	15	11	22	20	26	13	27	25	5
Д	5	4	6	21	27	19	24	6	8	20	19	22
Е	6	8	21	27	3	16	8	4	2	26	1	6
Ж	7	16	26	4	15	29	2	19	25	7	17	28
З	8	6	7	1	12	8	6	3	12	11	5	30
И	9	10	18	22	24	17	5	8	6	16	15	10
К	10	20	4	17	30	4	19	28	23	18	27	19
Л	11	15	17	23	9	3	11	22	9	3	9	4
М	12	17	23	13	17	14	28	12	18	13	12	1
Н	13	24	15	30	4	6	30	21	24	4	22	27
О	14	9	19	6	20	30	3	24	1	23	10	17
П	15	30	10	26	25	23	18	23	14	28	18	25
Р	16	12	30	10	8	5	15	10	21	21	3	15
С	17	25	13	16	1	26	7	13	17	6	16	23
Т	18	11	28	14	29	13	25	1	10	24	30	12
У	19	1	29	19	19	25	16	16	3	29	4	2
Ф	20	28	11	18	18	10	1	29	11	30	14	20
Х	21	27	9	29	14	12	12	2	22	15	7	9
Ц	22	5	25	24	10	21	23	25	7	17	23	18
Ч	23	29	1	3	5	27	27	27	16	9	11	21
Ш	24	26	14	12	23	20	29	15	4	12	2	29
Щ	25	2	22	9	26	7	17	18	19	8	29	11
Ы	26	18	8	11	7	11	10	11	26	22	26	3
Ь	27	21	27	2	6	24	21	14	5	25	28	24
Ю	28	14	5	28	22	9	4	17	30	10	21	13
Я	29	13	12	8	2	2	22	30	28	1	6	16
Й	30	19	16	25	13	28	26	20	20	14	13	8

SPECIAL NOTE: The column on the far right side of the table shows the output contacts that are connected to the 30 input contacts of multi-adjustable rotor "K" when the removable modular wiring maze has been removed and reversed so that side "2" faces outwards and the index mark points to the Cyrillic letter "A". For a further description of this setting, please see the information on the multi-adjustable rotors later in this chapter.

Rotor Advance Blocking Pin Locations for Non-adjustable and Multi-adjustable Modular-wiring-maze Rotors for Russian M-125-MN and M-125-3MN Fialka Cipher Machines

Copyright 2005: Tom Perera PhD and David Hamer PhD

Rotor Contact Letter	No	А 1	Б 2	В 3	Г 4	Д 5	Е 6	Ж 7	З 8	И 9	К 10
А	1			x	x			x		x	
Б	2	x								x	
В	3		x		x	x		x		x	
Г	4				x		x	x	x	x	
Д	5	x	x		x	x		x			x
Е	6				x			x		x	
Ж	7		x		x	x		x			
З	8					x		x		x	x
И	9			x	x		x				
К	10	x			x			x			
Л	11	x	x					x	x	x	x
М	12				x		x	x	x	x	
Н	13	x	x					x	x		x
О	14				x	x		x		x	x
П	15	x	x		x			x			x
Р	16		x	x	x					x	
С	17	x	x		x	x	x				
Т	18	x	x	x				x	x		
У	19		x		x		x				
Ф	20		x		x		x	x			x
Х	21	x			x			x		x	x
Ц	22	x	x	x	x			x	x	x	
Ч	23		x		x	x	x	x		x	
Ш	24				x					x	x
Щ	25	x	x	x				x	x	x	x
Ы	26				x		x	x		x	
Ь	27	x			x		x	x			x
Ю	28		x		x		x	x			x
Я	29	x	x	x						x	x
Й	30		x		x		x	x	x		

EXAMPLE OF THE USE OF THIS TABLE:
Insert all Fialka rotors such that the rotors are in the order shown at the top of the table. Set all Fialka rotors to the letter "A" position. Suppose you would like to know which positions of the drive rotor number 2 will lead to the rotation of rotor 4. Remember that the actual drive cog engages the drive rotor at position 18 (this is important). Note from this table that there is a rotor advance blocking pin at position 18. This means that the first letter typed in will rotate drive rotor number 2 but it will be blocked from rotating rotor 4. After you type in the first letter, drive rotor number 2 will rotate one step. This means that the drive cog will engage position 17 where there is also an advance blocking pin in place. Thus rotor number 4 will be blocked from turning, and so on.

Sample Rotor Advancing Data for all Ten Rotors for the First Twenty Letters Typed into a Fialka after Setting Rotors to the Starting Positions: A A A A A A A A A A

Copyright 2005: Tom Perera PhD and David Hamer PhD.

Number of letters typed in	ROTOR IDENTIFICATION LETTER AND NUMBER										Conversion of number to Cyrillic letter	
	А 1	Б 2	В 3	Г 4	Д 5	Е 6	Ж 7	З 8	И 9	К 10		
Start 0	1	1	1	1	1	1	1	1	1	1	1	А
1	1	30	1	1	1	1	1	1	2	1	2	Б
2	1	29	1	1	1	1	1	1	3	1	3	В
3	1	28	1	1	1	1	1	1	4	1	4	Г
4	1	27	1	1	1	1	1	1	5	1	5	Д
5	1	26	1	30	1	30	1	1	6	10	6	Е
6	1	25	1	30	1	30	1	1	7	1	7	Ж
7	1	24	1	29	1	30	2	1	8	1	8	З
8	1	23	1	29	1	30	3	1	9	1	9	И
9	1	22	1	28	1	30	3	1	10	1	10	К
10	1	21	1	27	1	30	4	1	11	1	11	Л
11	1	20	1	26	1	30	4	1	12	1	12	М
12	1	19	1	26	1	30	4	1	13	1	13	Н
13	1	18	1	25	1	29	4	1	14	1	14	О
14	1	17	1	25	1	29	4	1	15	1	15	П
15	2	16	2	24	2	29	5	1	16	1	16	Р
16	2	15	2	24	2	29	5	1	17	1	17	С
17	2	14	2	23	2	28	6	30	18	30	18	Т
18	2	13	2	22	2	28	6	30	19	30	19	У
19	2	12	2	22	2	28	7	30	20	30	20	Ф
20	2	11	2	22	2	28	8	30	21	30	21	Х
											22	Ц
											23	Ч
											24	Ш
											25	Щ
											26	Ы
											27	Ь
											28	Ю
											29	Я
											30	Й

Use the right hand columns ONLY to convert the numbers in this table into their respective Cyrillic letters.

EXAMPLE OF THE USE OF THIS TABLE
Insert all Fialka rotors such that the rotors are in the order shown at the top of the table. Set all Fialka rotors to the letter "A" position. Let us assume that you would like to predict the rotation of rotor 4 as you type in five letters.
1. Remember that the drive cog for rotors 2, 4, 6, 8 & 10 is located at position 18 (very important).
2. Look at the table that shows the locations of the rotor advance blocking pins.
3. Note that there is an advance blocking pin in location 18.
4. This means that when you type in the first letter, the drive wheel "2" will rotate but the advance blocking pin will prevent rotor "4" from being turned.
5. You will see in this table that rotor "4" does not rotate as the first letter is typed.
6. Now type in another letter. The drive rotor, number "2" has moved so that the drive cog engages position 17 and the table shows that position 17 has an advance blocking pin in place preventing rotor 4 from turning.
7. Typing in two more letters advances the drive rotor "2" two more positions but rotor advance blocking pins are in place in positions 16 and 15 so rotor 4 still does not turn.
8. Now, type in another letter. The drive cog now turns the drive rotor at position 14 where there is NO rotor advance blocking pin. Without a drive advance blocking pin in place, rotor "4" is also rotated and turns to position 30. This means that the drive advancing cog is now located at position 17. Since the table shows that rotor 4 has a drive blocking pin in position 17, it does not allow rotors 6, 8, or 10 to turn. Drive blocking pins prevent the even numbered rotors to the right from turning.

is so difficult and complex that for field and operational use, it can safely be assumed that these pins are always to be found in the positions shown in the table.

The table gives the locations of the advance blocking pins for the non-adjustable and multi-adjustable Fialka rotors. These pins determine whether the rotor will advance or not as each letter is typed in. These pins block the advance of rotors by blocking specific advance cogs underneath the rotor stack. The advance blocking pins (marked with an "x" for each rotor in the table) are located at the position identified by the Cyrillic letter and contact number shown in the column on the left.

Example: For rotor "A" there is no rotor advance blocking pin in position 1 which is marked with the Cyrillic letter "A". There is, however, a blocking pin located at position 2.

Please note that this table only gives the actual physical location of the advance blocking pins. The rotor advance sequence is as shown but the actual point of advance is different from these locations. The actual position where the cogs engage and drive the rotors is described below:

Please also note that the non-adjustable and multi-adjustable rotors are identical *only* when the multi-adjustable rotors are set to their overall 'BASE' setting. In the overall BASE setting, the outer lettered ring is set so that the Cyrillic letter "A" is Adjacent to the Cyrillic letter "A" on the main rotor frame. Then the internal modular wiring maze is removed and placed back into the rotor so that its index mark points to the Cyrillic letter "A" and so that its side "1" is facing outward. Please see the accompanying text for an explanation of the special multi-adjustable modular-wiring-maze rotors.

Notes on the rotation of the rotors

The actual advancing of rotors 2, 4, 6, 8 and 10 (reading from left-to-right) is activated by a drive cog that engages the rotor at position 18 (when the rotor is set to the "A" position). An advance blocking pin in the rotor in this position (position 18) will block the rotation of any of these even-numbered rotors to the right of that rotor. As the rotors rotate, the place that the advancing cog engages the rotor changes accordingly.

Rotors 2, 4, 6, 8 and 10 rotate their upper letters away from the keyboard. Their rotation is driven by rotor 2 which drives rotors 4, 6, 8 and 10 in that order. For these five rotors, any rotor advance blocking pins existing in the drive slot of a rotor to the left of a given rotor will prevent it from rotating. In other words, a rotor advance blocking pin blocks the rotation of any of these five rotors to the right of the rotor that has the pin. The rotor advance blocking pin locations are given in the accompanying table.

The advancing of rotors 1, 3, 5, 7 and 9 (reading from left-to-right) is activated by a drive cog that engages the rotor at position 21 (when the rotor is set to the "A" position). An advance blocking pin in the rotor in this position (position 21) will block the rotation of any of these odd-numbered rotors to the left of that rotor. As the rotors rotate, the place that the advancing cog engages the rotor changes accordingly.

Rotors 9, 7, 5, 3 and 1 rotate their upper letters toward the keyboard. Their rotation is driven by rotor 9 which drives rotors 7, 5, 3 and 1 in that order. For these five rotors, any rotor advance blocking pins existing in the drive slot of a rotor to the right of a given rotor will prevent it from rotating. In other words, a rotor advance blocking pin blocks the rotation of any of these five rotors to the left of the rotor that has the pin. The rotor advance blocking pin locations are given in the accompanying table.

Sample Rotor Rotation Data

Sample rotation data for all ten rotors for the first twenty letters typed into the M-125-MN and M-125-3MN Fialka are shown in a table opposite:

The table gives sample rotor advancing data after the rotors have been set to starting position: A A A A A A A A A A. This table applies to both the non-adjustable and multi-adjustable rotors when the multi-adjustable rotors are set to their BASE ring setting. This BASE setting of the multi-adjustable rotors has all Cyrillic letter "A"s on the outer ring set adjacent to the Cyrillic letter "A"s on the inner ring of the rotor. The table has been constructed in the following way:

First, each of the ten rotors was inserted into the Fialka as shown at the very top of the table with rotor "A (1)" on the far left and rotor "K (10)" on the far right. The rotors have been given numbers for convenience in understanding the paragraphs in the next section.

Then all ten rotors were manually rotated to position "A". The state in which all rotors are set to position "A" is shown in the table as 1, 1, 1, 1, 1, 1, 1, 1, 1, 1 in the top row of the table.

Finally, twenty letters were typed into the Fialka. Each letter caused some of the rotors to rotate. The position that each of the ten rotors had reached after each letter was entered is shown in the table by a number that corresponds to a Cyrillic letter on the outer ring of the rotor.

These numbers may be converted into their Cyrillic letter equivalents by using the column on the right side of the table which is just placed there as a convenience in making the conversions.

See the earlier paragraph "Notes on the rotation of the rotors" for more detailed information.

MULTI-ADJUSTABLE MODULAR-WIRING MAZE ROTOR SET

This set consists of ten black-colored rotors that are identified by the first ten letters of the Russian Cyrillic Alphabet.

Each rotor has thirty contacts that are identified by thirty letters of the Cyrillic Alphabet. They receive electrical voltages

The thirty input contacts for multi-adjustable rotor "A".

from the input wheel on the right side of the Fialka and are called the input contacts. These contacts are on the right side of the rotors when they are inserted into the Fialka. The right side of the rotors face the input wheel which on the far right side of the Fialka and which carries the voltages from the keyboard to the rotor stack.

The other side of the rotors have the thirty output contacts that pass the electrical voltage out of the rotor and left to the next rotor in the stack or to the reflector at the far left. Each of these output contacts is identified by a letter from the Russian Cyrillic Alphabet. If you look closely at the output contacts you may be able to see the "A 1" that identifies side 1 of the removable modular wiring maze for rotor "A".

The thirty output contacts for the multi-adjustable rotor "A".

This is a closer view of the BASE ring setting in which the outer letter "A" is set across from the inner letter "A".

Adjusting the Multi-adjustable Rotors

The ten multi-adjustable rotors can have their ring settings set to any one of thirty possible locations. They can also have their removable modular wiring mazes set to any one of sixty possible locations. These settings are explained below.

Ring settings: The outer ring has thirty Cyrillic letters and any one of these letters may be set across from the index mark by pushing a spring-loaded locking pin inwards as shown below.

In the picture of the input contacts (bottom left), the Cyrillic letter "A" has been set to the index mark which, as you will see from the next photograph, is also the outer ring setting letter "A". When the outer ring is set to this position, it is said to be in the BASE ring setting position.

This is a view of the spring loaded locking pin on a different rotor. Again, the outer ring has been set to the BASE ring setting in which the outer letter "A" is set across from the inner letter "A".

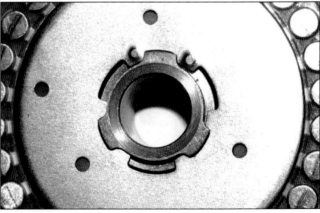

The removable modular wiring maze is removed by first releasing this metal disc by rotating it so that it is no longer retained by the central brass cylinder.

Here, the retaining disc has been released from the brass cylinder.

The modular wiring maze has been removed from the rotor.

The retaining disc has been moved aside to reveal the modular wiring maze. Note that the maze has a Cyrillic letter and a number. The Cyrillic letters on the mazes correspond to the letters of the ten rotors but *any maze* may be inserted into *any* of the ten rotors. You are looking at side one of the modular wiring maze "A". It can be flipped upside down to reveal side two. Please also note that the modular wiring maze has a white line index mark that is pointing to the Cyrillic letter "A". When the index mark on side one of the modular wiring maze is facing outwards and pointing to the Cyrillic letter "A", the wiring maze is in the "BASE" position. When the maze *and* the ring setting are in the BASE position, the rotor is in the OVERALL BASE SETTING and it exactly corresponds to the like-lettered non-adjustable rotor.

Setting the removable modular wiring mazes: The thirty wired connections between the thirty input contacts and the thirty output contacts are made by a modular removable wiring maze. The modular wiring maze is removed from the rotor by following the steps shown in the photographs on this page.

In the following photograph, the modular wiring maze has been removed from rotor "K" and flipped upside down so that side two is facing outwards. The index mark on the modular wiring maze is pointing to the Cyrillic letter "A". Note that this is the setting of adjustable rotor "K" shown in the far right column of the wiring table shown earlier in this chapter. The heading of this column is: "Reversed maze K".

This is a close view of the index mark on the modular wiring maze. The maze is oriented so that side 1 is facing outwards. The large figures "A1" show that you are looking at side 1 of modular wiring maze "A". The small figures A 1 printed around the outside of the modular wiring maze are put in that position to allow the letter and number of the maze to be read even when the metal disc holding the modular wiring maze is locked in place.

In this photograph, the index mark of the modular wiring maze has been set to the Cyrillic letter "B" position.

This photograph shows rotor "K" with its removable modular wiring maze flipped over or reversed so that side two of the maze is facing outward and its index mark is pointing to the letter "A" position. This is the setting of rotor "K" that is referred to as "Reversed maze K" in the column on the right side of the rotor wiring table. The wiring data shown in the right column of the table show the connections between the input contacts and the output contacts when the modular wiring maze is reversed in rotor "K" so that it is in this position.

This is a close view of the rotation advance blocking pins for multi-adjustable rotor "A".

This means that multi-adjustable rotor "K" has had its internal modular "K" wiring maze flipped to the position shown in this photograph. The special wiring data set in the right column is shown to try to help clarify what happens to the wired relationship between the thirty input contacts and thirty output contacts when the removable modular wiring maze is reversed in the way shown in this photograph.

Of course, there is a total of sixty possible orientations of the removable modular wiring maze within the rotor but it is hoped that showing the data for this one orientation will help researchers extrapolate all of the other possibilities from this known wiring.

It is important to remember that the wiring mazes from one rotor can be removed and reinserted into any other rotor in sixty different orientations. Please notice that the modular wiring maze has both an index mark and a Cyrillic letter and a number 1 or 2. The modular wiring maze can be inserted into a rotor with the index mark pointing to any of the thirty Cyrillic letter-identified locations around the rotor. The modular wiring maze can be inserted into the rotor with either side 1 or side 2 facing up. The "BASE" positioning of a modular wiring maze is when the index mark points to the Cyrillic letter "A" and side one is facing outward.

In addition to the sixty possible insertion positions of the modular wiring maze, remember that these multi-adjustable rotors can also have their outer Cyrillic letter ring rotated to any of thirty positions. When letter "A" on the outer ring is adjacent to letter "A" on the rotor, the rotor is set to the BASE ring setting.

Specific wiring data for all multi-adjustable rotors: When the multi-adjustable rotor is set to the base position with the modular wiring maze index pointed to the Cyrillic letter "A" and side one facing out *and* when the outer letter ring is set so that the Cyrillic letter "A" on the outer ring is adjacent to the Cyrillic letter "A" on the output face of the rotor, the rotor is in its OVERALL BASE position.

The exact wiring between the thirty input and thirty output connections for the ten multi-adjustable rotors set to the

OVERALL BASE position is identical to the wiring of the non-adjustable rotors and it is shown in the previous wiring data table. This table shows the Cyrillic and the corresponding numerical identifier for each of the thirty input contacts in a column on the left side of the table.

The output contact that is wired to each of the input contacts is given by the number in the table under the Cyrillic letter identifying each of the ten rotors. To convert this number back into its corresponding Cyrillic letter, just use the column on the left.

Remember that the table applies to both the non-adjustable rotor set and the multi-adjustable rotor set as long as the multi-adjustable rotors are set to the BASE position. One final column is presented in the table to show the internal wiring of multi-adjustable rotor "K" when the rotor ring setting is first set to the base position and then the modular wiring maze is flipped upside-down so that side two is facing out and the index mark is adjacent to the Cyrillic letter "A". With this wiring data it is possible to determine by extrapolation, the exact internal wiring data for the multi-adjustable rotors for any of the sixty possible insertion positions of the modular wiring maze.

Rotor rotation advance blocking pins: The actual rotation of the rotors is controlled by the placement of the metal pins adjacent to each of the contacts. These pins block or lock-out the drive mechanism and determine which rotors will not rotate. This photograph shows several of the pins and several of the un-pinned locations. A detailed table of the locations of all of the pins in all of the rotors may be found earlier in this chapter.

FIALKA POWER SUPPLY AND CABLES

This section describes and shows one of the two models of Fialka 24 volt power supplies.

This model uses a multi-conductor Tempest data cable to connect to the Fialka and compensate for Fialka solenoid operations that might provide Tempest information to enemy agents nearby. Every time a solenoid is activated, a compensating circuit in the power supply corrects for any slight voltage transients that might be picked up by enemy monitoring equipment.

The other model of power supply does not have this compensating circuit and thus is more susceptible to remote interception of messages.

(right) The front of the Fialka 24 volt DC power supply.

The right side of the Fialka 24 volt DC power supply showing the compartment for storing the cables that connect the Fialka to the power supply.

The right side of the Fialka 24 volt DC power supply after the cover is removed. The power transformer and filter condensers are visible.

The left side of the Fialka 24 volt DC power supply after the cover is removed. The voltage regulating and "Tempest" eliminating circuitry is visible. The "Tempest" compensating circuits are fully described in Reuvers and Simons [2008]

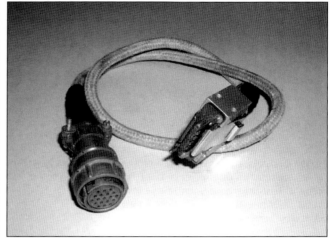

A third cable that connects the Fialka to its 24 volt power supply. This is the data cable that carries the "Tempest" information. [Reuvers and Simons, 2008]

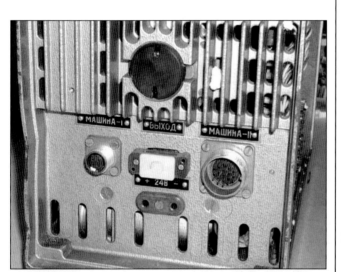

A close view of the back of the Fialka 24 volt DC power supply showing the cable connectors.

FIALKA COVER AND ACCESSORIES

This section describes and shows the metal cover for the Fialka and a set of accessories that may accompany the machine.

A metal cover protects the Fialka from damage in transit and contains a number of accessories.

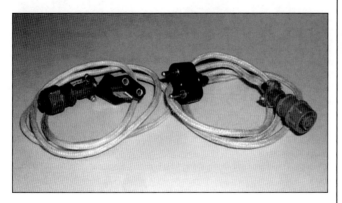

Two of the cables that connect the Fialka to its 24 volt power supply.

The back of the cover has two metal skids that hold it up.

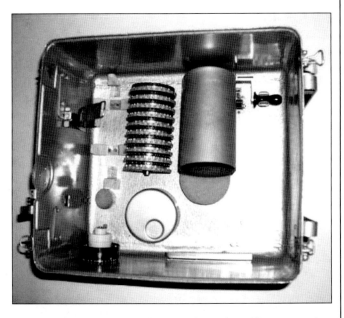

The inside of the cover may contain accessories as shown. These accessories may include a hand crank, a spacer, additional print wheels, and a different set of rotors.

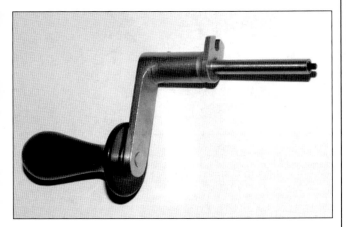

The hand crank that may be found inside the cover.

The additional print wheels, if included, are stored inside protective white plastic covers and stacked on a shaft along with a spacer that allows a reduced number of rotors to be installed on the shaft.

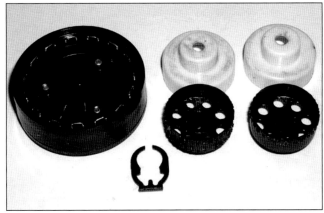

The additional print wheels are shown along with the retaining clips and spacer after their protective white covers have been removed.

A closer view of the additional print wheels.

The tool kit used for maintenance and adjustment of the Fialka

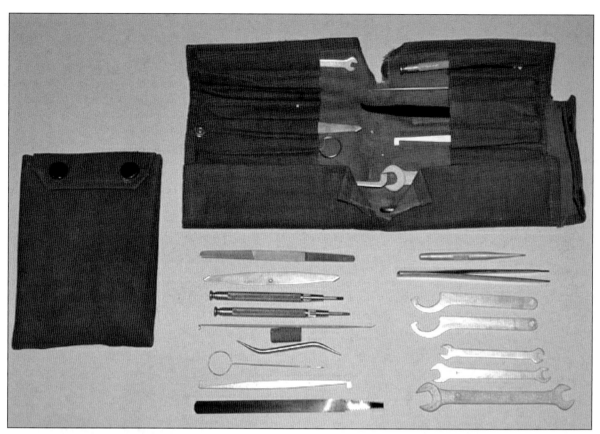

This is a closer view of the input or right side of the special test reflector. These contacts receive voltages from the input wheel and reflect them right back to adjacent contacts on the input wheel. To use this test reflector, all rotors are removed from the rotor shaft, the 'E' clips are installed to hold the test reflector at the far right end of the shaft, and the shaft is placed in the Fialka. The test reflector has every pair of adjacent contacts connected together. The voltages from the input wheel are therefore 'reflected' directly back to the input wheel.

This is a closer view of the left side of the special test reflector. Notice that adjacent pairs of pins are connected together so that a voltage coming in on one pin is reflected back out on the adjacent pin.

The additional set of rotors, if provided with the Fialka cipher machine, is stored in a protective metal case.

SPARE MODULAR WIRING MATRIX ROTOR SET
An additional set of rotors may be provided. This rotor set may be a duplicate of the brown, non-adjustable rotors (pictured earlier in this chapter) or a set of the black multi-adjustable modular wiring matrix rotors, The set pictured is a multi-adjustable one.

(pictured right) The special set of black multi-adjustable modular wiring maze rotors. The retaining clip that holds the rotors on the shaft is also shown.

(below) The input contact side of all ten black multi-adjustable modular wiring maze rotors after they have been removed from the shaft.

The special retaining clip location that allows eight of the rotors to be mounted on the shaft instead of ten. An accessory spacer fills in the rest of the rotor stack width.

Close view of the input contacts on one of the ten black multi-adjustable modular wiring maze rotors.

The output contact side of all ten black multi-adjustable modular wiring maze rotors after they have been removed from the shaft.

The output contacts on one of the ten black multi-adjustable modular wiring maze rotors.

MORE INFORMATION ON THE FIALKA CIPHER MACHINE

The most complete and comprehensive source of information on the Fialka is the extraordinary Fialka reference manual written by Paul Reuvers and Marc Simons. Some of their material has been included in the preceding discussions and much more information and ordering procedures can be found in their website: www.cryptomuseum.com.

Hundreds of additional detailed photographs and descriptions of Fialkas are on display in the W1TP.com Enigma Museum at: www.w1tp.com/enigma, and in the CD-ROM "The Story of the Enigma: History, Technology, and Deciphering" (see page 4). The CD also includes a German language manual for both models of the M125 Fialka.

This Fialka reference manual by Paul Reuvers and Marc Simons describes, explains and provides photographs and diagrams of every aspect of this complex cipher machine. (Ordering information at: http://cryptomuseum.com)

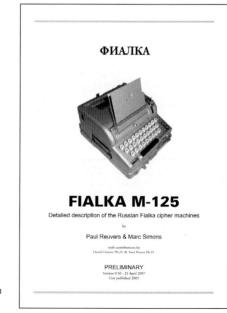

ФИАЛКА

FIALKA M-125

Detailed description of the Russian Fialka cipher machines

by

Paul Reuvers & Marc Simons

with contributions by
David Hamer Ph.D. & Tom Perera Ph.D.

PRELIMINARY
Version 0.50 - 23 April 2007
First published 2005

Appendix 1

Original Enigma Manuals (translated)

Reproduced from Radio Equipment of the Third Reich *©1991 by Charles Barger, with permission from Paladin press, Boulder CO.*

The ENIGMA Coding Machine

Army Manual g. 13
Inspection Number 9875
Air Force Manual g. 13

SECRET

OPERATING INSTRUCTIONS FOR CODING MACHINE ENIGMA

dated 12 - 1 - 1937

Unchanged Reprint

BERLIN 1940

Printed by the Imperial Printing Office

I. GENERAL INFORMATION

A. The ENIGMA coding machine is a secret item within the meaning of the Classified Items Regulation. In accordance with this regulation, the item will be kept in places inaccessible to unauthorized persons.

B. Users of this machine must be aware that its construction calls for careful handling and maintenance so that the machine is at all times operational.

Figure 9.1 *Clockwise from top right: spare light bulbs (37), lamp-filter latch (9), spare patch cords (34), spring-loaded buttons (2), spring support levers (3), latch (1), front cover (25), letter transparencies (10), windows (16), cover plate (4), lamp filter / Zellon plate (8).*

Figure 9.2 *Clockwise from top right: lamp-filter latch (9), operating instructions (32), patch cord (14), double-plug cables (30), metal cover (17), cover hinges (11), terminals for battery (28), key levers (29), retainer screws (18), battery switch (7), socket board (15), plug sockets (31), keys (6), cover plate (4), setting disks (5), windows (16).*

II. PREPARING MACHINE FOR OPERATIONS

A. Prior to use of the machine, check for faultless operation. For this purpose, open the wooden container, release the support mechanism by lifting the spring-loaded buttons, and swing the support levers around. The cover plate can now be lifted and the setting disks will become visible.

B. Turn setting disks several times in opposite directions so that the coding cylinder contacts become clean, then close the cover plate and secure it by operating the support levers.

C. To clean the key contacts, push down hard on all keys and release quickly. Do this several times prior to switching on the power supply. During this operation, hold one key in the down position to avoid unnecessary movement of the cylinders.

D. If the battery has recently been charged, move the battery switch from *Aus* to *Dunkel* (dark). When the battery charge deteriorates after prolonged use, move the battery switch to the *Hell* (light) position to ensure the brightness of incandescent lights. Moving the switch to *Hell* too early during operation causes premature failure of the incandescent bulbs.

E. In sunshine and for eye protection, it is advisable to remove the green *Zellon* plate from under the wooden cover by lifting and turning the spring buttons and, using the same components, securing it over the letter transparency. The *Zellon* plate softens the glare of the incandescent lights and covers all other letters, allowing only one letter to be illuminated.

F. For protection against bright sunlight, the machine can be shaded by pulling forward the joints of the cover hinges and half closing the wooden cover.

G. A clip to retain the sheet of paper is located on the underside of the cover to ensure easy reading of the passages to be encoded.

III. SETTING THE CYPHER

Figure 9.3 Clockwise from top right: battery box (27), coding cylinders (12), light bulbs (38), testing light sockets (39), hooks (26), unused patch panel sockets (41), patch cord test socket (40), code numbers (13), reversing cylinders (20), lever (19), metal cover (17).

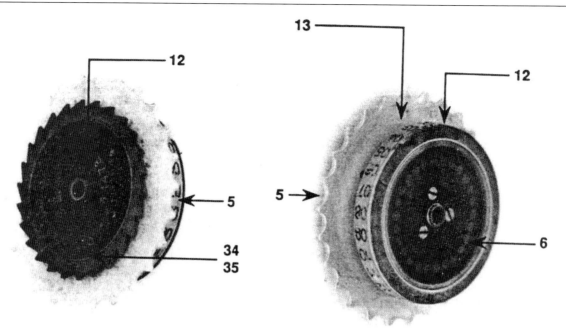

Figure 9.4A (top left): coding cylinders (12), setting disks (5), spring-loaded contact pins (34), coding cylinder contact pins (35). ***Figure 9.4B (top right):*** setting disks (5), code numbers (13), coding cylinders (12), smooth contact points (36). ***Figure 9.4C (right):*** axle collar (21a), spring stud (24), retainer spring (22), axle (21), retainer spring button (23).

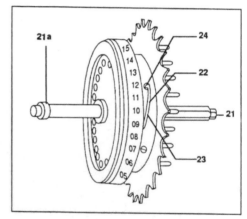

Figure 9.5 Close-up view of the operating instructions and patch cords.

A. The cypher issued for the machine determines the following four settings:
  1. Sequence of coding cylinders (position of cylinder).
  2. Setting of number or letter rings on the three coding cylinders (ring position).
  3. Setting of numbers or letters to be visible in the windows (normal position).
  4. Plug connections on the socket board using double-plug cables (plug-in connections).

B. The setting of the cypher is accomplished by opening the metal machine cover by unscrewing both retainer screws, lifting the cover up by the screws, and pulling it forward.

C. The cylinders are marked with Roman numerals on the sides where the spring-loaded contact pins are located, and with a number of black dots corresponding to these numerals, so that the cylinder sequence may be checked initially without removing them.

1. To obtain the correct cylinder position, the lever in the left-rear corner is folded forward right up to the stop and the reversing cylinder is pushed sharply to the left. After this, compress the coding cylinders by pushing the setting disks to the left with your right hand. The coding cylinders are then removed together with the axle.

2. Push the cylinders onto the axle in the sequence determined by the cypher and, by compressing them, place them back into the machine. When pushing the cylinders onto the axle, make sure that the sides with the smooth contact areas are at all times pointing to the side of the axle collar and that, when placing the cylinders that have been pushed onto the axle back into the machine, the axle collar with the smooth contact areas is always turned toward the reversing cylinder. After placing the cylinders back into the machine, move the lever back to the rear until it clicks into position.

3. When removing and subsequently placing coding cylinders back into the machine, make sure that the necessary care is taken to ensure that the protruding contact pins of the reversing cylinder are not bent by the left bearing stud. Care must also be taken that, after pushing back the lever, the cylinders snap in position properly, which can be verified by checking if the numerals or numbers are located in the center of the windows (check by turning individual coding cylinders).

D. To set the correct ring positions, lift the retainer springs of the rings that show the numerals and numbers by grasping the knob provided on each spring with the right hand and turning the rings with the left hand until the spring stud—which, from machine No. 1253 on, is provided with a red marker—snaps into the hole located next to the numeral prescribed by the cypher. Then close the metal cover and tighten both screws.

E. To set the normal position, open the cover plate and use the adjusting knobs to turn the coding cylinders until the numerals and letter prescribed by the cypher for the normal position become visible in the windows. Close the cover plate.

F. To establish plug-in connections, loosen the hooks located at the front plate and let down the plate. This gives access to twenty-six pairs of plug sockets that are marked by letters A through Z and, simultaneously, with corresponding numerals 1 through 26. The cable-connected pairs of double plugs are pulled out individually by the plug handles (do not pull on the cable). In accordance with the plug connec-

Figure 9.6 The ENIGMA *coding machine in use.*

tions as prescribed by the cypher, establish connection between a number of pairs of sockets using the cable-connected double plugs. Sockets and plug pairs have been designed so that they cannot be confused. Be sure to push the plugs as far down as possible into the sockets to prevent a simultaneous lighting up of several incandescent lights. Close the front cover and secure with it hooks.

G. Having set the cypher, feed the message text in the clear letter by letter into the machine in the same manner as you would do on a typewriter. Depress the keys all the way down until a letter lights up in the transparency and/or the *Zellon* plate placed over it. The next key must not be depressed before the preceding key has been released and has snapped back into its normal position. For details of the coding procedure see *Schluesselanleitung zur Chiffriermaschinen Enigma* (Army Manual g.14).

V. DECODING

Set the machine in accordance with the prescribed cypher (see III above) and then decode in the same manner as when encoding (see IV above), but instead of the letters of the clear text, key in the letters of the encoded message.

VI. KEYING ERRORS AND MALFUNCTIONS

A. In the event that errors have been made when encoding or decoding by pushing the wrong keys or by machine malfunctions (failure of incandescent lights), repeat the encoding or decoding procedure starting at the *beginning of the message*. To do so, set the cypher in the windows in the same manner as at the start of the procedure. However, in the event that an error is made at the end of the decoding or encoding process, set the key again and depress any one key as often as letters were correctly keyed prior to the occurrence of the error to avoid having to repeat the entire coding process.

EXAMPLE: If, during coding, the thirty-second letter is fed in erroneously, a random letter is keyed thirty times after resetting the cypher in the window, whereupon the thirty-first letter of the message is fed in by depressing the appropriate key for control purposes and comparing it with the letter that was produced by the first encoding. In the event that this comparison produces the same letter as during the first encoding, proceed normally with the thirty-second letter and the letters following thereafter.

B. If long messages must be processed, the correction of mistakes can be simplified considerably by writing down the numeral that simultaneously appears in the window after about every fiftieth letter. To correct the mistake, proceed back to the last letter taken down in the aforementioned manner and, after setting the appropriate numeral in the window, repeat the coding process from there on.

Figure 9.7 The ENIGMA machine in transport configuration. This particular example has a wooden case; others have metal cases.

VII. POWER SOURCE, INCANDESCENT LIGHTS

A. General operating instructions are printed on the inside of the cover of the machine; this is to ensure that, without having to consult the operator's manual, insignificant malfunctions may be remedied.

B. Battery 4.5 KZT 5 must be used in the machine. Such batteries may be obtained from the Ordnance Depot (comm), where they are held in storage. In the event that no usable batteries are available, connect into any power source (flashlight battery, storage battery, and such like) using the two thumbscrews provided. Care must be taken to ensure that the power source has a maximum voltage of 4 volts. To operate the machine with a power source connected to the machine through the two thumbscrews, turn the battery switch to *Sammler* (storage battery).

C. When replacing the battery, the cover of the battery box, which has become accessible after opening the metal cover, must be opened and the old battery pulled out and replaced by a new one. In doing so, care must be taken to ensure that the contact springs of the new battery point to the right (see also position of mating contact springs within the battery box).

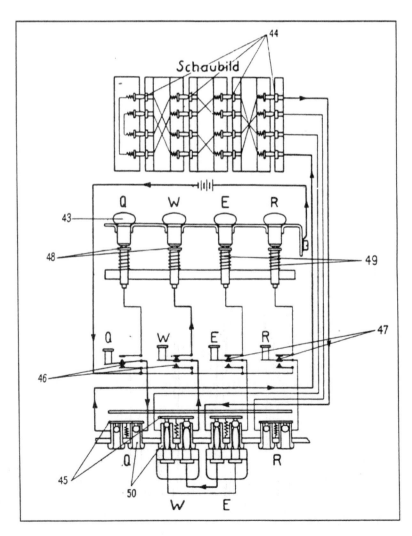

Figure 9.8. Clockwise from top: rotor contacts (44), lamp contact springs (49), key contacts N.C. (47), jacks in patch panel (50), bypass contacts for unused patch panel sockets (45), key contacts N.O. (46), lamp contacts (48), light bulbs (43).

D. Incandescent lights used in the coding machine comply with the following specifications: hemispherical, 12 millimeters, 3.5 volts, .2 amperes, acid-free soldering, base-nickel plated. There are twelve spare bulbs on a strip of metal located at the upper edge of the wooden cover. Commercial torch batteries with a diameter of 12 millimeters may be used in emergencies; they must, however, be replaced as soon as possible since they are prone to malfunctions. Machines marked with number 4388 and higher have an opening to the right of the incandescent lights area marked "testing." By inserting individual bulbs into this opening and placing the arm of the switch in position *Dunkel* or *Hell*, individual bulbs may be tested as to their serviceability (be sure to pull the bulbs out of this opening immediately following the test).

E. Each machine is provided with eight double-plug cables, two of which may be accommodated under the cover of the machine. As of machine number 4388, two sockets (the extreme left and the extreme right—with red markings—of the middle row on the socket board) and the light marked *Kabelprüfung* (cable test) are located on the left side of the incandescent light area so that the conductivity of the double-plug cables and their serviceability may be tested. The two sockets cannot be confused and are switched in a manner by which, when inserting the respective plug prong of each double plug into these sockets, the test light comes on. At the same time, check the double-plug cable for breaks.

VIII. MALFUNCTIONS

A. Malfunctions that can be rectified by operators are usually bad connections that are traced and identified as follows.

B. To ascertain whether or not incandescent lights, cylinder contacts, and metal short-circuit strips of the socket board are in working order, the Q key must be depressed in any cypher setting, whereby any letter (e.g., letter W) will light up. While keeping the Q key depressed, depress the key of the corresponding light (in our case the W) whereby, after releasing the Q key, letter Q will light up. The W key is kept depressed and, for example, the E key is now pushed, which again causes a letter, (e.g., letter R) to light up. Now release the key and depress the R key, then release the E key, which will cause the letter E to light up. Then, for example, push the T key and so on. In this manner you can test the whole alphabet without having to change the cypher setting in the windows.

C. If this test is conducted and a malfunction of one or two of the corresponding lights is ascertained, the following tests must be conducted and/or malfunctions eliminated:
1. The contact prongs of the coding cylinder and those of the reversing cylinder are cleaned within the machine or after their removal from the machine by rubbing the tops clean with a polishing cloth. At the same time, check if individual prongs stick, in which case clean them with a cleansing agent and thinly coat them with acid-free grease. If the machine is continuously used, the contact points of the cylinder must be sanded every six to eight weeks—or, accordingly, at longer intervals—and treated with a damp oil cloth. All key contacts, bulb contacts, metal short-circuit strips, and other contacts must be thoroughly protected from contact with oily liquids.
2. When testing bulb contacts, the incandescent lights must be removed from their positions. Then the mating contacts must be depressed, after which, by retightening the nonoperating lights, these must be tested for proper contacts, having already previously tested the serviceability of the two incandescent lights (see VII D above). If the machine does not have instrumentation for testing lights, use the two poles of the battery to test lights.
3. The cables of the double plugs must be tested in accordance with VII E above. (If the machine is not yet equipped with instrumentation to test cables, establish direct contact

with the two poles of the battery using an incandescent light.) If required, exchange defective cables.

4. By repeatedly inserting double plugs into and removing them rapidly from the corresponding pairs of sockets, the spring-loaded contact lamellas (metal short-circuit sheets) must be pushed away from the sockets and allowed to jump back sharply against the sockets.

CHIFFRIERMASCHINEN

AKTIENGESELLSCHAFT

BERLIN W 35

STEGLITZER STR. 2

◆

FERNSPR.: NOLLENDORF 2699
TEL.-ADR.: CHIFFRIER BERLIN

Figure 9.9 Front cover from an original commercial sales brochure for the Chiffriermaschinen. Originally designed for commercial business use, the machine was impractical and unsuccessful until adapted for military use.

5. To clean the two respective key contacts, the associated keys must be depressed several times vigorously and released quickly (as in II 5 above) while keeping a third key depressed permanently so as to prevent the cylinder from moving to the next position.

6. Under no circumstance should individual contacts be touched with hands.

D. In the event that *all* lights fail to function, it is likely that the battery is empty or the ends of the prongs are in contact with the springs of the battery box. Eliminate this malfunction by changing the battery in accordance with VI B above or by bending the spring and thus establishing contact.

E. If malfunctions cannot be eliminated after tests conducted in the above manner, further repair work can only be done in the workshops of signal battalions and army ordnance supply depots and/or air force signal supply depots in accordance with special instructions.

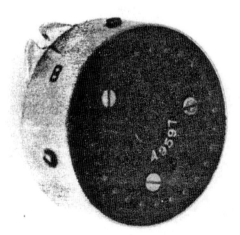

Figure 9.10 Close-up view of an internal section of the rotor. Note the contact pins and serial number near the center hole.

F. *Under no circumstance will repair work be carried out on coding machines. If repairs are necessary, machines will be sent to the army ordnance depot (signals) by units in the army high command area;*

for those in the high command of the air forces area, machines will be sent to the air force signal supply depot.

IX. MAINTENANCE

A. The axles of the coding cylinder and the drive-shaft bearings will be cleaned and treated with acid-free and nonresinous oil every six to eight weeks if the machine is operated permanently; in normal operations, maintain at three-month intervals. Great care must be taken that no oil comes in contact with any of the key contacts, bulb contacts, and short-circuit strips.

B. To protect the inside of machine from dust and similar substances, always keep the metal cover and cover plate closed. As soon as the machine is no longer operated, move the battery switch to *Aus* and close the wooden-box cover.

Berlin, 12 January 1937

The Imperial Minister of War and
Commander in Chief of the Armed Forces
by direction
Fellgiebel

Coding Instructions for the ENIGMA Coding Machine

Army Manual g. 14
Navy Manual No.-168
Air Force Manual g. 14

Control No. 9875

<u>SECRET</u>

Coding Instructions
for
Coding Machine ENIGMA
dated 13 Jan 40

Reprint with included Change Sheets 1 - 8

Berlin 1940
Printed by the Imperial Printing Office

I. DEFINITIONS OF TERMS AND MARKINGS

    A. "Coding" may be encoding or decoding.

    B. "Coding means" is the supplemental equipment required; i.e., coding machine (hereafter called "cyphering machine").

    C. "Coding procedure" is the rule on which the coding process is based.

    D. "Coding table" is the listing of individual cyphers for an extended time period.

    E. "Cypher" is the alternating documentation used to prepare the coding machine for coding in accordance with individual procedures.

    F. "Decoding" is changing an encoded text into a clear text.

    G. "Encoding" is changing the clear text into an encoded text.

    H. "Identification group" is used to identify the cypher that is used to process the message.

    I. "Secret text" or "encoded text" is a clear text that has been changed in accordance with a certain cypher.

    J. "Text in clear" or "open wording" is a message written in open speech.

II. GENERAL DATA

    A. The extent to which the ENIGMA coding machine is to be used will be the subject of a separate order to be issued by the supreme command for the individual elements of the German armed forces.

    B. The general rules for coding are contained in armed forces manual *Allgemeine Schlüsselregeln* (general coding instructions; army manual g.7, navy manual 534, air force manual g.7). The instructions for the operation of the ENIGMA coding machine are contained in the *Gebrauchsanleitung für die Schlüsselmaschine ENIGMA* (operator's manual for ENIGMA Coding Machine; army manual g.13, air force manual g.13).

    C There is no minimum length prescribed for a message to be encoded or decoded on the ENIGMA Coding Machine. The maximum length of a message to be transmitted must not exceed 250 letters.

    D The message heading contains:
        1. The time, four digits; e.g., 1755.
        2. The number of letters including the five letters of the identifier group.
        3. The selected normal position, e.g., WEP, and the encoded message cypher, e.g., HFI.

III. CODING DOCUMENTATION

    A. The cypher changes daily ("daily cypher") at 0000 hours. The cyphers and their identifiers (see IV below) are issued in a *Schlüsseltafel* (coding table) containing a summary of individual daily cyphers and identifiers which, as a rule, are issued for one month.

B. The following information, which changes daily, is supplied with the cypher and changes daily:
   1. Cylinder position (Roman numerals).
   2. Ring position (Arabic numerals or letters).
   3. Plug-in connections (letters).

C. In so far as code information is expressed by letters or numerals, the latter will be used in place of letters or vice versa according to their sequence within the alphabet.

A	B	C	D	E
01	02	03	04	05

(Note that there is a separate letter J in addition to the I in the coding machine, meaning that the alphabet has 26 letters!)

D. Examples.
   1. The cylinder position denotes the sequence in which the individual coding cylinders are to be inserted into the ENIGMA coding machine from left to right.
   2. The ring position denotes the positioning of letter or numeral rings on each individual cylinder.
   3. Specifying the plug-in connections identifies the socket pairs that must be connected by the double-plug cable.

NOTE: Each letter identifies a certain socket pair, and two letters printed together denote those socket pairs that have to be connected, e.g.:

AO   BI   DV   EH   GZ   KW   LX   MU   RY   QT

IV. IDENTIFYING THE CYPHER

A. The cypher used for a message is identified by a five-digit letter identifier group. The first two letters (filler letters) of this group may be selected at random and, in order not to disclose the identifier group, must be changed for each message. The *last three* letters ("identifier group letters") are taken from the *Kenngruppentafel* (identifier group table). Each cypher area and day has several identifier groups consisting of three letters each. These groups of letters must be used alternatingly; in so doing, the sequence of the individual letters within this group must be changed for each message.

B. In messages consisting of several parts, *each individual part* will be identified using different identifier group letters and different filler letters.

C. The identifier group (two filler letters plus three identifier group letters) must be placed at the beginning of the message as the first group before the encoded message cypher. The five letters of the identifier group must be counted towards the number of letters contained in the message heading. *Identifier groups will not be encoded.* Prior to encoding the message, they will be written on the message form as the first group and, after establishing the cypher area, must be deleted prior to encoding the message.

V. ENCODING

A. The ENIGMA coding machine is prepared for transmission on the basis of the coding information contained in the daily cypher. This process is identical for all agencies using the same cypher (i.e., cypher for armed forces machines). The encoder takes three identifier group letters from the coding table and fills them up by placing two randomly selected filler letters in front, thus creating a group of five letters that he writes down on the message form as the first group of the message to be transmitted. The encoder then selects a special normal position for *each* message and adjusts the machine accordingly. The normal position prescribes the numerals or letters that have to be set in the windows of the coding machine from left to right. For example:

W E P - 23 05 16.

B. The normal position must differ for each message; if messages consist of several parts, *it has to be different for each part*. In messages consisting of several parts, under no circumstances may the position resulting in the windows of the coding machine at the end of the preceding part be selected as the normal position or message cypher for the following part of the message. When selecting the normal position, the instructions for selecting the message cyphers must be observed. *The normal position and message cypher may not be identical.*

C. Each message must be encoded in accordance with a particular message cypher, which is selected by the encoder himself, from the letters and/or numerals for the three rings A A A through Z Z Z (01 01 01 through 26 26 26). When selecting individual cyphers, it is not permitted to use identical letters (AAA), words (sic: ist), abbreviations (sic: Rgt.), call signs of the transmission area, code signs (QRM), letters in the key sequence of the coding machine (ERT), or letters in alphabetical sequence (forward or reverse: ABC, CBA). For *every* message and *for each part* of a message consisting of several parts, a new message cypher will be used.

D. The message cypher selected by the encoder (e.g., XFR - 24 06 18) will be keyed once into coding machine ENIGMA, which has been set on the basis of the daily cypher and the selected normal position. The three illuminated secret letters will be added to the three letters of the normal position contained in the message heading.

E. The encoder then sets the letters selected as the message cypher (e.g., XFR - 24 06 18) under the windows and keys the clear text. The letters illuminated during this procedure are written on the message form behind the five letters of the identifier group as the sixth, seventh, and eighth letters and combined to form five-digit letter groups.

VI. DECODING

A. From the received encoded text, the cypher that was used must be identified on the basis of the identifier group tables printed onto the individual coding tables. The identifier group must then be deleted (see also IV above). The coding machine must then be set in accordance with the valid daily cypher; the normal position is to be taken from the heading of the encoded message received.

B. To decode, the coder must first establish the cypher (see V: B and C) used in the message. To do so, the three letters of the encoded message cypher, which are located in the message heading behind the three letters of the normal position, are keyed. They represent the three-digit message cypher.

C. The coder then places the cylinder in position under the windows of the machine in accordance with the message cypher obtained and, from the sixth letter, keys the encoded message. The letters that are illuminated in this process are written down and represent the message text in clear.

VII. ALTERNATE AND EMERGENCY CYPHERS

A. Every cypher has a replacement cypher or manual cypher, of which the latter is issued in accordance with the *Wehrmacht-Handschlüsselverfahren* (armed forces manual cyphering procedure; army manual g 15a and 15b). In the event of a compromise or loss of the machine cypher, the replacement cypher then replaces the machine cypher and will be used by all units and agencies working with the same cypher table.

VIII. EXAMPLE

A. The effective daily cypher is extracted from the cypher table applicable to the encoding of the clear message text (e.g., armed forces machine cypher for the month of May).

Date	Drum Position	Ring Position
4th	I III II	16 11 13

Plug-in Connection	Identifier Group
BN KE VZ CO DI FR HY JW LS TX	adq nuz opw vxz

This daily cypher is to be used to set the coding machine (see III B, C, and D above).

B. Encoding.
　1. The text to be encoded in the following example has been selected at random. For security reasons, it was not keyed with the coding machine. The message to be encoded:

> *Tag 4.5., Abgangszeit 17.55 Uhr, Gen. Kdo VI, angreift 5. Mai 0345 Uhr mit 3. und 10. Div. Feind bei Maisach. Gef. Stand Milbertshofen Nordausgang.*

> (Day 4.5, Time transmitted: 17.55 hours, VI Army Corps to attack 5 May 0345 hrs with 3rd and 10th division enemy near Maisach. CP at northern exit of Milbertshofen.)

　2. For the encoding of this message, the clear text will be written down as follows in accordance with army manual g.7, navy manual 534, and air force manual g.7:

> gen kdo roem s e q s angreift fuenften mai null drei vier fuenf uhr mit dritter und zehnter div feind bei maisach x gef stand milbertshofen nordausgang

> (Roman six army corps to attack fifth may zero three four five hrs with third and tenth division enemy near maisach x comd post northern exist milbertshofen)

3. The coder then sets the ENIGMA coding machine according to the daily cypher. He then enters the identifier group as the first group on the message form, selects for each message or, respectively, for each part of a message (in the event that a message consists of several parts) one special normal position (such as WEP - 23 05 16) and sets this normal position in the windows of the ENIGMA coding machine (see V: A above).

4. He then selects a message cypher (e.g., XFR - 24 06 18) and keys these letters in once, which results in the generation of letters HFI that will have to be written down after the normal position (WEP) in the message heading.

5. Now the coder enters the letters that were selected as the message cypher (e.g., XFR - 24 06 18), with the coding machine remaining set as before, and allows them to appear in the windows. He then keys in the clear text. The letters thus resulting are written down subsequent to the five letters of the identifier group as letters 6, 7, 8, and so on; at the same time, groups of five letters are formed. The following coded text then results:

ulznu	sgexu	nfopr	salme
ydrjq	qarzu	bhfem	ooxzl
gredl	fijya	eivdg	nhyex
mjyra	qztls	siwfu	wfhel
narzq	eduwj	vsfab	skqud
ihxgf	ncjpa	fohwe	gaimf
ojrle	khhd		

6. While prefixing the message heading at the same time (see also II D above), the message is now ready for transmission and reads:

1755 - 129 wep hfi

ulzno	sgexu	nfopr	salme
ydrjq	qarzu	bhfem	ooxzl
gredl	fijya	eivdg	nhyex
mjyra	qztls	siwfu	wfhel
narzq	eduwj	vsfab	skqud
ihxgf	ncjpa	fohwe	gaimf
ojrle	khhd		

1755 = time group
129 = number of letters including the 5 letters of the identifier group
wep = normal position as selected by the encoder
hfi = encoded message key
ulzno = identifier group

7. To identify the cypher that is to be used for the encoding of the message, one of the four identifier groups (e.g., NUZ) is to be selected from the daily cypher (see VIII A above). This group is rearranged to read, for example, ZNU and, after prefixing two filler letters, such as UL, is entered as the first group.

sgexu nfopr . . . = encoded clear text

C. Decoding.

1. The message to be decoded is as in B6 above.

2. The first group of the encoded text is the identifier group. Having deleted the first two filler letters and arranged the remaining three letters in alphabetical order, the following identifier group letters result: NUZ. With these identifier group letters, the cypher that was used is identified and the coding machine is adjusted on the basis of the cypher applicable on that particular day.

3. The normal position to be used is taken from the message head (for example, WEP - 23 05 16) and set in the windows of the ENIGMA coding machine.

4. The three secret letters (HFI) of the message key that are located behind the three letters of the normal position (WEP) are keyed. The letters XFR that light up are the message cypher.

5. The encoder then arranges message cypher letters XFR (24 06 18) in the windows of the ENIGMA coding machine and keys the coded text. This procedure will produce letters as follows:

> gen kdo roem seqs angreift fuenften mai null drei vier fuenf uhr mit dritter und zehnter div feind bei maisach x gef stand milbertshofen nordausgang.

The final clear text reads as follows:

> *Gen. Kdo. VI angreift 5. Mai 0345 Uhr mit 3. und 10. Div Feind bei Maisach. Gef. Stand Milbertshofen Nordausgang.*

IX. GENERATION OF TRAINING KEYS

When generating training keys, the following will be observed:

A. Position of the cylinder must change daily. Cylinders I through V must be used.

B. To come up with the ring position, it is useful to cut out twenty-six pieces of cardboard (as in the Lotto game) and allocate them numbers 1 through 26. In this manner and as in the Lotto game, eight lines (e.g., eight days) may be identified in the *Ringstellung* column (two numbers are logically omitted each time). For example:

Day	Position of Ring	Day	Position of Ring
31st	24 14 08	27th	16 05 11
30th	17 01 13	26th	23 03 07
29th	25 15 19	25th	02 22 21
28th	26 12 10	24th	18 09 06

Thus, all numbers, with the exception of 04 and 20, have been used. In the same manner the ring position is established for the remaining days of the month.

C. To establish the ten plug-in connections, twenty-six little pieces of cardboard are cut out, of which twenty are randomly selected and placed together in pairs of two as plug-in connections. They are written down in a manner ensuring that within one letter pair, the letters ascend alphabetically (for example: KV IT BY FG CO EJ DP MR QS LX).

D. To designate the type of cypher to be used, four identifier groups of three letters each will be added to the daily cypher. While the identifier groups of the cyphers for the secret message traffic are determined by the supreme commanders of the individual armed forces services, the training cyphers may be selected simply by randomly establishing four-letter combinations, each consisting of three letters, such as BLV, KUX, RTZ, SWY. The supreme commanders of the individual armed forces services are also free to issue identifier groups for training purposes or special cyphers.

Appendix 2

American M-209 Handbook

Reproduced here are appropriate excerpts from the US War Department's Technical Manual for the widely used M-209 Enigma. The original booklet is 152mm x 118mm and bound in a brown paper cover.

   This book is included to give the reader a clear and detailed understanding of the complex procedures that American military personnel were expected to follow as they set up their M-209 Cipher Machines to encode and decode messages.

WAR DEPARTMENT,
WASHINGTON 25, D. C., 17 MARCH 1944.

TM 11-380, Converter M-209, M-209-A, M-209-B, is published for the information and guidance of all concerned.

(A. G. 300.7 (31 Jan. 44).)

BY ORDER OF THE SECRETARY OF WAR:

G. C. MARSHALL,
Chief of Staff.

OFFICIAL:

J. A. ULIO,
Major General,
The Adjutant General.

DISTRIBUTION: IR 5, 7, 17, (2); IBn & H 1 (2); IBn 5, 6, 7, 9, 10, 11, 17 (5); IC 2, 5-11, 17, 18, 44 (3).

(For explanation of symbols see FM 21-6.)

TABLE OF CONTENTS

LIST OF ILLUSTRATIONS

the cover of the converter are clamps for holding a screw driver, a pair of tweezers, an oil can, an ink pad can, and the roll of paper tape in use. When desired, a hand-carrying strap may be attached to the left side of the machine.

3. MAIN COMPONENTS AND ACCESSORIES.

a. Converter M-209-(*) consists of the following main component parts with weights and dimensions as shown (fig. 1):

Quantity	Part	Dimensions (inches)	Weight (pounds)
1	Converter M-209-(*)	7¼ x 5½ x 3½	6
1	Case, canvas (complete with straps)	8¼ x 6½ x 6	1
1	Strap, hand-carrying (complete with snaps)	11⅝ long	..

b. The following accessories are issued with the converter:

Quantity	Part	Dimensions (inches)
1	Can, oil, with cover	2½ x ⅝
1	Can, ink pad, with cover	2½ x ⅝
1	Screw driver	4 long (2⅜ blade, ¼ tip)
1	Tweezers	4 long
5	Pad, ink (inside ink pad can)	....
2	Tape paper rolls (1 in use, 1 spare)	4 diam. approx.; ⅜ wide
4	Clips, message	....
2	TM 11-380	....

c. The total weight of Converter M-209-(*), including its accessories, is approximately 7¼ pounds. It weighs about 10 pounds when packed for shipment in this country, and has a volume of about 0.37 cubic foot.

4. IDENTIFICATION OF PARTS.

a. Preliminary Procedure. Open the outer cover of the machine by pushing the button located in the center of the front of the cover. Raise the inner lid from the front by lifting it off its spring catch.

2

① Canvas case.   ⑤ Screw driver.   ⑨ Ink pads.
② Converter M-209-(*). ⑥ Message clips.   ⑩ Ink pad can.
③ Carrying strap.   ⑦ Tweezers.   ⑪ Paper tape.
④ Hand strap.   ⑧ Oil can.

FIGURE 1. Main components and accessories.   3

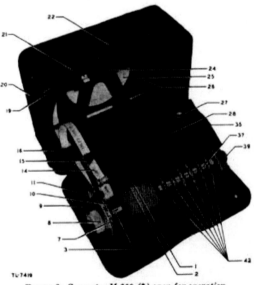

FIGURE 2. Converter M-209-(*) open for operation.

b. Numbered Reference List. Operators of Converter M-209-(*) can identify all the parts of the device by referring to the following list and figures 2 and 3. Numbers in parentheses such as (10) correspond to those in figures 2 and 3, and should be studied with an opened converter nearby so that each part may be located. These numbers will be used throughout this manual to assist in identifying parts.

4

---

(1) Letter counter window.   (23) Paper guard catch.
(2) Letter counter.   (24) Paper guard.
(3) Indicating index.   (25) Paper roll.
(4) Ink pad.   (26) Tweezers.
(5) Typewheel.   (27) Reset button.
(6) Reproducing disk.   (28) Inner lid.
(7) Indicating disk.   (29) Number plate.
(8) Setting knob.   (30) Drum disks.
(9) Encipher-decipher knob.   (31) Drum bar.
(10) Reading window.   (32) Drum bar lug.
(11) Paper feed knob.   (33) Interlock lever.
(12) Paper feed ratchet.   (34) Guide arm.
(13) 5-letter cam.   (35) Drive knob.
(14) Paper tape.   (36) Intermediate gear.
(15) Paper pressure arm.   (37) Key wheel bench mark.
(16) Cover support.   (38) Key wheel gear.
(17) Ink pad container.   (39) Reset knob.
(18) Screwdriver.   (40) Ineffective pin.
(19) Oil can.   (41) Effective pin.
(20) Outer cover.   (42) Key wheels.
(21) Catch for inner lid.   (43) Typewheel gear.
(22) Cover catch button.

5. PRINCIPAL OPERATING PARTS.

a. Key Wheels (42). (1) Letters of the alphabet in normal sequence are engraved on the rims of the six key wheels. On each wheel, from left to right, there is a decreasing number of letters. The letters are arranged on the key wheels as follows:

Wheel No.	No. of letters	Letters
1	26	A – Z
2	25	A – Z, omitting W
3	23	A – X, omitting W
4	21	A – U
5	19	A – S
6	17	A – Q

5

(2) Near the rim of the key wheels, and just below each letter, a small pin projects from one side or the other of the key wheels. The *key wheel pins* may be pushed from side to side in the slots in which they are set. The letters and pins are arranged as part of the preliminary setting of the device and are explained in detail in paragraph 7. The key wheels are mounted on a shaft, on the right end of which is the *reset knob* (39). The key wheels may be turned as a unit in either direction when the *reset button* (27) is depressed and the reset knob twisted. Individual wheels may be turned by hand in one direction only.

b. Indicating Disk (7). The indicating disk is the larger of two disks located on the left-hand side of the converter. Letters of the alphabet are arranged on its rim in normal order. The disk can be rotated freely in either direction, allowing any letter to be aligned on a white bench mark, called the *indicating index* (3). The large knob on the left of the indicating disk is used for turning the disk to the desired letter.

c. Reproducing Disk (6). The letters of the alphabet are engraved in reverse order upon the reproducing disk, the smaller disk located just to the right of and on the same shaft as the indicating disk. When the inner lid is closed, four of the letters can be seen through the *reading window* (10) on the edge of the inner lid. The first letter, nearest the front of the machine, is read when this disk is used (pars. 10*b*(5) and 22*b*).

d. Typewheel (5). The typewheel is mounted on the same shaft with the two disks mentioned above. On its rim are raised letters for printing. These letters are also in reverse order. The last letter printed and the letter which is read on the reproducing disk are the same.

e. Paper Feed Knob (11). The paper tape is advanced automatically when the converter is operated, and also can be fed through the rollers by turning the paper feed knob. The knob turns toward the rear of the machine only.

6

Note that Page 7 was a double-page pull-out (shown below).

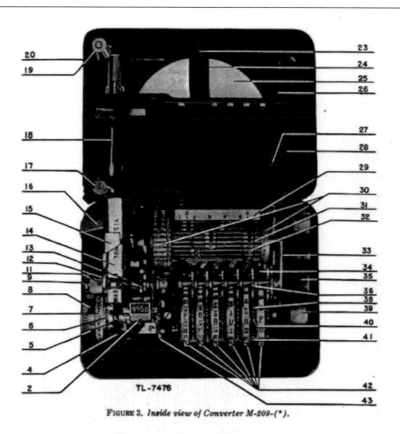

FIGURE 3. *Inside view of Converter M-209-(*).*

7

f. Paper Pressure Arm (15). On the front end of the paper pressure arm is a small, knurled roller which is held firmly against a larger roller by spring tension. To raise the roller, push down on the rear end of the pressure arm. The roller and arm are used to guide the paper tape. A *cutting edge* is provided on the end of the pressure arm to facilitate tearing off the tape.

g. Letter Counter (2). The letter counter is visible through a window in the left front corner of the converter. It counts letters enciphered or deciphered up to 9999. The counter is returned to zero by turning the *reset knob* (39) in either direction while depressing the *reset button* (27) on top of the inner lid.

h. Encipher-Decipher Knob (9). Just below the paper feed knob is the encipher-decipher knob. When turned to the "C" position, the converter is set for enciphering clear text; when set in "D" position, it is ready to decipher cryptographed text. The position of this knob should be checked before operation.

i. Drive Knob (35). The large black operating handle on the right-hand side of the machine is the drive knob. Each time the indicating disk is moved, the drive knob may be turned once and then locks. At each turn of the drive knob, the machine enciphers or deciphers a letter and prints the equivalent letter on the tape.

j. Drum. When the inner lid is open, the drum can be seen at the rear of the machine. On the drum are 27 *drum bars* (31), which occupy about two-thirds of the circumference of the drum and are numbered at the right of the drum. On each drum bar are two movable lugs which may be set in any one of eight positions, numbered 1 $\overset{0}{\cdot}$ 2 3 4 5 $\overset{0}{\cdot}$ 6. Each lug fits into a small hole at each position. It must be pushed slightly toward the front of the machine before it can be disengaged from one hole and slid along the bar into another. When placed at any position, *the lug must always be fitted into the hole provided for it.*

SECTION II

INSTALLATION AND OPERATION

6. CRYPTOGRAPHIC SYSTEMS.

a. Definition. A military cryptographic system comprises a prearranged set of rules and equipment chosen for cryptographing messages sent from one unit to another. All systems fall into one of two classifications, *code* or *cipher*. In code systems, groups of letters or numbers represent words, phrases, or entire sentences. A cipher system normally uses single letters to represent other single letters. Converter M-209-(*) is a cipher device since, when operated, it substitutes a letter for a letter.

b. Cipher Keys. Every cipher system must be provided with a guide, or *cipher key*, for its operation. The cipher key should be changed as often as is necessary to preserve the security of the system. The key for systems using Converter M-209-(*) must include two tables which make up a *cipher-key* list and are published periodically in a system publication or the signal operation instructions of a using unit. The tables, changed only by order of the signal or communication officer, govern preliminary settings which must be made before enciphering or deciphering a message. The proper use of cipher-key lists is explained in paragraph 8.

c. Converter M-209-(*) Systems. Any cipher system employing the Converter M-209-(*) must consist of the following:

(1) The Converter M-209-(*).

(2) This manual which contains operating instructions for the Converter M-209-(*).

(3) The cipher-key list which is in effect at the time.

(4) A system publication describing the particular system in use at the time, or personal instruction in such a system.

7. KEYING ELEMENTS.
Units using Converter M-209-(*) must make certain that the following keying elements are set identically if they are to exchange messages:

a. External Keying Element. The external keying element is composed of the six key wheels (42). Letters on the key wheels are selected at random by the enciphering operator, and lined up from left to right along the white bench mark. *Different letters must be selected for every message.* These six letters make up the message indicator and are transmitted with the message (par. 9).

b. Internal Keying Elements. There are two internal keying elements; each is initially set, and changed, in accordance with a cipher-key list. The first internal keying element is made up of the key wheel pins (40), (41). When placed to the right, or effective, position, the pins affect the operation of the machine; to the left, they are in a *noneffective* position. The second internal keying element is made up of the movable lugs (32) on the drum bars (31). Lugs are effective in any position except the two marked " $\overset{0}{\cdot}$." Instructions for setting the keying elements are in paragraph 8.

c. Changes of Keys. A high degree of cryptographic security is provided when Converter M-209-(*) is used. Systems using Converter M-209-(*), however, can be solved, especially if a large volume of traffic is enciphered without changing the arrangement of the keying elements. A *daily* change in the internal keying elements is advisable, although the frequency of change will depend upon the tactical situation. This is the responsibility of the signal or communication officer. *Changes in the external keying element are the responsibility of the*

operator alone, and must be made for every message he enciphers. There is no reason for allowing the enemy to "break" a message enciphered with Converter M-209-(*) because the keying elements were not changed often enough. The key wheel alignments should be noted to prevent using the same arrangement of letters for future messages.

8. PREPARING FOR OPERATION.

a. General. The procedure given in this paragraph is intended to show the operator how to install the converter and make all preliminary settings.

b. Installation. Normally Converter M-209-(*) will be operated under cover to protect the machine from dust and dampness. Usually the converter will be set up on a table or some solid support. If necessary, the machine may be secured to the operator's knee in the following manner: Attach the carrying strap to the bottom of the converter and pass it under the operator's foot. Shorten or lengthen the strap so that the converter will be held firmly in place on the knee. The base of the machine is shaped to fit the curvature of the knee (fig. 4).

c. Key Wheel Pins. Open the outer cover of the converter, and raise the inner lid. If the machine has been properly zeroized (par. 12), all of the key wheel pins will project from the left-hand side of the key wheels. If any project from the right-hand side, use the screw driver provided and push them to the left. This will make the setting easier. Set the pins as indicated in table I, *Position of key wheel pins.* The columns of letters and dashes represent the six key wheels, from left to right. The pins associated with the letters which are printed in the columns are to be pushed to the right, or effective, position. Where a dash appears, the pin associated with the omitted letter will remain at the left, or ineffective, position. Thus, following the example table, the pin under

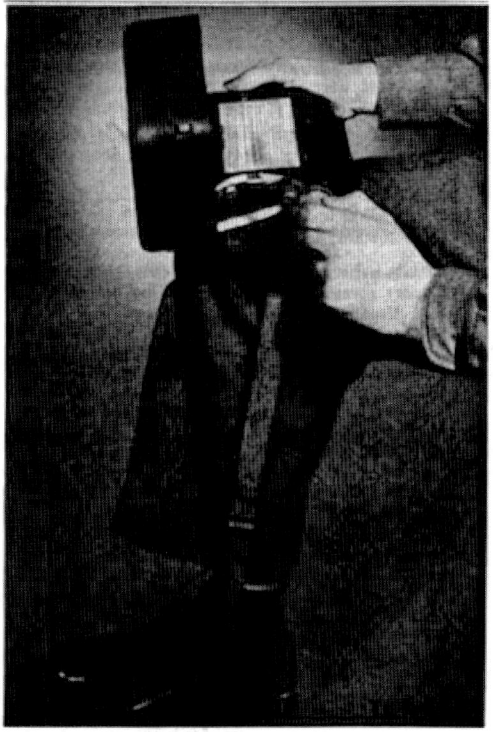

FIGURE 4. *Converter M-209-(*) strapped to knee.*

letter A on wheel number 1 should be moved to the right or effective position. The pin under letter C on wheel number 1 will remain at the left, or ineffective, position. A knife blade or the special screw driver provided may be used to set the pins (fig. 5). Each pin must be moved all the way to the left

TABLE I. *Position of key wheel pins.*

Period (date) to (date).

No. 1 (26)	No. 2 (25)	No. 3 (23)	No. 4 (21)	No. 5 (19)	No. 6 (17)
A	A	A	—	—	A
B	—	B	—	B	B
—	—	—	C	—	—
D	D	—	—	D	D
—	E	—	E	E	—
—	—	—	F	F	—
—	G	G	—	—	—
H	—	H	H	H	H
I	—	I	I	I	—
—	J	J	—	—	—
K	K	—	—	—	K
—	L	L	—	—	—
M	—	M	M	M	—
N	—	N	N	—	N
—	O	—	—	—	O
—	—	—	P	P	—
—	—	—	—	—	Q
—	R	R	—	—	—
S	S	S	S	S	—
T	—	T	T	—	—
—	U	U	U	—	—
V	—	—	—	—	—
W	X	X	—	—	—
—					
—					

TL-7474

FIGURE 5. *Setting key wheel pins.*

or right. A garble will result if pins are left in an intermediate position. Care in making the setting will prevent loss of time later. The effective period for that particular setting must be known in order that a new setting will be made at the proper time. (Information regarding the preparation of a table of pin settings will be found in appendix I.)

TABLE II. *Position of drum bar lugs.*

Period (date) to (date).

1. 3–6	10. 2–0	19. 2–0
2. 0–6	11. 2–0	20. 2–5
3. 1–6	12. 2–0	21. 2–5
4. 1–5	13. 2–0	22. 0–5
5. 4–5	14. 2–0	23. 0–5
6. 0–4	15. 2–0	24. 0–5
7. 0–4	16. 2–0	25. 0–5
8. 0–4	17. 2–0	26. 0–5
9. 0–4	18. 2–0	27. 0–5

26-letter check

T N J U W A U Q T K C Z K N U T O T B C W A R M I O

d. Drum Bar Lugs. With the inner lid open, the drum will be seen in the rear of the machine. Each of the 27 drum bars has 2 movable lugs which may be placed in effective positions 1 through 6, or in 2 noneffective positions labeled "0." Consult table II, *Position of drum bar lugs.* The 2 columns of numbers, 1 through 14, and 15 through 27, represent the 27 drum bars. The numbers opposite each drum bar number denote the positions which the two lugs on each drum bar will occupy. These positions are indicated on the machine by the number plate behind the drum. For example, on bar 1, the left-hand lug will be moved to position 3 and the right-hand lug to position 6. On bar 2, the left-hand lug will be moved to the

TL-7475

FIGURE 6. Setting drum bar lugs.

16

left zero position, and the right-hand lug to position 6. Turn the setting knob (8) to release the drum lock and to allow the drive knob to rotate the drum. Use the special screw driver provided to move the lugs from one position to another (fig. 6). When correctly placed, each lug will lock in position in a small hole. When moving a lug, push it slightly toward the front of the machine to release it, before attempting to slide it to another location. *Be sure that the lug catches in the hole at the new position.* If a lug is allowed to remain in an intermediate position, it will jam the machine. A click can be heard when the lug is properly placed. It is recommended that the left-hand lugs on each drum bar be placed in positions 1, 2, 3, and the left zero, and that the right-hand lugs be placed in positions 4, 5, 6, and the right zero. When all lugs have been properly set, turn the drive knob until the drum locks into place. (Information on the preparation of a table of lug settings may be found in appendix I.)

e. Twenty-six-letter Check. Every cipher-key list will include a 26-letter check. Using this check, the operator of Converter M-209-(*) may verify his preliminary settings. The operator must always make the check immediately after completing his pin and lug settings. The following steps are necessary: Insert the paper tape according to instructions given in paragraph 24d. Make certain that the ink pad contains enough ink for legible printing. (If it does not, replace the pad from the ink pad can clamped to the outer cover.) Turn the setting knob several times to ink the typewheel thoroughly. With the inner lid closed, depress the reset button and turn the reset knob to zeroize the letter counter. The right-hand zero of the letter counter must be completely in view. A click will be heard when it comes into place. Set the encipher-decipher knob in the C position. Set the initial alignment of AAAAAA on the key wheels by turning them individually until the letter A of each wheel lines up with the white bench mark (fig. 7). Turn the indicating disk until the letter A is on line

17

① Counter set on 0000.
② Encipher-decipher knob set in the C position.
③ Key wheels aligned to AAAAAA.
④ First letter A located on indicating disk.

TL-7418

18   FIGURE 7. Converter set to make 26-letter check.

with the indicating index, and encipher it by operating the drive knob. Be sure that the drive knob is turned until it locks in place. Continue the encipherment of "A's" in the same manner until the letter counter shows that 26 letters have been enciphered. If the letter A is already aligned on the indicating index at the end of an operating cycle, the indicating disk must be moved to another letter and returned to A in order to release the drum lock, which prevents turning the drive knob. Advance the paper tape by turning the paper feed knob until the paper can be torn off at the cutting edge. Compare the tape with the 26-letter check in the cipher-key list. If the tape and the 26-letter check are identical, the pin and lug settings are correct; if they differ by one or more letters, there is an error in the initial settings of the converter which must be corrected before proceeding with any encipherment or decipherment. Refer to the cipher-key list composed of tables 1 and 2, and make the preliminary settings. Verify these settings by means of the 26-letter check in table II.

9. INDICATORS.

a. General. Every message enciphered with Converter M-209-(*) will be accompanied by certain *indicators* which are transmitted with the message. The purpose of these indicators is to show the deciphering operator what settings to make on his machine before deciphering that message. The various methods of determining and using the indicators are described in system publications.

b. Types. Three types of *indicators* are used. The number required will depend upon the system.

(1) The *system indicator* discloses to the receiving operator the system which is in use. It will appear in the system publication or the signal operation instructions.

(2) The *message indicator* reveals to the deciphering operator the initial key wheel alignment which was used to encipher

19

the message (par. 7a). In some systems this indicator will be enciphered before transmission to provide additional security.

(3) The *cipher-key indicator* designates the particular cipher-key list which was in effect at the time of encipherment. This indicator will appear in the SOI with the cipher-key lists.

c. *Use.* The following method of using the indicators is intended as an example for training purposes only:

(1) The system indicator is composed of two letters, such as FW. This system indicator designates the method of cryptographing, and is placed as the first two letters of the first group of the indicators.

(2) The message indicator is taken from the six key wheels before encipherment is begun, by reading the letters which are aligned with the white bench mark. These six letters are divided in half, the first half forms the last three letters of the first indicator group, and the second half forms the first three letters of the second indicator group. These appear as the first two groups of a message, and are sent in the clear. Assume, for example, that the initial key wheel alignment is QAHNKE. These letters make up the message indicator, and are written in the form shown below.

(3) The cipher-key indicator will appear as two letters, such as LP, accompanying each cipher-key list. These letters are inserted as the last two of the second indicator group.

(4) The two indicator groups would be made up and transmitted as follows:

FWQAH   NKELP
(1)   (2)   (3)

This is only a sample method of showing the indicators.

d. The indicators will always be placed in the order shown above, and will be inserted before the first group of cipher

20

text. They also appear (in the same order) as the last two groups of the message, following the last group of cipher text. The indicators must be added in pencil in both cases.

10. ENCIPHERMENT.

a. *General.* The student should follow the procedure on a converter which has been set and checked with the cipher-key list composed of tables I and II.

b. *Preliminary Instructions.* The following steps for enciphering a message with Converter M-209-(*) are presented in a numbered sequence designed to help an operator learn the process by performing the operations:

(1) Make certain that the drive knob is in the locked position. If it is not locked, turn it until it clicks and will turn no more. The knob cannot be turned again until the indicating disk has been moved. Leave the drive knob in the locked position until all adjustments have been made.

(2) Turn the encipher-decipher knob so that the letter C is up and facing the front.

(3) Zeroize the letter counter. This will insure that the enciphered text will be printed in groups of five letters, and will show the exact number of letters enciphered.

(4) Align the key wheels at random. In selecting the key wheel alignment, the operator should move the key wheels individually, choosing the letters which line up on the white bench mark. These letters should not spell a word, nor should the same letter be found twice in one key wheel alignment. The flat end of the tweezers may be used for turning the key wheels individually. *Do not use an eraser tip.* Each key wheel upon coming into place will click audibly; do not leave a key wheel in an intermediate position. Make a note of the indicator so that it may be referred to later.

21

(5) Advance enough paper tape to allow insertion of the system and message indicators by hand. (If the supply of paper tape is exhausted, the cipher text may be copied from the reproducing disk, as each letter is enciphered.)

c. *Procedure.* Encipher the following message: REINFORCEMENTS URGENTLY NEEDED. Proceed as follows:

(1) Turn the indicating disk until the first letter to be enciphered (R) lines up with the indicating index, and release the knob.

(2) Turn the drive knob until it locks. Avoid a rapid or jerky movement of the drive knob. A moderate steady motion is preferable. Complete the operating cycle before enciphering another letter, or jamming of the mechanism will result.

(3) Locate the second letter of the message (E) on the indicating disk and rotate the drive knob again. This procedure is repeated for all letters of the clear text.

(4) Encipher the letter Z between the words of the clear text; i. e., between *reinforcements* and *urgently*, and between *urgently* and *needed*, in the above message. When the cipher text is deciphered, a space will appear at the proper place between the words. A thorough explanation of Z-spacing is included in paragraph 13b.

(5) Since the drive knob is locked at the end of each operating cycle, the indicating disk must always be moved before another letter can be enciphered or deciphered. Occasionally the desired letter is already in position before the indicating disk is moved. If this happens, move the disk to another letter and return it to the desired letter. This will release the lock and allow the drive knob to be turned.

(6) When the message has been completely enciphered, advance the paper tape two or three inches and tear it off at the cutting edge.

22

(7) Note that the cipher text has been automatically spaced into five letter groups. If the last group contains only 1, 2, 3, or 4 letters, add enough X's in pencil to make it a complete 5-letter group. DO NOT ENCIPHER THESE X's TO COMPLETE THE LAST GROUP. Such a practice reduces the security of the system and aids the enemy in solving the message.

(8) Now print at the beginning of the message the system, message, and cipher key indicators, and repeat them in that order at the end of the message. From this point, the code clerk will follow the procedure for cryptographed messages as outlined in FM 24-5, Basic Signal Communication, or the standing operating procedure of his unit.

11. DECIPHERMENT. The deciphering operator must have initial settings on his machine which are identical to those used by the enciphering operator. Retaining the settings of tables I and II, decipher the message which was enciphered in paragraph 10c. Proceed as follows:

a. Make certain that the drive knob is in a locked position.

b. Turn the encipher-decipher knob to the D position.

c. Zeroize the letter counter.

d. Check the message indicators at the beginning of the message with those at the end to make sure that they are the same, and align the key wheels in accordance with the message indicator.

e. Proceed as in encipherment; locate the cipher letters one by one on the indicating disk, and operate the drive knob in one complete cycle each time. Disregard the spaces between the groups of the cipher text. Carry in mind one 5-letter group at a time so that it will not be necessary to look at the text for each letter; this will keep errors at a minimum.

23

f. Upon completion of decipherment, advance the tape until the printed clear text is beyond the cutting edge, and tear it off. If the letter "Z" was used as a space between words when the message was enciphered, the clear text will appear in its original word form. Local message center procedure will be followed in servicing the message and delivering it to the addressee.

12. ZEROIZING THE MACHINE. When the converter is to be closed at the end of a day or a period of operation, the internal keying elements of the device must be zeroized. First, push all of the key wheel pins to the left or ineffective position. Second, move all lugs to the zero positions on the drum bars. Tear off any tape which contains printing, and close the outer cover of the machine. The converter should then be placed in the canvas case provided, and kept in a dry place until used again.

13. SPACING.

a. Automatic Spacing. Five-letter cipher groups are obtained only when the encipher-decipher knob is set in the encipher position. This spacing is automatic and is ignored by both enciphering and deciphering operators.

b. Z-spacing. If the operator enciphers a Z for each space between words of clear text, the deciphered message will appear in its original word form (par. 10c(4)). This is made possible by the elimination of the letter Z in the deciphering process. Such a word as ORGANIZED will appear in clear text as ORGANI ED, but the missing letter can easily be supplied from the context of the message. The printing of the Z is prevented only when the encipher-decipher knob is set for deciphering.

14. USE OF LETTER COUNTER. An operator who wishes to check a word or correct an error, or who has lost his place in the message he is enciphering or deciphering, need not

24

start at the beginning of the message if he has a proper understanding of the letter counter. Whenever it is necessary to check back in the message for any reason, proceed as follows:

a. Determine the place in the message where the error occurs. Count the letters from the beginning of the message to the error. If the count is made from clear text, remember to count spaces also. In cipher text, the number of groups can be multiplied by five (there are five letters in each group), and any extra letters which are correct can be added to the product. For example, in the message used in paragraph 10c, "REINFORCEMENTS URGENTLY NEEDED," a mistake might have been caused by skipping a letter in decipherment so that the following text resulted: "REINFORCEMENTS URGENQCTLV etc." A count of the letter in error will show that all letters through the 20th are correct.

b. Turn the letter counter back until it reads 20. Count the cipher text letters up through the 20th (four groups), and begin from there by deciphering the 21st letter. This process may be used for reenciphering or redeciphering any portion of a message as long as the indicators remain the same.

15. CAUSES AND CORRECTION OF GARBLES.

a. General. Faulty operation of a cryptographic device, errors made in transmission, or mistakes made by either the enciphering or deciphering operator may produce garbled text. The garble may be so slight that the text may still be read, or it may likewise be so serious that the text will be unreadable. It is important that operators of Converter M-209-(*) recognize the types of garbles and know their causes, and whenever possible, make correction. *The operator should always make every possible attempt to decipher a message before asking for a service on it.* There are five common causes of garbled text.

25

b. Incorrectly Set Key Wheel Pin. One incorrectly placed key wheel pin will result in garbled text. This type of garble is recognized by a single-letter error appearing periodically in the text, i. e., by errors which are an equal distance apart. Location of the incorrectly set pin is accomplished in the following manner:

(1) Count the number of letters including spaces from one garbled letter to the next. This number determines the key wheel on which the pin is located. If the count is 17, the incorrectly set pin will be found on wheel number 6 (numbering from left to right), because this wheel contains only 17 pins (table I). If the count is 19, the incorrectly set pin will be found on wheel number 5; if 21, on wheel number 4; if 23, on wheel number 3; if 25, on wheel number 2; if 26, on wheel number 1. The following message is slightly garbled as the result of an incorrectly set key wheel pin:

NOW IS L̲HE TIME FOR ALL X̲OOD MEN

If the deciphering were continued, the error would appear periodically at the same interval. A count shows that from the first error to the second, there are 17 letters and spaces, indicating that the incorrectly-set pin is on key wheel number 6.

(2) Following the directions given in paragraph 14, turn the letter counter to the number of the last letter deciphered before the garbled letter appeared. In the example above, the counter would be turned back to 7.

(3) By using the following table and counting over the top of the key wheel which contains the error, beginning with the letter which is on line with the bench mark, the pin which was in the operation at the time of the error will be located.

Wheel No.	1	2	3	4	5	6
Count back	16	15	14	13	12	11

26

If A were aligned on the key wheels, the pin in operation for the next letter would be the one associated with the letter P for wheel number 1, O for wheel number 2, N for wheel number 3, and so forth. After determining the pin in error, turn the wheel until that pin is visible, and move it to the other side. Reset the key wheel to its proper place and decipher the letter to determine whether the trouble has been corrected.

c. Incorrectly Set Drum Bar Lug. Garbles caused by an incorrectly set drum bar lug are recognized by a *nonperiodic* appearance of errors throughout the text, which may or may not be readable at first sight. Such garbles can be divided into three types according to the results produced:

(1) The first type is caused by a lug which has been made effective, when it should be noneffective. This condition adds one positive "kick" in the operation of the machine. In this case the letters which are in error will always be those letters which immediately follow the correct letters in the alphabet. The text might appear as follows:

NOX̲ IS THEA̲UIMF̲ FORA̲AML HOO̲E MEN

(NOW IS THE TIME FOR ALL GOOD MEN)

Note that each incorrect letter takes the place of that letter in the alphabet which just precedes it: X for W, A for Z (space), U for T, F for E, and so forth.

(2) The second type is caused by a lug which has been placed in a noneffective position, when it should be in an effective position. This condition results in one less "kick" in the machine's operation; that is, the letter in error will be that letter which immediately precedes the correct letter in the alphabet. The text might appear as follows:

NOV̲ IS THD̲ TIME FOR ̲KL GOODY̲MEN

(NOW IS THE TIME FOR ALL GOOD MEN)

27

Here it can be seen that the incorrect letter V precedes the correct letter W in the alphabet, that D precedes E, and so forth.

(3) A third type of error results when a lug is made effective in the wrong position. For this case there will be both plus and minus "kicks" in the operation of the machine. The result will be that some of the letters in error will be those letters which come immediately before the correct letters in the alphabet, others will be those which come immediately after the correct letters. The garbled text usually has no resemblance to the original clear text, and may appear as follows:

NNWAJTYSHDATHMF FNR   LKYGPPD MDN

(NOW IS THE TIME FOR ALL GOOD MEN)

Comparison of the clear text with the garbled text will show that the garbled letters are either immediately before or immediately after the correct letters in the alphabet.

> NOTE: There is no way of finding the particular lug which is in error in the above cases. However, it is possible to obtain clear text if the operator substitutes letters as directed in the preceding paragraphs.

d. Incorrect Setting of Indicator. This mistake will result if the enciphering operator fails to copy down the correct message indicator or cipher key indicator; if the receiving operator records the message improperly; or if the deciphering operator makes an accurate setting. In any case, unreadable text will be the result. Correction can be made only by referring to the correct indicators. Receiving operators must always check the indicators at the end of the message, as well as those at the beginning. These two indicators should be identical, but if they differ, the receiving operator will have to try them both in attempting to decipher the message.

e. Transmission Errors. The frequency of garbles due to transmission errors will depend upon the efficiency of transmitting and receiving operators and upon the quality of transmission. A knowledge of Morse code will help the deciphering operator to see the errors possible due to transmission, and to correct them.

f. Omissions or Repetitions. The deciphering operator's machine may produce readable text up to a point after which a garble appears. The cause of the garble will either be the omission of letters or groups, or the repetition of letters or groups. To determine the cause of the garble, the operator must make several checks.

(1) First, the cryptographed text is examined for the repetition of letters or groups. Identical groups will probably not appear side by side, but may appear as in the following example:

QHKLV NCRQH KLVOP

In this case the operator would turn the counter back to the number just preceding the number of the first repeated letter, and proceed with the decipherment omitting the repeated

(2) If no groups are repeated in the message, each group should be examined to determine whether any group contains more or less than five letters. If a group contains less than five letters, a letter, or letters, has been left out in transmission and the letter counter must be turned up the necessary number of times before proceeding. If a group contains more than five letters, a letter has been added and must be omitted when deciphering.

(3) Trouble may result due to the deciphering operator's carelessness or to an interruption in his work; in which case the letter counter must be turned back to the last letter of clear text (par. 14), before deciphering is continued.

(4) Omission of a code group within a message, during transmission or reception, is one of the most difficult errors to

locate. If an error occurs which is not of a type described in the preceding paragraphs, the operator can assume the omission of one or more groups. The letter counter should be moved up five points from the number of the last correct group before proceeding. If clear text is not obtained by moving the letter counter up 5 points, it should be moved up 10 points, or 15, until clear text is produced.

16. OPERATION CAUTIONS.

a. General. Most failures of Converter M-209-(*) can be credited to careless or faulty operation rather than to the machine. The converter is designed to withstand hard usage in the field, and is therefore rugged in its construction, but it must be handled with a reasonable amount of care if it is to give satisfactory service.

b. Check List. Certain cautions have been mentioned throughout this section of the manual which, if properly observed, will help to keep the machine running smoothly. These cautions appear below as a check list for the new operator:

(1) In making preliminary settings, each key-wheel pin must be pushed all the way to the right or left; do not leave a pin in an intermediate position.

(2) Drum bar lugs must be properly seated in the holes provided for them.

(3) The reset knob must click into place after being turned, and a complete figure must be visible on the letter counter.

(4) Key wheels will click when moved into position. Do not allow a key wheel to remain in an intermediate position.

(5) Turn the drive knob in a complete cycle until it locks. Avoid an excessively rapid or jerky motion.

(6) The indicating disk must not be moved until the drive knob has made a complete cycle.

TABLE 3. *Garble correction chart.*

Error	Cause	Correction
1. Periodic single-letter error.	Incorrectly set key wheel pin.	Count interval between errors; turn counter back to number before error; count around wheel to pin in effect, change this pin to proper position.
2. Nonperiodic errors (may or may not appear unreadable).	Incorrectly set drum bar lug.	Substitute letters which appear before and after garbled letters in alphabet, and attempt to read the message.
3. Unreadable text.	Incorrect indicator setting.	Obtain correct indicator setting.
4. Nonperiodic errors.	Poor transmission.	Determine meaning from context, or ask for service on message.
5. Clear text up to certain point, followed by garble.	(a) Repetition of letter. (b) Repetition of group. (c) Omission of letter. (d) Omission of group.	(a) Leave out repeated letter. (b) Omit repeated group. (c) Turn letter counter up one. (d) Turn letter counter up five points.

(7) NEVER USE FORCE TO CLEAR A JAMMED MACHINE. Paragraph 25 gives instructions for eliminating a jam.

17. SECURITY CAUTIONS.

a. Change the message indicator for each message sent.

b. Destroy all printed tape not pasted to a message blank.

c. Do not encipher X's to fill out the last cipher group of a message. Complete a group by adding X's in pencil.

d. Be very careful to avoid errors while enciphering. Errors may help an enemy to break down the cryptographic system in use.

SECTION III
FUNCTIONING OF PARTS

18. THEORY OF OPERATION.

Converter M-209-(*) operates on the cryptographic principal of reciprocal-substitution alphabets. The effect is that of sliding a normal-alphabet sequence against reversed normal alphabet. The manner in which the various elements of the converter shift the alphabets, with respect to each other, produces a high degree of irregularity in the letter substitutions during encipherment. For example, in the enciphering of a message, the alphabets might be arranged in the following manner for the first letter:

A B C D E F G H I J K L M N O P Q R S T U V W X Y Z

K J I H G F E D C B A Z Y X W V U T S R Q P O N M L

Thus, if K were the first letter to be enciphered, its cipher equivalent would be the letter A. For the second letter to be enciphered the alphabets might be arranged as follows:

A B C D E F G H I J K L M N O P Q R S T U V W X Y Z

R Q P O N M L K J I H G F E D C B A Z Y X W V U T S

If K were also the second letter to be enciphered, its cipher equivalent would be the letter H. The continual shifting of the alphabets is the factor which provides security for messages enciphered with Converter M-209-(*).

---

19. KEY WHEEL ASSEMBLY.

a. The key wheel assembly comprises the six key wheels (42) with their ratchets, pawls, and gears (38); the reset knob (39) and key wheel shaft; the key wheel intermediate gear shaft and gears (36); and the letter counter (2). The key wheel ratchet and pawl arrangement cannot be seen clearly unless the key wheels are removed from the shaft. Figure 8 below shows an inside view of each key wheel gear.

b. The key wheels are operated by the drive knob (35) on the right-hand side of the machine. The key wheel gears are driven by a set of intermediate gears located behind the six key wheels. A key wheel feed-cam assembly on the right drum disk moves the set of intermediate gears one notch each time the drive knob is rotated. The intermediate gears vary in circumference and number of teeth. The smallest gear has the greatest number of teeth, and is located on the left. The largest gear has the smallest number of teeth, and is located on the right. This variation is necessary due to a like variation in the key wheels driven by the intermediate gears. Letters of the alphabet appear in normal order on the outer rim of each key wheel. The key wheel on the left has the greatest number of letters, and the key wheel on the right has the smallest number of letters (par. 5a). For each letter on the key wheels there is one pin, and for each pin there is a tooth in the associated key wheel gear. To allow the key wheels to move simultaneously for one space during each operating cycle, the key wheel gears are so constructed that they compensate for the differences in the spacing of the key wheel pins.

c. A ratchet pawl permits turning the key wheels individually by hand, but in one direction only. When the relative positions of the pins are changed, different combinations of pins result without resetting all key wheel pins. The letter counter records numbers from 0000 to 9999, and is

---

driven by a gear on the left-hand side of the intermediate gear shaft. The counter will operate only when the key wheels are turned as a unit. The reset knob will zeroize the letter counter or turn the key wheels back to any previous setting.

d. A different pin on each wheel comes into play for each letter cryptographed, until the wheels have made one complete rotation. However, each key wheel pin is not necessarily in an effective position. Paragraph 8 explains that only those pins which are pushed to the right are effective.

20. GUIDE ARMS. Six guide arms, one for each key wheel, are located between the key wheel assembly and the drum (fig. 9). The guide arms form the link between the key wheels and drum bars. When a key wheel pin in the effective position comes into play the associated guide arm is released allowing the guide arm spring to push the guide arm toward the rear of the machine. In this position, the guide arm will, when the drum is rotated, make contact with the drum bar lugs in line with it. For example, the guide arm for wheel number 6 will contact those lugs which are in the number 6 position on the drum bars. When the drum is turned, the guide arm forces the drum bars it controls to the left, which is their effective position. A key wheel pin in the noneffective position holds the guide arm it controls in an inactive position. A guide arm held in an inactive position has no effect on the operation of the train of gears for that particular cycle.

21. DRUM ASSEMBLY.

a. The drum assembly (fig. 10) consists of the shaft and disks (30), the bars (31), and lugs (32), the step and lock arm (fig. 9), and the gear. Attached to the shaft, and operated by it, are the paper feed cam and the printing cam. Paragraph 23 explains the functions of the paper feed cam and the printing cam. The 27 drum bars are numbered on

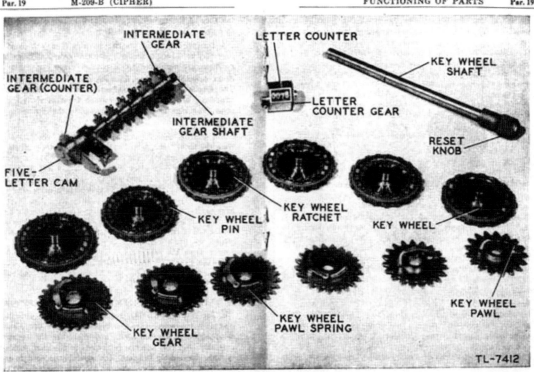

GUIDE ARMS

INTERMEDIATE GEAR LOCK
GUIDE ARM SHAFT
GUIDE ARM SPRING
INTERMEDIATE GEAR LOCK SPRING
GUIDE ARM COMB

DRUM STEP AND LOCK ARM
INK PAD HOLDER
KEY WHEEL BEARING SCREW

TL–7410

FIGURE 9. *Guide arms.*

the face of the right-hand drum disk to assist the operator in making the preliminary settings.

b. On each drum bar are two movable lugs. The drum bar lugs may be moved to any one of eight positions. These eight positions are numbered (on a number plate just behind the drum assembly), in the following order: 1 0 2 3 4 5 0 6. The zero positions are noneffective, but the other six are effective positions located directly in front of the six guide arms. The lugs are placed according to the cipher-key list in effect.

c. The drum assembly makes one complete revolution each time the drive knob is rotated, and the effective drum bar lugs are contacted by effective guide arms. The drum bar lugs are forced, one after the other, to the left. In the left position the drum bar lugs act as cogs of a wheel, meshing with the typewheel intermediate gear, which drives the typewheel. The typewheel is turned as many letters as there are bars projecting from the left of the drum. A retractor forces the bars back into neutral position after they have been used. At the end of the operating cycle, a cam on the left-drum disk pushes the drum lock arm into place; simultaneously a projection from the lock arm drops between two cogs of the typewheel gear. The drum remains locked until the typewheel is turned, moving the projection of the lock arm, and releasing the lock arm.

22. TYPEWHEEL ASSEMBLY AND PRINT ARM ASSEMBLY.

a. The setting knob (8), indicating disk (7), reproducing disk (6), typewheel (5), and typewheel gear (43), are all mounted on a common shaft and make up the typewheel assembly (fig. 11). A screw in the end of the shaft holds the typewheel assembly in place. The assembly is used to select the letter to be cryptographed or decryptographed and print the enciphered or deciphered letter on a paper tape.

INTERMEDIATE GEAR
LETTER COUNTER
KEY WHEEL SHAFT
INTERMEDIATE GEAR (COUNTER)
INTERMEDIATE GEAR SHAFT
LETTER COUNTER GEAR
RESET KNOB
FIVE-LETTER CAM
KEY WHEEL PIN
KEY WHEEL RATCHET
KEY WHEEL
KEY WHEEL GEAR
KEY WHEEL PAWL SPRING
KEY WHEEL PAWL

TL-7412

FIGURE 8. *Key wheel assembly.*

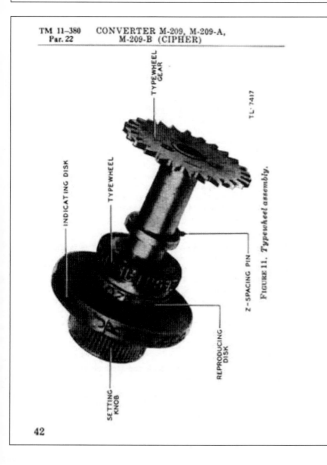

FIGURE 10. Drum assembly.

Labels: DRUM BAR; DRUM BAR LUG; RIGHT DISK (NUMBER DISK); LUG POSITIONS; DRUM LOCK ARM CAM; RETRACTOR; TL-7411; DRUM BAR PROJECTIONS; LEFT DISK; SHAFT; PRINTING CAM; PAPER FEED CAM

b. The indicating disk, containing the letters of the alphabet in normal order, is set to the desired letter by alignment of that letter with the indicating index mark (3) on the inner lid. During the operating cycle, the intermediate typewheel gear meshes with the effective drum bars and drives the typewheel gear. The typewheel prints the letter in position at the end of the cycle; printing is accomplished through the action of the print hammer. The letter printed may also be seen as the first letter visible on the reproducing disk. If the supply of tape or ink pads should become exhausted, the cipher text may be copied from the reproducing disk, one letter after each operating cycle.

c. The print arm assembly is mounted on the shaft of the encipher-decipher knob and includes the print arm, print hammer, and print arm stop. A spring attached to the print arm and the base of the converter keeps the required tension on the assembly.

d. Printing is accomplished at the end of each operating cycle, when the printing cam (fig. 10) on the drum shaft allows the print arm to be pulled forward suddenly by the print arm spring. The print hammer, a piece of hard rubber clamped in the teeth of the print arm, strikes the tape against the inked typewheel, printing a letter. The printing cam, continuing its cycle, brings the print arm back to its original position.

e. The print arm stop prevents printing of the letter Z when the machine is being used to decipher. A cam on the shaft of the encipher-decipher knob controls the operation of the print arm stop. When the encipher-decipher knob is set in the D position, the printing cam pushes the print arm stop forward and holds it. On the typewheel shaft there is a small pin offset from the letter Z, which rests against the print arm stop when Z is to be printed. As a result, the print hammer is not allowed to strike the typewheel and a blank space ap-

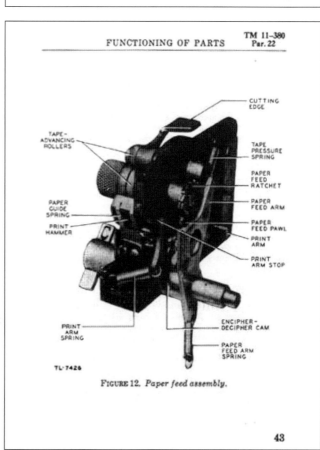

FIGURE 11. Typewheel assembly.

Labels: TYPEWHEEL GEAR; TL-7417; INDICATING DISK; TYPEWHEEL; Z-SPACING PIN; REPRODUCING DISK; SETTING KNOB

FIGURE 12. Paper feed assembly.

Labels: CUTTING EDGE; TAPE-ADVANCING ROLLERS; TAPE PRESSURE SPRING; PAPER FEED RATCHET; PAPER GUIDE SPRING; PAPER FEED ARM; PRINT HAMMER; PAPER FEED PAWL; PRINT ARM; PRINT ARM STOP; PRINT ARM SPRING; ENCIPHER-DECIPHER CAM; PAPER FEED ARM SPRING; TL-7426

pears on the tape. When the encipher-decipher knob is set in the C position, the print arm stop is held back and does not touch the pin.

23. PAPER FEED ASSEMBLY.

a. The paper feed assembly consists of a large cam on the drum shaft (fig. 10), an arm which rides on this cam, a pawl and ratchet, a small 5-letter cam (13), a paper feed stop, and a knob (fig. 12).

b. The revolution of the paper feed cam causes the paper feed arm to move the paper feed pawl and ratchet one notch for each operating cycle, advancing the paper tape one space. Double spacing between groups is accomplished by the 5-letter cam. A projection from the paper feed arm rides on the outer rim of the 5-letter cam which has two indentations on opposite sides. As the projection rides into one of the indentations, the paper feed arm moves the pawl and ratchet two notches, advancing the tape two spaces. After five letters have been enciphered, the projection will again ride into an indentation on the cam and permit double spacing.

c. Automatic spacing is not desired during deciphering, and is prevented by the paper feed stop. The paper feed stop is in contact with the cam of the encipher-decipher knob. When the encipher-decipher knob is set in the D position, the arm of the paper feed stop is raised and aligned on a fixed projection of the drum shaft bracket. The projection of the paper feed arm is prevented from following the contour of the 5-letter cam, resulting in continuous single spacing.

SECTION IV
MAINTENANCE

24. CARE OF CONVERTER.

a. Preventive Checks. Converter M-209-(*) will offer few maintenance problems if it is operated correctly and cared for properly. In many cases a thorough cleaning and lubrication will remedy mechanical difficulties. As the machine is used from day to day, a few simple checks during operation will help to keep the device in good operating condition. Operators should check the following items:

(1) Spring tension of the various visible springs on machine.

(2) Proper lubrication.

(3) Amount of lateral play in the key wheels on the key wheel shaft (par. 26). (Key wheels must be sufficiently tight to avoid slipping to one side, but not so tight that easy turning is prevented.)

(4) Dried ink on typewheel or dust in operating parts.

(5) Proper positioning of lugs on drum bars.

(6) Tightness of screws on drum base.

b. Cleaning. From time to time certain parts of the machine will require cleaning.

(1) TYPEWHEEL. The typewheel may become caked with ink and print indistinct or illegible characters. Brushing the

---

typewheel with a small stiff-bristled brush may be sufficient to clean it. If the dried ink has hardened, use a sharp instrument to loosen the ink before applying the brush. Do not damage the letters on the typewheel with the instrument.

(2) GENERAL. When the converter is used in the field, dust may collect in the operating parts and impede their action, especially if the machine has been oiled excessively. If the machine becomes clogged, remove the parts as directed in paragraph 34 and clean with a dry cloth. Lubricate the machine before replacing the parts. Remove the dust from corners and openings occasionally with a small brush. Always close the outer cover when the converter is not in use.

c. Oiling. The oil rod provided with Converter M-209-(*) is attached to the cover of the oil can, and should always be used to oil the machine. The bearings should be lubricated occasionally (for every 256 hours of operation) by placing one to four drops of oil in the lubricating holes provided. The drum bar slots on the left-hand side of the drum should be kept well oiled, but all other moving parts should be lubricated sparingly.

d. Paper Tape Supply. To insert fresh tape into the paper feed mechanism, release the hinged guard which holds the roll of paper in place and allow the guard to tilt forward against the inner lid. Remove the empty spool and place a new roll of tape over the pin. (The tape must unroll in a counter-clockwise direction.) Pass the end of the tape through the slot in the hinged guard, bring the tape forward, and insert it in the tape slot just above the encipher-decipher knob. Push the tape through the tape channel until it appears between the typewheel and the tape-advancing rollers. The tape must pass under the paper guide spring immediately behind the typewheel. Next pass the paper tape between the tape-advancing rollers (fig. 12), while depressing the paper pressure arm.

---

e. Ink Pads. Additional ink pads will be found in one of the small metal containers held by spring clamps in the outer cover of the machine. To insert a fresh pad, open the inner lid of the converter, use the tweezers to remove the old pad, and insert a new one. The life of the pad, before replacement is necessary, can be prolonged by turning it end for end. The ink pads should be re-inked with the special ink developed for the ink pads, or with any standard purple or black stamp pad ink. Hectograph ink should not be used because it dries the ink pad and makes it unfit for further use.

f. Minor Repair. The operator of Converter M-209-(*) should be able to make certain minor repairs on the machine. Paragraphs 25 through 32 explain the common minor troubles and include information for correcting such troubles. Paragraph 34 explains how to dismantle the machine and limits operator's maintenance to minor repairs.

25. JAMMING.

a. Description and Location. Converter M-209-(*) is jammed when the drive knob will not revolve. Jamming may occur at any phase of an operating cycle and is generally the result of faulty operation. DO NOT USE FORCE IN AN ATTEMPT TO CLEAR THE MACHINE. The operator should first make the following checks to locate the cause of the trouble:

(1) Move indicating disk slightly and realign letter to be enciphered or deciphered. Try drive knob.

(2) Move reset knob until it snaps into place (if not already in place). Try drive knob.

(3) Open inner lid. Rock drum back and forth several times. Try drive knob.

b. Causes. If none of the checks listed clears the jam, the operator must determine whether the trouble is due to one of the following causes:

(1) A DRUM BAR LUG OUT OF LINE, A BENT DRUM BAR LUG, OR A BENT DRUM BAR TOOTH (fig. 10). Open the inner lid. If the drum has been moved through only part of the operating cycle, proceed as follows:

(a) Using the flat side of the screwdriver, push to the right drum bars projecting beyond the left side of the drum. The drum bars must be pushed until flush with left side of the drum.

(b) Turn drive knob until it locks.

(c) Check for a lug not fitted into a hole. Check also for a bent lug, or for a bent drum bar tooth.

(d) If a lug or tooth is bent, straighten it with a pair of pliers and use it until a new lug or bar can be obtained.

(2) BENT GUIDE ARM (fig. 9). Check each guide arm to determine if one is bent and touching a drum bar or the base of a drum bar lug. If a bent guide arm is found, pull it back toward the front of the machine, and turn the drive knob to complete the cycle. Bend the guide arm back to its proper position with a pair of pliers. The guide arm must make contact with the side of the lug projection only. Do not bend the guide arm into the comb (fig. 9), or the guide arm will not operate freely.

(3) EXCESSIVE PLAY IN THE KEY WHEELS. Open the inner lid. Check each key wheel to determine whether one has slipped to the right and become disengaged from the key wheel intermediate gear (fig. 8). Key wheels slip as a result of the loosening of the right-hand shaft screw or of the key wheel bearing screw (fig. 9). Re-engage the key wheel gear, and tighten the right-hand shaft screw and the key wheel bearing screw until the key wheels have no play to the left or right. It may be necessary to tap two or three times on the end of the reset knob before tightening the screws in order to slide the shaft over to its proper location.

48

CAUTION: When tightening the key wheel bearing screw, do not use too much pressure. The screw is made of very soft metal and is easily broken.

(4) BENT TYPEWHEEL DETENT. The typewheel detent is located below and slightly toward the rear of the typewheel gear. The typewheel detent rides on the typewheel gear and makes the clicking noise heard when the setting knob is turned. If the typewheel detent becomes bent to either side of the typewheel gear, the entire mechanism of the converter may jam. Raise the inner lid and remove the letter counter (par. 34). If the typewheel detent is bent, bend it back to the proper position, and turn the drive knob. See paragraph 35 for information on replacing the letter counter.

26. MINOR KEY WHEEL REPAIRS.

a. Key Wheel Rotates in Both Directions. (1) Move the key wheels to the left or right to determine if there is play on the shaft. If play is discovered, add enough shims under the left-end shaft screw to overcome the looseness, and tighten the screws on both ends of the shaft. Test the rotation of the key wheels.

(2) If a key wheel continues to rotate in both directions after the procedure in the above paragraph has been applied, remove the key wheels according to the directions for dismantling the machine in paragraph 34. Separate the faulty key wheel from its intermediate gear by turning the gear in a clockwise direction, pulling the gear away from the key wheel at the same time. Bend the end of the key wheel pawl away from the intermediate gear, so the key wheel pawl will fit closely against the key wheel when the two are placed together (fig. 8). To fit the key wheel and the intermediate gear together, place the gear against the key wheel, and rotate the gear in a clockwise direction while pushing it against the wheel. Replace the key wheels according to instructions given in paragraph 35.

49

---

b. Key Wheels Stick. Key wheels operating sluggishly or sticking in intermediate positions probably are set too tightly on the shaft. Check the key wheel bearing screw to determine whether it has been properly set in the indent on the shaft. If not, slide the screw until it is fitted into the indent. If this is not the trouble, remove enough shims from either end of the shaft to permit free movement of the key wheels.

c. Key Wheel Pins Stick. Place a drop of oil in the key wheel pin slots (fig. 8), and push the pins back and forth several times. If the key wheels are dirty, wash them in a solvent before lubricating the pin slots.

27. MINOR GUIDE ARM REPAIRS. A guide arm may become bent at the point where it runs through the guide arm comb (fig. 9). If a guide arm is bent it may operate sluggishly or may not become effective at the proper time, due to scraping against the side of the comb. Adjust the guide arm by bending with a pair of long-nosed pliers. Be certain not to bend any other part of the guide arm.

28. MINOR DRUM ASSEMBLY REPAIRS.

a. Sprung Drum Bar (fig. 10). Remove a sprung drum bar in the following manner: Grasp the left end of the bar just inside the left-hand drum disk, and lift the bar slightly. Now push the bar to the left. When the drum bar has cleared the right drum disk, grasp the right end of the bar and move it in an arc to the left. Work the left end of the bar free of the disk spring. Insert a new bar by following the above instructions in reverse order. It is not worthwhile to attempt to straighten a sprung drum bar.

NOTE: Drum bars can be replaced by fourth and fifth echelons only. This part is not supplied to first, second, and third echelons.

50

---

b. Drum Bars Stick. If the drum bars stick, place a drop of oil in each of the drum bar slots on the left-hand drum disk (fig. 10).

c. Drum Not Locking. Bend the projection from the drum lock arm (fig. 9), so that the projection rides on the cam on the left drum disk when an operating cycle is completed. If the trouble is not corrected, the converter must be serviced by a repairman.

29. MINOR TYPEWHEEL ASSEMBLY REPAIRS. If the indicating disk turns hard, check one of the following troubles:

a. Insufficient Space on Key Wheel Shaft. Check the key wheel bearing screw to determine that it is properly fitted into the indent on the shaft. If not, slide the shaft until the screw fits. If there are too many shims, remove as many as necessary.

b. Locking Arm Not Releasing Properly. The projection of the drum lock arm, which locks the typewheel gear, should fit snugly between the cogs of the gear. Adjust the locking arm by bending to the proper position.

c. Bent Typewheel Detent (see par. 25b (4)).

d. Lack of Oil on Shaft (fig. 8).

30. IMPROPER PRINTING.

a. Loose or Missing Print Arm Spring (fig. 12). If the spring is loose, shorten it and use it until another spring is available.

b. Misaligned Hammer Pad. If the rubber pad which is mounted in the print hammer becomes oil-soaked or worn on one side, it will fail to print properly. To remove the pad from the print hammer; remove the typewheel, the paper guide spring, and the hammer guard (fig. 12). Next loosen the

51

clamps on the hammer and lift out the pad. Trim the pad until it is smooth, or turn it end for end, and replace it in the clamps. (Proper size of the print hammer is $\frac{7}{16}$" long, $\frac{5}{16}$" wide, and $\frac{3}{16}$" thick.) Do not clamp the pad too tightly or the outer surface will become rounded.

c. Sprung Paper Guide Spring (fig. 12). If sprung, bend the side of the paper guide spring which is out of line, until both sides of the spring apply an equal amount of pressure to the tape. When adjusting the paper guide spring, remember that the print hammer must fall between the two arms of the spring.

d. Sprung Ink-pad Holder. This trouble may result in the printing of only a part of a character. Bend the holder into its proper shape and use it until a new holder can be obtained.

31. IMPROPER FEEDING OF PAPER TAPE. The paper tape may feed improperly, or cease to feed, due to one of the following causes:

a. Clogging of the Tape at the Rollers (fig. 12). The tape will clog when improperly inserted between the rollers (either placed in crooked or not reaching to the end of the paper pressure arm), or when stuck to the rollers. Remove the clogged tape and insert the end of the tape between the rollers, advancing it to the end of the paper pressure arm. If gummed tape is used and continues to stick, try turning the tape over so that printing appears on the gummed side.

b. Flattened Roller. Regroove the roller with a sharp instrument.

c. Insufficient Lubrication on Top Roller. Oil both ends of the roller.

d. Weak Paper Pressure-arm Spring (fig. 12). This spring is located on the inside of the left side-plate, toward the rear

52

---

of the machine. Shorten the weak spring to provide sufficient tension, until a new spring is available.

e. Misaligned Paper Pressure Arm. This trouble will cause the paper tape to move out of line and become clogged in the sides of the rollers. Bend the arm until the two rollers are properly fitted.

f. Missing Paper Feed Arm Spring (fig. 12).

32. IMPROPER COUNTING. The letter counter will not operate correctly if improperly mounted. Follow the directions for mounting the counter as given in paragraph 35. The counter will be inaccurate if a tooth is broken off either the counter gear (fig. 8), or the intermediate gear which meshes with the counter gear.

33. COMMON MECHANICAL FAILURES.

a. General. It is impracticable to list all of the failures possible with Converter M-209-(*). A summary of some of the more common mechanical failures is given below as a check list for the repairman, including those which have already been discussed under the operator's "minor repair" headings.

b. Check List for Repairmen.

(1) Defective key wheel feed, allowing key wheels to remain stationary.

(2) Too much play in key wheels on shaft.

(3) Jamming of lock on typewheel gear teeth.

(4) Inoperative drum lock, i. e., drum moves past stop.

(5) Drum out of line due to previous jam cleared by force.

(6) Sprung drum bar.

(7) Bent or burred drum bar tooth.

(8) Bent drum bar lug.

(9) Sticking of drum bar.

53

---

(10) Failure in operation of feed stop pawl for key wheels.

(11) Partial advancement of key wheels due to bind in key wheel feed pawl.

(12) Irregular or binding paper feed.

(13) Weaving of paper tape.

(14) Guide arms binding irregularly, or sticking in active or inactive positions.

(15) Weak, detached, or broken spring on paper feed pawl.

(16) Irregular printing due to broken or bent paper guide spring.

(17) Irregular printing due to worn or loose printing hammer rubber.

(18) Failure to print due to weak or broken printer spring.

(19) Broken key-wheel-pawl ratchet spring.

(20) Key wheel pawl slipped out of ratchet.

(21) Key wheel pin sticking.

(22) Failure of typewheel detent (safety catch) to function properly.

(23) Detached or broken typewheel detent spring.

34. PROCEDURE FOR DISMANTLING.

a. Operator. Converter M-209-(*) can be sufficiently dismantled for the operator to make any *minor* repairs necessary by following the numbered steps below:

(1) Remove ink pad.

(2) Remove letter counter (two screws).

(3) Remove key wheel left-end shaft screw.

(4) Loosen key wheel bearing screw (fig. 9).

(5) Withdraw key wheel shaft (fig. 8) by pulling the reset knob (with the screw still in it) to the right, while rocking the key wheels with the palm of the left hand.

54

---

(6) Remove typewheel assembly (fig. 11). Pull the ink pad holder back when lifting the assembly out.

(7) Remove key wheels (fig. 8).

b. Repairman. If a converter requires more than minor repair it must be serviced by a repairman. In addition to the dismantling procedure authorized an operator, a repairman will continue dismantling as follows:

(1) Revolve the drum in the usual manner until 27 on the number disk is the only number visible; then remove the drum bar lug number plate (fig. 3, (29)) by taking out the two screws, lockwashers, and spacing washer. (After removing number plate, complete the drum cycle.)

(2) Remove the right side-plate (4 screws). Note the dowel which is fitted into the end of the rear plate of the machine. The side-plate must be pulled straight out in order to prevent bending the dowel.

(3) Remove the intermediate gear assembly (2 screws). Do not bend the dowel between the two screws (fig. 8).

(4) Remove the left side-plate, proceeding as follows:

(a) Unhook the print arm spring and the paper feed arm spring from the spring clip (fig. 12).

(b) Remove the screw on the left of the underside of the base. This screw holds the encipher-decipher knob detent ball and spring in place. Remove the ball and spring.

(c) Remove the screw in the inset on the underside of the base.

(d) Remove the screw on the lower back of the left side-plate.

(e) Remove the screw spring and latch assembly on the upper back of the left side-plate.

(5) Remove the two screws on the bottom of the drum shaft bracket, and lift out the drum. Do not bend the dowel.

55

(6) Remove the guide arm shaft, guide arms, and intermediate gear lock (fig. 9).

c. *Parts Accessible without Dismantling.* After the repairman has dismantled the converter as directed in the above paragraphs, a number of parts are accessible without any further dismantling. These parts are as follows:

(1) The paper feed assembly and print arm assembly (parts of the encipher-decipher knob shaft) on the left side-plate (fig. 12).

(2) The paper guide spring and hammer assembly (fig. 12).

(3) Parts mounted on the base casting as follows:

(a) Ink pad holder and spring (fig. 9).

(b) Print arm and paper feed spring clip.

(c) Guide arm spring (fig. 9).

(d) Intermediate gear lock spring (fig. 9).

(e) Key wheel feed-arm assembly (fig. 9).

(f) Intermediate gear release-arm assembly (right side-plate).

(g) Key wheel feed-pawl spring clip (upper right corner).

35. PROCEDURE FOR REASSEMBLING. To reassemble Converter M-209-(*) follow in reverse order the procedure given above for dismantling. Note the following special instructions:

a. *The Guide Arms.* Mount the guide arms as follows: Place any guide arm numbered 156 in the first position on the guide arm shaft (counting from left to right). Follow the guide arm numbered 156 with the three guide arms numbered 234. Next, place on the shaft the remaining two guide arms numbered 156, and place the intermediate gear lock (fig. 9) in the extreme right position. The smaller end of the shaft is inserted in the lower bearing in the key wheel bracket, and

the bent ends of the guide arms are placed through the slots in the guide arm comb. Each guide arm must rest on a part of the flat spring. The intermediate gear lock rests on its own spring. The right side-plate must be mounted before any adjustment is made. Then adjust for tension, freedom of movement, and alignment. Adjustments may be made by loosening the three screws holding the guide arm comb in place, and sliding the comb back and forth until the proper alignment is obtained. If necessary, a guide arm which scrapes against the comb may be adjusted by bending it with a pair of long-nosed pliers. Bend only that portion of the guide arm which operates in the slots of the comb.

b. *The Left Side-plate.* As the left side-plate is slid into position, lift the paper feed arm so it rests on the paper feed cam of the drum. Replace the detent ball and spring in the underside of the base, and hook the springs to the spring clip.

c. *Key Wheels.* To replace the key wheels, proceed as follows: Insert the key wheel shaft through the hole in the right side-plate so the shaft reaches the position for key wheel number 6. Each key wheel is numbered according to its position with the exception of number 6 which is blank. The key wheel numbers are visible through a hole in the key wheel gear and are engraved on the key wheel pawl. Place key wheel number 6 in position and slide the shaft through it. Follow with each key wheel in reverse order, i. e., 5, 4, 3, 2, 1. Slide the shaft completely through the typewheel assembly. Push the reset knob against the key wheels until they fit closely together in place, and tighten the key wheel bearing screw. (Do not twist off the head of the screw.) Next tighten the two screws at the ends of the shaft and test the typewheel and key wheels to determine if they turn freely, and check for play to right and left. A certain amount of play is permissible for the typewheel, but no play is allowable for the key wheels.

d. *Letter Counter.* Before mounting, the counter must be set to 0000 or any multiple of five. The 5-letter cam must be properly positioned to assure coordination between the cam and the counter. Proper positioning is accomplished by turning the drive knob a sufficient number of times to bring the dowel pins of the intermediate gear shaft to a vertical position. The counter gear must mesh properly with its intermediate gear, so that a full series of numbers is visible through the letter counter window.

36. INSPECTION CHECK. The following check list should be used after repairs and adjustments have been completed. This inspection check will assure that the machines are returned to service in proper working condition. The troubles listed below are followed by suggestions for correction only where such suggestions are necessary.

a. *Encipher-decipher Knob.*

(1) Binding of knob. REALIGN LEFT SIDE-PLATE.

(2) No detent in knob.

b. *Letter Counter.*

(1) Faulty alignment of numbers. MESH TEETH PROPERLY.

(2) Gear out of line.

(3) Poor meshing of gears. ADD OR TAKE OFF SHIMS.

c. *Drum.*

(1) Drum jamming. CHECK POSITION OF DRUM BAR LUGS.

(2) No detent in bar.

(3) Sprung bar. INSERT NEW BAR.

(4) Sticking bar. CLEAN SLOT OR CHANGE BAR.

(5) Inoperative lock. ADJUST DRUM, AND CHECK LOCK SPRING.

(6) Binding. CHECK ALIGNMENT.

(7) Improperly set bracket slot.

(8) Slipping of drum when intermediate lock is open.

(9) Number disk not pinned.

d. *Drum Lugs.*

(1) Too loose or too tight.

(2) Improperly fitted in drum bar slots.

e. *Guide Arms.*

(1) Too weak or too strong. ADJUST GUIDE ARM SPRING.

(2) Too far from, or too close to, pins on key wheel. ADJUST BY BENDING.

(3) Sticking, causing improper encipherment and decipherment. ADJUST BY BENDING.

(4) Improperly adjusted to lugs on drum. ADJUST BY BENDING.

(5) In wrong position, causing false encipherment. CHECK GUIDE ARM NUMBERS; SEE PARAGRAPH 35.

f. *Intermediate Key Wheel Gears.*

(1) Too much play in key wheel release. USE SHIMS.

(2) Lock arm riding on drum. ADJUST BY BENDING.

(3) Drive gear making contact with drum bar. POSITION DRUM PROPERLY.

(4) Faulty alignment of gears.

(5) Faulty timing of feed arm.

g. *Paper Feed.*

(1) Defective cam or loose taper pin.

(2) Defective paper.

(3) Jamming.

(4) Weaving of paper. ADJUST PAPER PRESSURE ROLLER.

(5) Inoperative. CHECK FOR FREEDOM OF MOVEMENT.

h. Pins (key wheel).

(1) Sticking. WASH WHEEL IN SOLVENT; LUBRICATE.

(2) No detent. REPLACE KEY WHEEL.

i. Key Wheels.

(1) Defective. REPLACE.

(2) Excessive side play. TIGHTEN RIGHT-END SCREW ON KEY WHEEL SHAFT, OR INSERT SHIM IF NECESSARY.

(3) Incorrectly positioned.

(4) Improper alignment.

(5) Ratchet defective.

(6) Binding and difficult to move.

j. Key Wheel Gears.

(1) Bent. STRAIGHTEN IF POSSIBLE; OTHERWISE REPLACE.

(2) Out of line. REPLACE.

k. Key Wheel Release.

(1) Sticking lever.

(2) Lack of play in reset button.

(3) Excess play in lever.

(4) Inoperative reset button.

l. Printing.

(1) Double print. ALIGN PRINTING HAMMER.

(2) Light on one side; ink pad not centered. ALIGN PRINTING HAMMER.

(3) Parts of letter not printed. ALIGN PRINTING HAMMER; CHECK TENSION OF PAPER GUIDE SPRING.

(4) Poor spacing.

(5) Prints Z with machine set to decipher. CHECK PIN ON TYPE WHEEL.

(6) Groups irregular. CHECK INTERMEDIATE FEED ARM ON RIGHT OF DRUM.

(7) Letters appearing in groups of 10, 15, or 20, but not 5. CHECK PAPER FEED.

m. Screws.

(1) Loose.

(2) Marred.

(3) Missing.

n. Springs.

(1) Deformed. REPLACE.

(2) Missing.

(3) Unattached.

o. Typewheel.

(1) Binding.

(2) Detent stiff.

(3) Excess play.

(4) Typewheel gear riding on counter shaft.

(5) Inoperative lock. ALIGN DRUM.

(6) Drum lock jamming on typewheel gear tooth.

p. Washers.

(1) Missing.

APPENDIX I

PREPARATION OF PIN AND LUG SETTINGS

1. PIN SETTINGS.

a. Prepare a table of the key wheels by listing, in alphabetical order, the letters appearing on the face of each wheel: the first wheel, A to Z; the second wheel A to Z, omitting W; the third wheel A to X, omitting W; the fourth wheel A to U; the fifth wheel A to S; and the sixth wheel A to Q.

b. Prepare a set of 156 lettered cards, 78 of which are marked R (right) and the remainder L (left). Shuffle the cards thoroughly and draw one at a time. Start with A on wheel number 1, and prepare the key list in accordance with the cards drawn: if a card bears an L, cross out the letter; if a card bears an R, do not cross out the letter. Only letters with effective pins are then shown in the key list (table I, page 13). More than six consecutive effective or noneffective pins on any wheel must be rearranged in order to prevent use of such a sequence. A random arrangement, in which from 40 to 60 per cent of the pins are in the effective position is assured by this method.

2. LUG SETTINGS.
To prepare a table of favorable lug settings, proceed with the following steps in the order given:

a. Selection of Numbers. Select a set of six numbers from either group A or group B in appendix II. Sets of numbers selected from group B must not exceed 10 per cent of the

total sets selected. The sets are selected at random from the table, and a set is not used a second time as long as other unused sets are available. Sets of numbers from group B should be used at irregular intervals and should not succeed each other in a key list.

b. Rearrangement of Numbers. Rearrange the numbers so that they appear in random order.

c. Distribution of Overlaps. When the two lugs on a bar are both placed in effective positions, an *overlap* results. The total overlap is found by subtracting 27 (the number of bars on the drum) from the total of the six numbers in a set. The overlaps required for each set of numbers have been calculated, and are given with the sets appearing in appendix II. Distribute the overlaps among the numbers according to the following four rules:

(1) Most of the six numbers should be involved.

(2) Overlaps should include numbers which are separated, and numbers which are side by side.

(3) Several small overlaps should be used in preference to one large overlap.

(4) There must not be more than four overlaps between any two numbers. It is permissible, however, for a number to have a combined overlap of more than four. (The number 12 in subpar. *h* below has a combined overlap of five).

The above rules offer a general guide for overlap distribution, but some deviation can be made from all but the rule appearing in subparagraph (4) above, which must always be followed.

d. Checking Placement of Overlaps. The overlaps must be so placed that a single number, or the sum of any two, three, four, five, or all six of the numbers, yields all the values from 1 to 27, inclusive. Remember that the result of two effective lugs on the same drum bar is one. As an example, in table III there are three effective lugs in column 6, and one effective lug in column 3, giving a total of four. However, two of the effective lugs are on one bar which cancels the effect of one lug, yielding a result of only three. Hence, the proper total for columns 3 and 6 is three (two plus one), and not four.

e. Preparing Lug Setting Work Sheet. The effective lugs (represented by X's) are now entered on a work sheet similar to that shown in table III; lugs in the same column are placed on successive drum bars in as many cases as the overlap condition permits. The completed work sheet should be checked carefully for accuracy with the results of the previous steps. The two zero positions need not be shown on this chart.

f. Preparing Lug Setting Table. Convert the lug positions set up on the work sheet to the form illustrated in table II, page 15, by writing the numbered positions of the lugs opposite the number representing the drum bar. Determine the positions by referring to the number plate (29) at the rear of the drum bar cage.

g. Complete Preparation of Lug Setting. The following example serves to illustrate the preparation of a lug setting. The steps are numbered to correspond to the steps described in subparagraphs 2a to 2d.

(1) Select a set of numbers from group A.

   1, 2, 3, 5, 10, 12   Overlap=6

(2) Rearrange the numbers.

   2, 12, 1, 5, 10, 3

---

(3) Distribute the overlaps.

(a) All of the six numbers are involved.

(b) Columns side by side: Columns separated:
    4 and 5   1 and 5
                                   1 and 6
                                   2 and 5
                                   3 and 6

(c) Small overlaps are used in preference to one large one.

(d) Overlaps involving only two numbers do not exceed four.

(4) All values from 1 to 27, inclusive, are obtained. For example:

   1 is given by column 3.
   2 is given by column 1.
   3 is given by column 6.
   4 is given by columns 1 and 6.
   5 is given by column 4.
   6 is given by columns 3 and 4, and so on.

---

h. Alternate Overlap Distribution. Overlap distribution of the following form produces a good key but does not follow strictly the rules for overlap distribution. Lug settings of this nature should be kept to a minimum in key lists.

3. PURPOSE. The foregoing limitations are imposed to provide the greatest amount of security possible in the shifting of the alphabets, and to add to the difficulties of enemy cryptanalysts engaged in making a mathematical analysis of the messages.

TABLE III. *Position of drum bar lugs work sheet.*

	1	2	3	4	5	6
1.........			X			X
2.........						X
3.........	X					X
4.........	X				X	
5.........				X	X	
6.........				X		
7.........				X		
8.........				X		
9.........				X		
10........		X				
11........		X				
12........		X				
13........		X				
14........		X				
15........		X				
16........		X				
17........		X				
18........		X				
19........		X				
20........		X		X		
21........		X		X		
22........				X		
23........				X		
24........				X		
25........				X		
26........				X		
27........				X		

APPENDIX II
SETS OF NUMBERS AND OVERLAPS FOR LUG SETTINGS

1. GROUP A.

Sets	Overlaps
1 2 3 4 8 10	1
1 2 3 4 7 11	1
1 2 3 4 6 12	1
1 2 3 4 5 13	1
1 2 3 5 8 9	1
1 2 3 5 7 10	1
1 2 3 5 6 11	1
1 2 3 6 7 9	1
1 2 4 5 7 9	1
1 2 4 5 6 10	1
1 2 3 4 9 10	2
1 2 3 4 8 11	2
1 2 3 4 7 12	2
1 2 3 4 6 13	2
1 2 3 5 8 10	2
1 2 3 5 7 11	2
1 2 3 5 6 12	2
1 2 3 6 8 9	2
1 2 3 6 7 10	2
1 2 4 5 8 9	2
1 2 4 5 7 10	2
1 2 4 5 6 11	2
1 2 4 6 7 9	2
1 2 3 4 9 11	3
1 2 3 4 8 12	3
1 2 3 4 7 13	3
1 2 3 5 9 10	3
1 2 3 5 8 11	3
1 2 3 5 7 12	3
1 2 3 5 6 13	3
1 2 3 6 8 10	3
1 2 3 6 7 11	3
1 2 3 7 8 9	3
1 2 4 5 8 10	3
1 2 4 5 7 11	3
1 2 4 5 6 12	3
1 2 4 6 8 9	3
1 2 4 6 7 10	3
1 2 3 4 10 11	4
1 2 3 4 9 12	4
1 2 3 4 8 13	4
1 2 3 5 9 11	4
1 2 3 5 8 12	4
1 2 3 5 7 13	4
1 2 3 6 9 10	4
1 2 3 6 8 11	4
1 2 3 6 7 12	4
1 2 3 7 8 10	4
1 2 4 5 9 10	4
1 2 4 5 8 11	4
1 2 4 5 7 12	4
1 2 4 5 6 13	4
1 2 4 6 7 11	4
1 2 4 6 8 10	4
1 2 4 7 8 9	4
1 2 3 4 10 12	5
1 2 3 4 9 13	5
1 2 3 5 10 11	5
1 2 3 5 9 12	5
1 2 3 5 8 13	5
1 2 3 6 9 11	5
1 2 3 6 8 12	5
1 2 3 6 7 13	5
1 2 3 7 9 10	5
1 2 3 7 8 11	5
1 2 4 5 9 11	5
1 2 4 5 8 12	5
1 2 4 5 7 13	5
1 2 4 6 9 10	5
1 2 4 6 8 11	5
1 2 4 6 7 12	5
1 2 4 7 8 10	5
1 2 3 4 11 12	6
1 2 3 4 10 13	6
1 2 3 5 10 12	6
1 2 3 5 9 13	6
1 2 3 6 10 11	6
1 2 3 6 9 12	6
1 2 3 6 8 13	6
1 2 3 7 9 11	6
1 2 3 7 8 12	6

Sets	Overlaps
1 2 4 5 10 11	6
1 2 4 5 9 12	6
1 2 4 5 8 13	6
1 2 4 6 8 12	6
1 2 4 6 9 11	6
1 2 4 6 7 13	6
1 2 4 7 9 10	6
1 2 4 7 8 11	6
1 2 3 4 11 13	7
1 2 3 5 11 12	7
1 2 3 5 10 13	7
1 2 3 6 10 12	7
1 2 3 6 9 13	7
1 2 3 7 10 11	7
1 2 3 7 9 12	7
1 2 3 7 8 13	7
1 2 4 5 10 12	7
1 2 4 5 9 13	7
1 2 4 6 8 13	7
1 2 4 6 9 12	7
1 2 4 6 10 11	7
1 2 4 7 9 11	7
1 2 4 7 8 12	7
1 2 4 8 9 10	7
1 2 3 5 11 13	8
1 2 3 6 11 12	8
1 2 3 6 10 13	8
1 2 3 7 10 12	8
1 2 3 7 9 13	8
1 2 4 5 11 12	8
1 2 4 5 10 13	8
1 2 4 6 9 13	8
1 2 4 6 10 12	8
1 2 4 7 10 11	8
1 2 4 7 9 12	8
1 2 4 7 8 13	8
1 2 4 8 9 11	8
1 2 3 5 12 13	9
1 2 3 6 11 13	9
1 2 3 7 11 12	9
1 2 4 5 11 13	9
1 2 4 6 10 13	9
1 2 4 6 11 12	9
1 2 4 7 10 12	9
1 2 4 7 9 13	9
1 2 4 8 10 11	9
1 2 4 8 9 12	9
1 2 3 6 12 13	10
1 2 3 7 11 13	10
1 2 4 5 12 13	10
1 2 4 6 11 13	10
1 2 4 7 11 12	10
1 2 4 7 10 13	10
1 2 4 8 9 13	10
1 2 3 7 12 13	11
1 2 4 6 12 13	11
1 2 4 8 11 12	11
1 2 4 8 10 13	11
1 2 4 7 12 13	12
1 2 4 8 11 13	12

2. GROUP B.

Sets	Overlaps
1 1 2 3 8 13	1
1 1 2 4 9 11	1
1 1 2 4 8 12	1
1 1 2 4 7 13	1
1 1 2 5 9 10	1
1 1 2 5 8 11	1
1 1 2 5 7 12	1
1 1 2 5 6 13	1
1 1 3 4 9 10	1
1 1 3 4 8 11	1
1 1 3 4 7 12	1
1 1 3 4 6 13	1
1 1 3 5 8 10	1
1 1 3 5 7 11	1
1 1 3 5 6 12	1
1 1 3 6 8 9	1
1 1 3 6 7 10	1
1 2 2 3 9 11	1
1 2 2 3 8 12	1
1 2 2 3 7 13	1
1 2 2 4 8 11	1
1 2 2 4 7 12	1
1 2 2 4 6 13	1
1 2 2 5 8 10	1
1 2 2 5 7 11	1
1 2 2 5 6 12	1
1 2 2 6 8 9	1
1 2 2 6 7 10	1
1 2 3 3 9 10	1
1 2 3 3 8 11	1
1 2 3 3 7 12	1
1 2 3 4 9 9	1
1 2 3 5 5 12	1

Sets	Overlaps
1 2 3 6 6 10	1
1 2 4 4 8 9	1
1 2 4 5 5 11	1
1 2 4 6 6 9	1
1 1 2 4 8 13	2
1 1 2 5 9 11	2
1 1 2 5 8 12	2
1 1 2 5 7 13	2
1 1 3 4 9 11	2
1 1 3 4 8 12	2
1 1 3 4 7 13	2
1 1 3 5 9 10	2
1 1 3 5 8 11	2
1 1 3 5 7 12	2
1 1 3 5 6 13	2
1 1 3 6 8 10	2
1 1 3 6 7 11	2
1 2 2 3 9 12	2
1 2 2 3 8 13	2
1 2 2 4 9 11	2
1 2 2 4 7 13	2
1 2 2 5 9 10	2
1 2 2 5 8 11	2
1 2 2 5 7 12	2
1 2 2 5 6 13	2
1 2 2 6 10 11	2
1 2 2 6 7 11	2
1 2 3 3 9 12	2
1 2 3 3 8 12	2
1 2 3 3 7 13	2
1 2 3 5 5 13	2
1 2 3 5 9 9	2
1 2 3 6 6 11	2
1 2 3 7 7 9	2
1 2 4 4 7 11	2
1 2 4 4 5 13	2
1 2 4 5 5 12	2
1 1 2 4 9 13	3
1 2 3 6 8 10	3
1 1 2 5 9 12	3
1 1 2 5 8 13	3
1 1 3 4 10 11	3
1 1 3 4 9 12	3
1 1 3 4 8 13	3
1 1 3 5 9 11	3
1 1 3 5 7 13	3
1 1 3 6 9 10	3
1 1 3 6 8 11	3
1 1 3 6 7 12	3
1 2 2 3 9 13	3
1 2 2 4 10 11	3
1 2 2 4 9 12	3
1 2 2 4 8 13	3
1 2 2 5 9 11	3
1 2 2 5 8 12	3
1 2 2 5 7 13	3
1 2 2 6 9 10	3
1 2 2 6 8 11	3
1 2 2 6 7 12	3
1 2 3 3 10 12	3
1 2 3 3 9 13	3
1 2 3 4 10 10	3
1 2 3 6 6 12	3
1 2 3 6 9 9	3
1 2 3 7 7 10	3
1 2 4 4 9 10	3
1 2 4 4 8 11	3
1 2 4 4 7 12	3
1 2 4 4 6 13	3
1 2 4 5 5 13	3
1 2 4 5 9 9	3
1 2 4 6 6 11	3
1 2 4 7 7 9	3
1 1 2 5 10 12	4
1 1 2 5 9 13	4
1 1 3 4 10 12	4
1 1 3 4 9 13	4
1 1 3 5 10 11	4
1 1 3 5 9 12	4
1 1 3 5 8 13	4
1 1 3 6 9 11	4
1 1 3 6 8 12	4
1 1 3 6 7 13	4
1 2 2 4 9 13	4
1 2 2 5 10 11	4
1 2 2 5 9 12	4
1 2 2 5 8 13	4
1 2 2 6 9 11	4
1 2 2 6 7 13	4
1 2 3 3 10 12	4
1 2 3 3 9 13	4
1 2 3 6 6 13	4
1 2 3 6 9 9	4
1 2 3 7 7 11	4
1 2 3 7 9 9	4
1 2 4 4 9 11	4
1 2 4 4 7 13	4
1 2 4 6 9 9	4
1 2 4 7 7 10	4
1 1 2 5 10 13	5
1 1 3 4 10 13	5
1 1 3 5 10 12	5
1 1 3 5 9 13	5
1 1 3 6 10 11	5
1 1 3 6 9 12	5

Sets	Overlaps
1 1 3 6 8 13	5
1 2 2 4 10 13	5
1 2 2 5 10 12	5
1 2 2 5 9 13	5
1 2 2 6 9 12	5
1 2 2 6 8 13	5
1 2 3 3 10 13	5
1 2 3 4 11 11	5
1 2 3 6 10 10	5
1 2 3 7 7 12	5
1 2 4 4 10 11	5
1 2 4 4 9 12	5
1 2 4 4 8 13	5
1 2 4 6 6 13	5
1 2 4 7 7 11	5
1 2 4 7 9 9	5
1 2 4 8 8 9	5
1 1 3 5 10 13	6
1 1 3 6 10 12	6
1 1 3 6 9 13	6
1 2 2 4 11 13	6
1 2 2 5 11 12	6
1 2 2 5 10 13	6
1 2 2 6 9 13	6
1 2 3 3 11 13	6
1 2 3 5 11 11	6
1 2 3 7 7 13	6
1 2 4 7 7 12	6
1 2 4 8 9 9	6
1 1 3 5 11 13	7
1 1 3 6 11 12	7
1 1 3 6 10 13	7
1 2 2 4 12 13	7
1 2 2 5 11 13	7
1 2 2 6 11 12	7
1 2 2 6 10 13	7
1 2 3 6 11 11	7
1 2 4 4 11 13	7
1 2 4 4 10 13	7
1 2 4 5 11 11	7
1 2 4 7 7 13	7
1 2 4 7 10 10	7
1 2 4 8 8 11	7
1 1 3 6 11 13	8
1 2 2 6 11 13	8
1 2 3 5 12 12	8
1 2 4 4 11 13	8
1 2 4 6 11 11	8
1 1 3 6 12 13	9
1 2 2 6 12 13	9
1 2 3 6 12 12	9
1 2 4 4 12 13	9
1 2 4 5 12 12	9
1 2 4 7 11 11	9
1 2 4 8 8 13	9
1 2 2 6 13 13	10
1 2 3 5 13 13	10
1 2 4 8 11 11	10
1 2 4 8 11 13	10
1 2 3 6 13 13	11
1 2 4 7 12 12	11
1 2 3 7 13 13	12

6919-Phila-44-24 (45M) (10 Apr 44)

Appendix 3
Additional Sources of Information

MUSEUMS AND ARCHIVES

- In the USA, the **NSA / National Cryptologic Museum** is a wonderful source of information on the Enigma, Ultra, and the history of coding and decoding messages. Its displays are frequently updated and expanded, and human and electronically-guided tours are available. The Archives consist of a very extensive library of original documents and books. The museum is open daily and the website provides more information: http://www.nsa.gov/about/cryptologic_heritage/museum/.

- The UK's **Bletchley Park Museum** is another excellent source of information on the Enigma and Ultra. It is the place where most of the decoding of messages took place during WW2. Ongoing work includes expanding the exhibits and the reconstruction of the cryptologic Bombe computer. The website provides much more information: http://www.bletchleypark.co.uk.

- The British Public Records Office, which is now called the **British National Archives**, contains many documents related to the Enigma which have recently been declassified. These include many intercepted messages. Although some documents have not been scanned yet, many are available on their website at: http://www.nationalarchives.gov.uk/records/looking-for-subject/secondworldwar.htm, and they have download services available.

WEB SITES

There are excellent annotated lists of links on the following web pages:

- www.Cryptomuseum.com
- www.cryptocellar.org/Enigma
- http://home.comcast.net/~dhhamer/
- www.enigma-replica.com
- www.enigmatixuk.com

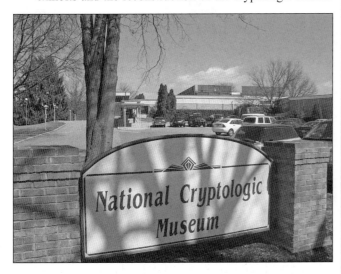

The National Cryptological Museum at the National Security Agency in Maryland, USA.

Bletchley Park, the UK's home of decoding.

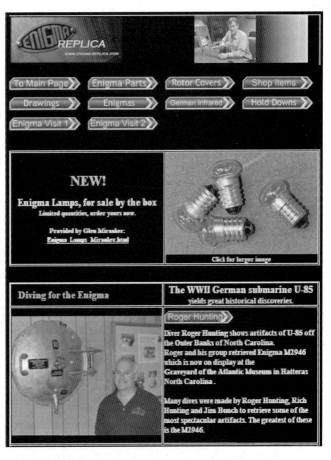

Part of the front page of www.enigma-replica.com/. This site not only has a large amount of information, but it is also a source of hard to find spare parts.

- http://jproc.ca/crypto/
- www.ilord.com
- www.users.telenet.be/d.rijmenants/en/enigma.html
- www.cryptomuseum.com/bp/index.htm
- The *Cryptologia* website lists the articles published in this journal since 1977: www.dean.usma.edu/math/pubs/cryptologia/.
- A great deal of additional information can be found by searching at google.com for: 'enigma cipher machines'.
- An excellent website with a list of all current museums and museum ships is located at: www.marinefunker.de. There is also information about ordering Enigma simulator programs. The two simulator programs are available from Franz Fick, Kiefernberg 19, 21075 Hamburg, Germany.
- Please also visit my Enigma Museum site: http://w1tp.com/enigma where, among other things, cumulative updates and/or corrections of the material in this book are posted as needed.

VIDEOS

- *Cipher Machines in Action*: by Tom Perera. The Enigma being set up and used by authentic German re-enactors and descriptive videos of the American WW2 M-209, the 1948 Swiss NEMA, and the Cold War Era Russian FIALKA. The Enigma video is included in the CD *The Story of the Enigma* (see page 6).
- *Decoding Nazi Secrets*: Available from: Public Television (PBS), WGBH Boston Video, P.O.Box 2284, S. Burlington, VT 05407-2284. Tel: (800) 949-8670 / FAX: (802) 864-9846.
- *The Secret Wireless War: Beyond Bletchley Park*. Also includes: *Black Propaganda*. Grindelwald Productions. P.O. Box 38, Princes Risborough, Bucks, HP27 9YL, Great Britain.

BOOKS AND CDs

Some good reference books on the Enigma, Ultra, and related topics are listed below. The online museum bookstore at Bletchley Park also has an extensive list of available publications.:

- Bauer, F. L. (1997). *Decrypted Secrets*. NY: Springer-Verlag. ISBN 3-540-66871- 3. Note: some of the illustrations in this book came from: Turkel, Siegfried, Chiffrieren mit Maschinen und Geraten, Graz (Austria) 1927.
- Beesly, P. (1977). *Very Special Intelligence*. NY: Ballantine. ISBN: 0-345- 29798-9.
- Bennett, R. (1979). *Ultra in the West: The Normandy Campaign of 1944-1945*. New York: Scribners. ISBN 0-684-16704-2.
- Bennett, R. (1989). *Ultra and Mediterranean Strategy 1941-1945*. Great Britain: Hamish Hamilton. ISBN 0-241-12687-8.
- Calvocoressi, Peter. (2001). *Top Secret Ultra*. Cleobury Mortimer, Shropshire: Baldwin, www.enigmatixuk.com
- Dulles, A. (1963). *The Craft of Intelligence*. NY: Harper & Row.
- Flicke, W. F. (1994). *War Secrets in the Ether*. Laguna Hills, CA: Aegan Park Press.ISBN: 0-89412-233-9.
- Freedman, Maurice. (2001). *Unraveling the Enigma*. South Yorkshire: Pen & Sword Books Ltd. ISBN 08052 810 0.

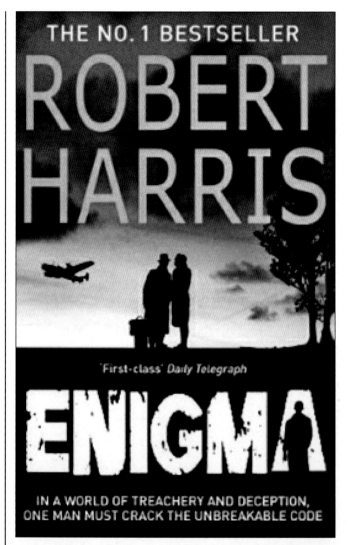

THE NO.1 BESTSELLER

ROBERT HARRIS

'First-class' *Daily Telegraph*

ENIGMA

IN A WORLD OF TREACHERY AND DECEPTION, ONE MAN MUST CRACK THE UNBREAKABLE CODE

- Gannon, Michael. (1999). *Black May: The Epic Story of the Allies Defeat of the German U-Boats in May*, 1943. New York: HarperCollins. ISBN 0-06-017819-1.
- Harper, S. (1999). *Capturing Enigma*. Gloucestershire: Sutton. ISBN 0-7509- 3050-0
- Harris, R. (1995). *Enigma*. (a dramatic novel & movie). NY: Ivy Books (Ballantine) ISBN: 0 8041 1548 6
- Haufler, H. (2003). *Codebreakers' Victory: How the Allied Cryptographers Won World War II*. New York: Penguin. ISBN 0-451-20979-6
- Hinsley, F.H., & Stripp, A. (1994). *Code Breakers: The Inside Story of Bletchley Park*. NY: Oxford Univ. Press. ISBN:0-19-285304-x
- Hoare, O. (2001). *Enigma: Codebreaking and the Second World War: The True Story through Contemporary Documents*. Public Records Office/Bletchey Park Trust.
- Hodges, A. (1983). Alan Turing: *The Enigma*. New York: Touchstone Books. ISBN: 0-671-49207-1.
- Kahn, David, (1967). *The Codebreakers: The Story of Secret Writing*. New York: Macmillan
- Kahn, David, (1978). *Hitler's Spies: German Military Intelligence in World War II*. New York: Collier Books. ISBN: 0-02-052440-4

- Kahn, David, (1991). *Seizing the Enigma*. New York: Barnes & Noble Books. ISBN: 0-7607-2672-8
- Keen, John. (2003). *Harold 'Doc' Keen and the Bletchley Park BOMBE*: Cleobury Mortimer, Shropshire: Baldwin, www.enigmatixuk.com
- Kozaczuk, W. (1979). *Im Banne Der Enigma. Militarverlag der Deutschen Demokratischen Republik*. ISBN 3-327-00423-4.
- Kozaczuk, W. (1984). *Enigma: How the German Cipher Machine was Broken and How it Was Read by The Allies in World War Two*. London:
- Kozaczuk, W. (2004). *Enigma: How the Poles Broke the Nazi Code*. New York: Hipocrene Books. ISBN: 0-7818-0941-X
- Lewin, R. (1978). *Ultra Goes to War*. New York: McGraw Hill. ISBN 0-07-037453- 8
- Lewin, R. (1983). *The American Magic*. Harrisonburg, VA: R.R.Donnelly. ISBN 0- 14-006471-0.
- Luke, Doreen. (2002). *My Road to Bletchley Park*. Cleobury Mortimer, Shropshire: Baldwin, www.enigmatixuk.com
- Mallman Showell, Jak P. (2000). *Enigma U-Boats: Breaking the Code*: Hersham, Surrey: Ian Allan Printing Ltd.
- Miller, A. R. (2002). *The Cryptographic Mathematics of Enigma*. Available on request from: NSA Center for Cryptologic History. NSA/National Cryptologic Museum. 9800 Savage Road Suite 6886. Fort George G. Meade, MD 20755-6886.
- Mowry, D. P. (2003). *German Cipher Machines of World War II*. Available on request from: NSA Center for Cryptologic History. NSA/National Cryptologic Museum. 9800 Savage Road Suite 6886. Fort George G. Meade, MD 20755-6886.
- Perera, T. B. (2006). (CD) *The Story of the ENIGMA: History, Technology, and Deciphering*. (4th. Edition). Artifax Books, 151 Barton Rd. Stow, MA 01775 http://artifaxbooks.com - email: artifaxbooks@yahoo.com or see: http://w1tp.com/enigma.
- Perera, T. B. (2006). (CD) *Telegraph Collectors Reference CD (Second Edition)*. Stow, MA: Artifax Books, 151 Barton Rd. Stow, MA 01775, http://artifaxbooks.com, email: artifaxbooks@yahoo.com or visit the author's website: http://w1tp.com.
- Perera, T. B. (1999). *Telegraph Collectors Guide (2nd Edition)*. Stow, MA: Artifax Books (see above).
- Reuvers, P, and Simons, M. (2009) *FIALKA M-125 Reference Manual*: http://cryptomuseum.com.
- Sale, Tony. (1998). *The Collossus Computer 1943-1996 and how it helped to break the Lorenz cipher in WW-2*: Cleobury Mortimer, Shropshire: Baldwin, www.enigmatixuk.com.
- Sebag-Montefiore, H. (2000). *Enigma: The Battle for the Code*. New York: Wiley
- Singh, S. (1999). *The Code Book*. NY: Doubleday. ISBN: 0-385-49531-5.
- Skillen, H. (1994). *The Enigma Symposium*. (and many other titles). Self Published. ISBN: 0-9515190-5-0.
- Smith, M. L. (2000). *The Emperor's Codes*. New York: Penguin. ISBN 0-14- 20.0233-X
- Stripp, A. (1989). *Code Breaker in the Far East*. New York: Oxford
- Terraine, J. (1989). *Business in Great Waters: The U-Boat Wars 1916-1945*. London: Leo Cooper. ISBN: 0-85052-7600

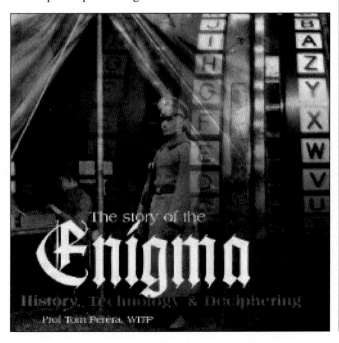

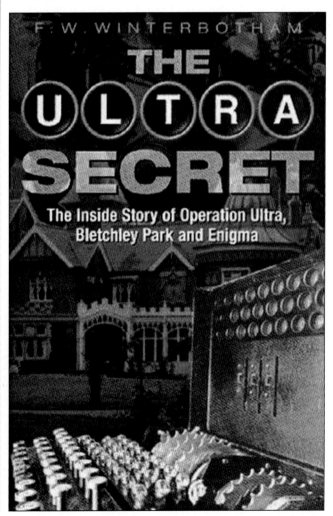

- Turkel, S. (1927). *Chiffrieren mit Maschinen und Geraten*, Graz (Austria)
- Ulsamer, Gregor. (2001). *Faszination Morsetasten: German Telegraph Keys Collector's Guide.* Gregor Ulsamer, Longumer Strasse 66, 26723 Emden, Germany.
- Welchman, Gordon. (1997). *The Hut Six Story.* Cleobury Mortimer, Shropshire: Baldwin, www.enigmatixuk.com
- West, N. (1988). *The Sigint Secrets.* NY: Morrow. ISBN: 0-688-07652-1
- Wilcox, J. (2002). *Solving the Enigma: History of the Cryptanalytic Bombe.* Available on request from: NSA Center for Cryptologic History. NSA/National Cryptologic Museum. 9800 Savage Road Suite 6886. Fort George G. Meade, MD 20755-6886
- Winkel, B. J., Deavours, C. A., Kahn, D., & Kruh, L. (2005). *The German Enigma Cipher Machine: Beginnings, Success and Ultimate Failure.* Boston: Artech House
- Winterbotham, F. W. (1974). *The Ultra Secret.* New York: Dell.
- Winterbotham, F. W. (1978). *The Nazi Connection.* New York: Dell. ISBN: 0-440- 16197-5

ARCHIVE MATERIAL ON THE CD: THE STORY OF THE ENIGMA

The following listings are available on the CD: *The Story of the Enigma*, by the author of this book. (See page 6 for how to order the CD):

- **The entire historical history archive / database of the NSA / National Cryptological Museum**: This searchable database is the entire 58 page listing of Enigma and Ultra materials in the NCM.
- **The entire Lou Kruh Collection Historical Archive / database**: This searchable collection database contains descriptions of over 3200 items in the Lou Kruh collection. It forms an unique historical record of important publications and materials.

Gordon WELCHMAN

THE HUT SIX STORY

FIA DPM WQ PE BCX SQW

Breaking the ENIGMA CODES

Foreword by Alan Stripp

Index

This index is limited to proper names as these may be difficult to locate by using the Contents page. To find details of the history and engineering of specific cipher machines, see the chapter listing on page 1.